second edition

modern
physics

F. W. VAN NAME, JR.

Professor, Department of Physics
University of Delaware

1962/Prentice-Hall, Inc.

Englewood Cliffs, N. J.

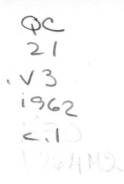

© 1952, 1962, by Prentice-Hall, Inc., Englewood Cliffs, N. J.

Library of Congress Catalog Card Number: 62–7243

Printed in the United States of America

59665C

preface to second edition

The purpose of this book is to present modern developments in physics beginning just before the start of this century and continuing through today. Some topics, such as relativity and quantum mechanics, have become almost classical; others, such as masers and Van Allen radiation, are matters of current research activity.

The material has been divided into three parts, roughly in the historical order of research activity in these fields. The main sections of the book are as follows:

I. Electron properties and special relativity.

II. Atomic and molecular spectra, structure and properties.

III. Nuclear physics and cosmic rays.

The material in this book can be covered in a typical full-year course meeting three hours per week. Most sections only require calculus as a prerequisite. Some derivations require more mathematical background, but these can be omitted if necessary, since only the results are needed. Problems are given at the end of each chapter both to illustrate physical principles concretely and to introduce collateral material or useful results. The reader is urged to work all the problems in order to gain a more complete understanding of each topic.

My thanks are due to Dean G. A. Hawkins of Purdue University, to Dr. C. B. Cooper of the University of Delaware for his helpful comments, and to Mrs. Virginia Bredermeier, Secretary of the Department of Physics of the University of Delaware, for her help in mimeographing much of the material for class use and for typing much of the final manuscript.

F. W. VAN NAME, Jr.

contents

modern physics

introduction

The developments in physics since the end of the nineteenth century constitute the contents of this book. About the year 1895, a definite break in the progress of physics occurred. The discontinuous increase in the number of the important fields of physics resulted, quite naturally, in the separation of the study of physics into classical and modern parts.

THE GOLDEN AGE OF PHYSICS

The nineteenth century was certainly the golden age of classical physics. During this period, tremendous advances were made in man's knowledge of nature, and scientific progress was much more rapid than during any earlier period. The greatest achievements of the century were the sweeping generalizations, and apparently unrelated phenomena were seen to be merely different aspects of a single, larger field of physics. Most of the material that one finds in an introductory physics textbook was found and organized during this fruitful period. Classical physics was essentially completed by 1890.

Perhaps the most important achievement during the nineteenth century was the formulation of the law of conservation of energy to apply to all fields of physics. The equivalence of heat and other forms of energy was gradually established by the work of Mayer, Joule, Kelvin, Helmholtz, and others. The intimate connection between heat and mechanics through the kinetic theory of matter was developed by Maxwell, Boltzmann, and others, during the second half of the century. During the same period classical thermodynamics was developed, using the conservation of heat energy along with other forms of energy as its First Law. Sound was also explained as a mechanical phenomenon, so that it was seen that three of the usual subdivisions of physics—heat, sound, and mechanics—were all included in a larger field, dynamics.

In fact, so great was the success of the mechanical approach to physical problems that many physicists came to feel that no theory was really satisfactory which could not be reduced to a mechanical model. One characteristic of much of modern physics is that this idea has had to be modified or abandoned. Concepts of space and time, derived from observations on large-scale bodies, are modified in the theory of relativity, which is applicable mainly to the smallest particles of nature. As another example, Bohr's mechanical model of the atom as a miniature solar system had to be replaced by quantum mechanics, for which no direct physical picture can be given or is required. Thus, in two of the greatest theories of the twentieth century we find an absence of a close connection between a mechanical model and the theory.

The first half of the nineteenth century saw the explanation of the nature of light in terms of the wave theory through the experiments of Young, Fresnel, and others. During this same period great advances were made, in the knowledge of electricity and magnetism by Volta, Oersted, Ampere, Faraday, and many others. These lines of advance were brought together by Maxwell in 1864 in his electromagnetic theory. Deductions from Maxwell's equations show that the fields of optics, electricity, and magnetism are all branches of a single larger science: electrodynamics. Again we find a number of subdivisions of physics synthesized into a single and wider field of knowledge.

A physicist of 1890 could hardly be blamed for feeling that major progress in his science was completed, and in fact this was almost true in some branches of physics. Application of the great theories of dynamics and electrodynamics could be expected to explain phenomena which still remained obscure. Of course, there would be engineering applications to be made, but pioneering work of important magnitude might easily have seemed quite unlikely. Only a writer of science fiction could have envisioned the revolutionary discoveries which were to be made in the next few years, as well as their tremendous effect on the industrial, military, and political life of the world during the twentieth century.

TWENTIETH CENTURY PHYSICS

The era of twentieth century physics began about 1895. Within three years, three fundamental discoveries were made which opened whole new fields of physics. In 1895 Roentgen discovered X-rays, in 1896 Becquerel discovered radioactivity, and in 1897 J. J. Thomson discovered the electron. Research was greatly stimulated by these and later discoveries in the atomic and sub-atomic worlds of nature. During the twentieth century the fields of X-rays, radioactivity and nuclear physics, and electronic physics took their places beside the classical fields of mechanics, heat, light, sound, and electricity and magnetism.

Let us consider the differences between nineteenth century physics and twentieth century physics. In the first place, new fields of physics, unknown in 1890, are of the greatest concern to the physicist of today. In addition, there has been a gradual abandoning of the mechanical approach to nature as the prerequisite of any physical theory. Theories have become more mathematical and abstract, and it is often difficult or impossible to explain them in terms of familiar mechanical analogues. The physicist of the nineteenth century was interested either in the phenomena of large-scale bodies or in phenomena which could usually be explained quite well in terms of a mechanical model. The third characteristic of twentieth century physics is its concern for phenomena which are beyond the direct reach of the senses. These sub-microscopic investigations are the subject of this book.

In addition to the extension of the knowledge of physics, another important development of the twentieth century has been the gradual merging of the various natural sciences. The joining of physics and chemistry has been essentially accomplished during this period, and great progress has been made in such fields as biophysics and biochemistry. The quantum mechanical explanation of the periodic table of elements is an example of the coalescing of physics and chemistry which is treated in some detail in the chapter on quantum mechanics. Just as the nineteenth century is most notable for combining various fields of physics into larger and wider fields of knowledge, it is likely that the most important product of twentieth century science will be the merger of astronomy, biology, chemistry, metallurgy, and physics into a single scientific discipline.

PROGRAM

In discussing the great progress which has been made in our knowledge of nature during the first half of the present century, no rigid historical pattern will be followed. Progress in a given field of knowledge is usually neither smooth nor logical until it is viewed later in retrospect.

This book is divided into three main sections dealing in turn with the electron, atoms and molecules, and nuclei. In general, each topic is presented in the historical order of its relation to one of these main divisions of twentieth century physics. However, after the discussion of a given field of physics has been completed, the clock may be turned back many years to begin the discussion of a new topic. In this way, the historical approach is partially preserved, and the material which has become an established part of our knowledge of nature is given a logical and integrated treatment.

The first three chapters are concerned with the properties of individual particles, especially the electron. The evidence for the existence of the electron and experiments for determining its properties are described in the first chapter. In the next chapter, various sources of electrons are described, such as thermionic and photoelectric emission. Black body radiation is also introduced in this chapter in connection with the theory of the photoelectric effect, so that the idea of energy quantization is available for later use in the discussion of other topics. The concluding chapter of the section on the electron deals with particles moving at speeds comparable to the speed of light. In this way, the equations from special relativity are introduced early in the course.

The next major section deals with atomic and molecular phenomena. The Bohr theory of atomic structure is introduced in connection with the explanation of spectral series, and the defects of the Bohr theory are discussed. The more successful quantum theory of atoms is treated in the next chapter on a fundamental mathematical basis, and then applications to various problems of atomic physics are made. This leads naturally to a study of X-rays and, as a simple generalization, to the study of molecules.

The last major section is concerned with nuclei and nuclear particles, without being concerned to any great extent with the extra-nuclear electrons of atoms and molecules. In the first chapter the discovery of natural radioactivity and the detection of nuclear particles is treated. In the following chapter the principles of nuclear reactions and the production of transmutations are discussed, as is the structure of nuclei. Since nuclear fission and other applications of nuclear physics are of great importance, they are treated in a separate chapter. The section on nuclear physics concludes with a description of reactions produced by cosmic radiations.

The plan of this book is thus to lead the student from a study of single particles to the study of the exterior parts of atoms and finally to the interior parts of atoms. In general, this follows the general progress of research during the twentieth century. The topics which most interest the research worker of today are those discussed in the last five chapters. To this extent, a historical pattern is maintained in the organization of this book, but the author's aim has been to treat the various topics in an integrated manner whenever possible, without being limited by the erratic nature of the progress of actual physical research. Various references are listed at the end of each chapter, and it is hoped that the reader will refer to them for additional information.

ADDITIONAL READING

Magie, William Francis, *A Source Book in Physics*. New York: McGraw-Hill Book Co. Inc., 1935. An excellent collection of outstanding works by the great physicists. Many of these original contributions are translated and many original diagrams are included. Every student of physics should read some of these original announcements of important discoveries.

Richtmyer, F. K., E. H. Kennard and T. Lauritsen, *Introduction to Modern Physics*. New York: McGraw-Hill Book Co. Inc., 1955 (5th Ed.). An excellent historical introduction to the field of modern physics is given in the first part of this book. In addition, many of the topics treated are the same as those dealt with in the present book.

part one

the electron

chapter one

the electron

In this chapter we will be concerned with the evidence for the existence of the electron, which culminated in the "discovery" of the electron by J. J. Thomson in 1897. This illustrates the fact that a major discovery is seldom made all at once; the growth of knowledge is gradual rather than precipitous. Thomson's crucial experiments were important because they directly confirmed views on the atomicity of electricity which had been held since the time of Faraday's researches on electrolysis, but the electron was not "discovered" in quite the same sense that radioactivity was.

Faraday investigated electrolysis about 1850 and found that the weight of a given monovalent ion deposited by a given quantity of electricity was proportional to the atomic or molecular weight of the neutral atom or molecule. The quantity of electricity which will deposit one gram-atom of a monovalent element is called the *faraday* and symbolized by the letter F. Experimentally, F is equal to 96,522 coulombs.

According to Avogadro's Law, the number of atoms in a gram-atom, N_0, is the same for all elements. If all monovalent ions carry the same electrical charge, e, then the magnitude of e would be given by

$$e = \frac{F}{N_0} \tag{1}$$

Similarly, multivalent ions would carry charges which are integral multiples of e. Stoney suggested the name *electron* for this natural unit of charge in 1874. However, at that time the value of N_0 was only very approximately known from kinetic theory considerations, so that the value of e could not be calculated exactly. Today, in fact, N_0 is most accurately measured by the ratio F/e from Eq. (1).

1.1. GASEOUS DISCHARGES

Although the evidence from electrolysis suggests that electricity is carried in discrete, equal units, the study of the conduction of electricity through gases provided the direct proof of this assumption.   Consider a glass tube containing two plane parallel electrodes, as shown in Fig. 1.   At pressures

FIG. 1

Apparatus for studying electrical discharges through gases.

near atmospheric pressure, a sufficiently high voltage applied between the electrodes will cause a disruptive spark to pass through the gas with considerable noise.   We shall define the sparking potential as the potential at which there occurs a discontinuous change from one more or less stable condition of current between the electrodes to another stable condition of current.   Both theoretically and experimentally the sparking potential is found to be a function of the product, pd, of the gas pressure, p, and the electrode separation, d.

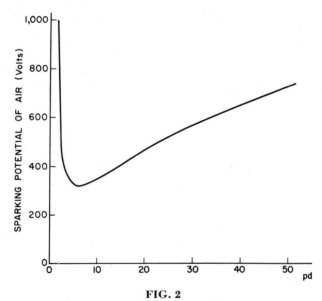

FIG. 2

Sparking potential curve for air (pressure in millimeters of mercury and electrode separation in centimeters).

The experimental sparking potential curve for air is shown in Fig. 2, with the gas pressure given in millimeters of mercury and the electrode separation in centimeters. The effect of the minimum of this curve is strikingly illustrated by constructing a tube in which there are two paths which the discharge can take, a short one and a long one. At high gas pressures the discharge takes the shorter path, so as to reduce the product, pd, and thus reduce the required sparking potential. At lower pressures, when pd is smaller than the minimal value, the discharge chooses the longer path, thus increasing the value of pd and decreasing the sparking potential.

As the pressure is lowered, the appearance of the discharge changes radically. At several centimeters of mercury pressure there is a wavy streamer of light between the electrodes, the streamer gradually filling the tube as the pressure is lowered. At about one millimeter of mercury pressure, we have the Geissler discharge, which is shown in Fig. 3. At any

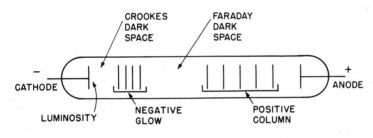

FIG. 3
Schematic representation of a gaseous discharge.

given pressure, the distance from the cathode to the beginning of the positive column is constant, the positive column merely filling the rest of the tube as far as the anode. In "neon" advertising signs, it is the positive column which is seen, each gas producing its characteristic color, such as red for neon and blue for mercury.

If the pressure in the discharge tube is now reduced to about 0.01 millimeter of mercury, the Crookes dark space expands so as to fill the tube almost completely and the glass walls of the tube fluoresce, giving off a green light. If a screen made of a fluorescent salt, such as zinc orthosilicate, is placed in the tube, an object placed between the cathode and the screen will cast a shadow on the screen. It appears that rays are being emitted at right angles to the cathode, more or less independent of the position of the anode, and thus we speak of *cathode rays*. As early as 1859, Plucker found that cathode rays could be deflected by a magnet, but not until 1897 did J. J. Thomson's experiments show conclusively that cathode rays were a stream of negatively charged particles.

1.2. ELECTROMAGNETIC DEFLECTION OF CATHODE RAYS

As a hypothesis suggested by the facts of electrolysis and the atomic theory, let us assume that cathode rays are a stream of charged particles of charge, q, and mass, m. In order to have a sharply defined beam of cathode rays to investigate, we construct a tube as shown in Fig. 4, which uses several slits as an anode. Once the cathode rays are through the slits, they will travel in a straight line and strike the screen practically at a single point.

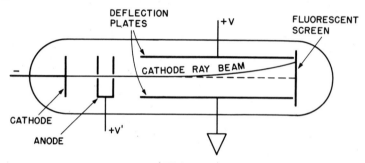

FIG. 4

Schematic of a cathode-ray tube, showing electrostatic deflection of the beam.

Consider the deflection of a beam of charged particles by an electrostatic field produced by a voltage, V, applied between the deflecting plates. For clarity, the region of electrostatic deflection is shown enlarged in Fig. 5. The electric field acting between plates separated a distance s is given by

$$E = \frac{V}{s} \qquad (2)$$

The acceleration produced by this electrostatic field on a particle of charge, q, and mass, m, in the vertical direction is

$$a = \frac{F}{m} = \frac{qE}{m} = \frac{qV}{ms} \qquad (3)$$

If the velocity of the particle when it enters the region between the plates is v, then the deflection of the particle from its undeflected point of impact with the screen is given by

$$d_E = \frac{1}{2} at^2 = \frac{1}{2} \frac{qV}{ms} \left(\frac{L}{v}\right)^2 = \frac{qVL^2}{2msv^2} \qquad (4)$$

We notice that three unknowns are present in the relation given by Eq. (4), namely, q, m, and v. To determine these quantities separately, additional information is needed.   This can be provided by measuring the deflection of the same beam by a magnetic field.

Before continuing the discussion of the electromagnetic deflection of cathode rays, the reader should be cautioned about the correct use of units in electromagnetic equations.   The MKS has become the most popular

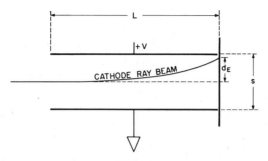

FIG. 5
Deflection of a beam of negatively charged particles by a
uniform electrostatic field.

system of units, since in this system nearly all of the units are the same as in the practical or laboratory system.   However, older texts and reference works employed the absolute electrostatic and electromagnetic systems of units, abbreviated esu and emu respectively.   In this book MKS units will be used in all electromagnetic equations.   Data given in esu or emu can be converted to MKS units by the use of the following identities:

	MKS	emu	esu	Symbol
Potential	300 volts	$= 3 \times 10^{10}$ emu	$= 1$ esu	V
Charge	10 coulombs	$= 1$ emu	$= 3 \times 10^{10}$ esu	q
Magnetic field	1 weber/m²	$= 10^4$ gauss		B

The equations above are identities between measured magnitudes.   Thus, fractions such as 1 esu/300 volts are equal to unity, and may be multiplied into any equation in order to convert units easily.

Let us now consider the effect on the cathode ray beam of a uniform magnetic field applied perpendicular to the beam.   Since the force exerted by a magnetic field on a moving charged particle is always at right angles to the velocity of the particle, the path of the particle will be a circle of radius R.   Let us take the X-axis in the direction of the undeflected beam, and the origin at the point at which the magnetic field begins to act on the beam, as shown in Fig. 6.   The equation of motion of a particle of charge q, mass m, and velocity v, is given by

$$\frac{mv^2}{R} = qvB \qquad (5)$$

Thus, the radius of the circular path of the particle is

$$R = \frac{mv}{qB} \qquad (6)$$

The trajectory of the particle is a circle of radius R, with its center at the point $(0, R)$. The equation of trajectory is then

$$x^2 + (y - R)^2 = R^2 \qquad (7)$$

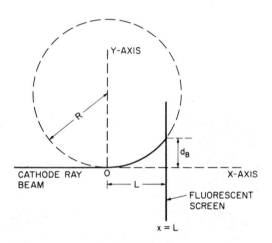

FIG. 6
Deflection of cathode rays by a magnetic field perpendicular
to the page.

The trajectory intersects the fluorescent screen at the line $x = L$. If we call the corresponding value of y d_B, Eq. (7) takes the form

$$L^2 + d_B^2 - 2d_B R = 0 \qquad (8)$$

If we solve Eq. (8) for R and use Eq. (6), we find:

$$R = \frac{mv}{qB} = \frac{L^2}{2d_B} + \frac{d_B}{2} \qquad (9)$$

Equation (9) gives a second relation between q, m, and v. Usually d_B is small compared to L, and so the second term on the right side of Eq. (9) can be neglected. If we eliminate v between Eqs. (4) and (9), we find

$$\frac{q}{m} = \frac{2V d_B^2}{B^2 L^2 s d_E} \qquad (10)$$

Similarly, for the velocity of the particle we find the expression:

$$v = \frac{d_B V}{d_E B s} \tag{11}$$

Thus, from measurements on the deflection of a beam of charged particles by electric and magnetic fields, we can determine the charge-to-mass ratio and the velocity of the particles.

1.3. THE DISCOVERY OF THE ELECTRON

In 1897 J. J. Thomson performed experiments on cathode rays similar to those analyzed in the preceding section. He found a value of q/m for cathode rays of approximately

$$5 \times 10^{17} \text{ esu/gm } (1.7 \times 10^{11} \text{ coulombs/kg})$$

The same value for q/m was obtained with various gases in the discharge tube and also when various metals were used for the electrodes. Considering the direction of the deflections, the cathode rays acted like negatively charged particles.

The conclusion from Thomson's experiments is that cathode rays are negatively charged particles, each having the same charge-to-mass ratio, which is usually denoted e/m. The name *electron*, originally suggested by Stoney to denote the charge carried by a monovalent ion in electrolysis, was gradually used for the corpuscles previously called cathode rays and is the universal usage today. There remained the problem of measuring the charge of a cathode ray particle, in order to show that they are identical particles, all with the same charge and mass, and not merely with a constant charge-to-mass ratio. Millikan's experiments for the measurement of the electron charge are described in Sec. 1.5.

1.4. APPLICATIONS OF CATHODE RAY TUBES

The deflection of a beam of electrons as described above has many applications in science and industry. In the early days a beam of cathode rays was obtained by the use of anode slits, as shown in Fig. 4. The velocity of the electrons emerging from the slits is not simply related to the voltage, V', applied between the cathode and anode, as will be seen from the following explanation of the mechanism of gaseous conduction.

According to present ideas, a few free electrons are present everywhere, being produced by cosmic rays, natural radioactivity contamination, and so forth. Each of these free electrons inside the tube is accelerated towards the anode, and if it does not suffer a collision with a gas molecule too soon, may acquire enough energy to knock an electron from a gas molecule. (The structure of atoms and molecules is discussed in later chapters, but the reader is assumed to have some knowledge of their structure from introductory work in physics.) The two electrons now present are both accelerated towards the anode, and each may gain enough energy before a collision with a gas molecule to knock another electron from the gas molecule. Continuing this process, we have an *electron avalanche*, which explains the currents found in gaseous discharges. However, because of the successive collisions each electron suffers, the velocity of an electron when it emerges from the anode slits is not simply related to the anode potential.

In present-day applications of cathode ray tubes and other vacuum tubes involving electron beams, the source of electrons is practically never an electron avalanche produced by ionization of a gas. Instead, the tube is highly evacuated and electrons emitted thermionically from a heated filament are accelerated by the anode potential. (Thermionic emission of electrons is described in Sections 2.1 and 2.2.) In this case, all of the electrons pass through the difference in potential between the cathode and anode, so they all have a common velocity. The velocity of electrons in this case is directly related to the anode potential, and in the following paragraph we will develop an equation relating these quantities.

Let us consider the acceleration of a particle of mass, m, and charge, q, through a potential difference, V'. According to the principle of conservation of energy, the work doné on the particle by the electrostatic field must equal the kinetic energy acquired by the particle. If the particle starts from rest, we have

$$qV' = \tfrac{1}{2}mv^2 \tag{12}$$

Solving Eq. (12) for the velocity of the particle, we have

$$v = \sqrt{2\frac{q}{m}V'} \tag{13}$$

Before using Eq. (13), one must be sure that the particles under consideration actually do pass through a common difference of potential, V'.

Instead of computing the energy gained by the electron in ergs from Eq. (12), it is common práctice to speak of the energy of an electron in *electron-volts*. One electron-volt is defined as the energy acquired by an electron in passing through a potential difference of one volt. Anticipating Millikan's measurement of the electronic charge, which is described in the following section, we will take $e = 1.60 \times 10^{-19}$ coulomb approximately. The definition of the electron-volt then gives us the following value for this unit of energy:

$$1 \text{ ev} = qV' = 1.60 \times 10^{-19} \text{ coul} \times 1 \text{ v} = 1.60 \times 10^{-19} \text{ joule}$$

Thus, if we say that a particle has an energy of 100 ev, we mean that the particle has the same kinetic energy as an electron which has been accelerated through a potential difference of 100 volts, which is 1.60×10^{-17} joule. It is now common practice to use the electron-volt as a unit of energy approximately equal to 1.60×10^{-19} joule even when referring to neutral particles, such as the neutron. Larger units are the kev (1000 ev), the mev (10^6 ev), and the bev (10^9 ev).

If we use the best modern value for e/m in Eq. (13), the velocity v of an electron accelerated through a voltage V' is found to be

$$v \, (\text{m/sec}) = 5.94 \times 10^5 \, \sqrt{V' \, (\text{volts})} \tag{14}$$

Equation (14) should not be used for electrons accelerated through very high voltages, since relativistic effects described in Chapter 3 modify the

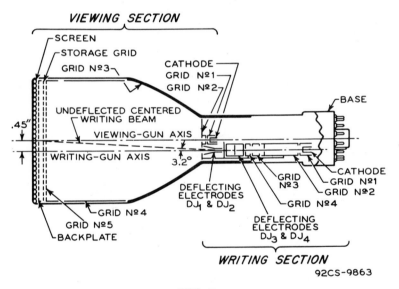

FIG. 7
Electrostatic focus and deflection, storage-type cathode ray tube, Type 7315. (Courtesy of RCA.)

results. For instance, with a potential difference of 10,000 volts the velocity calculated from Eq. (14) is about 1.5% higher than the correct value calculated according to relativity. At a potential difference of 1000 volts the error is less than 0.1%, which is usually negligible.

The deflection of beams of electrons by either electrostatic or magnetic fields or both has many applications. It should be noted that each type of deflection is proportional to the strength of the corresponding applied field.   Because of this linearity, the fluorescent screen of a cathode ray tube is well suited to the display of information.

In the laboratory, the cathode ray oscilloscope is widely used.   Two pairs of electrostatic deflecting plates at right angles are commonly used. By applying appropriate voltages to the two pairs of plates, amplitudes

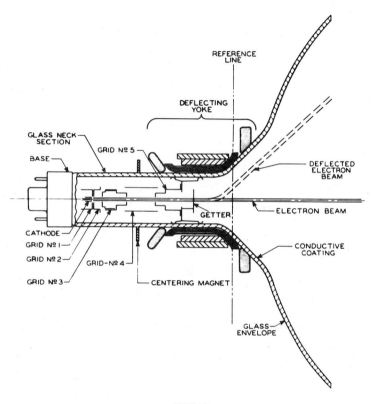

FIG. 8

Television kinescope using magnetic deflection and electrostatic focussing.   (Courtesy of RCA.)

and wave-forms of alternating voltages can be studied, frequency measure-ments can be made, and a wide variety of other useful information can be obtained.   It is indeed difficult to think of an instrument which would be more sorely missed from most physics laboratories.

Tubes which are essentially cathode ray tubes also have wide industrial and commercial applications.   The great importance of cathode ray tube displays in various types of military and navigational radar equipment is well known.   However, by far the greatest use of cathode ray tubes is in television.   Millions of television picture tubes with fluorescent screens up

to 30 inches in diameter are produced annually.   What was once a virtually
hand-made instrument for the scientific laboratory has become as common-
place as the car or the telephone.

The same principles of electromagnetic deflection of charged particles
yield information about the charge-to-mass ratio of heavy ions.   A variety
of such *mass spectrometers* has been built for various purposes.   The Bainbridge mass spectrometer is described in Section 8.6, but the deflection
principles are exactly the same as in Thomson's classic experiments on
cathode rays.

1.5. MILLIKAN'S MEASUREMENT OF THE CHARGE OF THE ELECTRON

Although Thomson's experiments showed that all of the particles in cathode
rays had the same charge-to-mass ratio, there still remained the problem of
actually measuring the charge, e, of each of these particles to show that all
of them were actually identical.   In 1909 Millikan made the first accurate
measurements of the electronic charge and at the same time verified the
hypothesis that the electronic charge is the basic unit of charge.   Millikan's
method, which is described below, is an improvement on a technique used
by Thomson, Townsend, and H. A. Wilson.

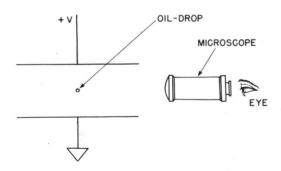

FIG. 9
Schematic diagram of Millikan's oil-drop experiment to
determine electronic charge.

Millikan's apparatus is shown in schematic form in Fig. 9.   An atomizer
is used to introduce a fine spray of oil droplets approximately 10^{-4} centimeter in diameter into the space between the parallel plates, which are a
few millimeters apart.   The droplets are illuminated transversely and
appear under the microscope as pinpricks of light.   One of Millikan's
improvements on the earlier method was the use of oil instead of water,

thus preventing evaporation of the droplets during the course of the measurements.

Now if a small piece of polonium or other radioactive material is held near the plates, ionization will be produced, giving the oil drops various positive or negative charges. To be specific, we will consider a drop with a negative charge, but the method is clearly applicable to either type of charge. A particular drop is observed and the time in which the drop traverses a known distance is measured in a scale fixed in the eyepiece of the microscope. Thus, the velocity of the drop when falling under the influence of gravity and rising under the influence of an electric field between the plates can be determined.

First consider the case when both plates are grounded. The drop under observation will fall slowly, subject to the downward force of gravity, the upward buoyant force given by Archimedes' Principle, and the upward force due to the viscous resistance of the air to the downward motion of the drop. The resistance offered by a viscous fluid to the steady motion of a sphere was investigated by Stokes in 1850. The result he obtained for a sphere of radius, a, moving with constant velocity, v, through a fluid with coefficient of viscosity, n, is the following expression for the viscous retarding force on the sphere:

$$F = 6\pi anv \tag{15}$$

For an oil drop which has reached its terminal velocity, v_0, the upward and downward forces just balance. If d and d' are the densities of the oil and of air respectively, we have then the following equation:

$$\frac{4\pi}{3} a^3 gd = \frac{4\pi}{3} a^3 gd' + 6\pi anv_0 \tag{16}$$

Since every quantity in Eq. (16) is known or measured except the radius, a, of the drop, the result of the free fall of the oil drop is a determination of its size.

Now let an electric field, E, be applied between the plates in such a direction as to make the drop move upward with a terminal velocity v_1. The viscous force again opposes the motion and thus acts downward in this case. If we assume that the drop has a charge, q, when it reaches its terminal velocity, the forces are in equilibrium and we have the following relation:

$$qE + \frac{4\pi}{3} a^3 gd' = \frac{4\pi}{3} a^3 gd + 6\pi anv_1 \tag{17}$$

If we add Eqs. (17) and (16), we get

$$qE = 6\pi an(v_0 + v_1) \tag{18}$$

If Eq. (16) is solved for the radius of the drop, a, and the result substituted in

Eq. (18), we find the following expression for the charge carried by the drop:

$$q = \frac{6\pi n (v_0 + v_1)}{E} \sqrt{\frac{9}{2} \frac{n v_0}{g(d - d')}} \tag{19}$$

Experimentally, the same electric field is used throughout all of the measurements, so that fine adjustments of the voltage applied between the parallel plates do not have to be made. A given drop is timed for several upward and downward flights over a known distance, and then the charge on the drop is changed by bringing the radioactive material near briefly. With some luck and skill, a given drop can be observed for many minutes, and a number of different charges will be observed on the same drop.

Millikan performed a series of experiments similar to that described above, both with different charges on the same drop and with different drops. It was found that the charge on a drop was always fairly close to an integral multiple of 5×10^{-10} esu, never a value differing radically from an integral value, such as 7×10^{-10} esu. As in the case of Thomson's experiments, electricity seems to consist of discrete, identical particles which are the basic unit of charge.

The value of electronic charge was found to depend somewhat on the radius of the particular drop used and on the air pressure. Millikan suspected that the difficulty might lie with Stokes' law, which assumes that air is a perfectly continuous fluid. Actually, we know from kinetic theory that air is made up of molecules executing a wild random motion. For a drop of radius 10^{-4} centimeter, air might not seem continuous at all, and instead the oil drop might fall through "holes" in the air.

If we let L be the mean free path of air molecules, that is, the average distance traversed by air molecules between collisions, kinetic theory (see Section 7.3 for derivation) gives the following expression for L in the case of a gas with N molecules per unit volume, each molecule being of diameter s:

$$L = \frac{1}{\pi s^2 N} \tag{20}$$

For a given type of molecule, the number of molecules per unit volume is proportional to the density of the gas and thus proportional to the pressure of the gas. Thus, L is inversely proportional to the gas pressure, p. Following Millikan, let us try a linear factor involving the ratio, L/a, of the mean free path of the gas molecules to the radius of the oil drop, as a correction to Stokes' law. Since L is inversely proportional to the pressure, p, the retarding force due to viscosity may be considered to be decreased by the factor $(1 + b/pa)$, where b is a constant. Equation (16) is then modified as follows:

$$\frac{4\pi}{3} a^3 g(d - d') = \frac{6\pi a n v_0}{1 + (b/pa)} \tag{21}$$

When the radius of the drop is large, the fluid will appear continuous and Stokes' law will hold exactly, but if the radius of the drop is comparable to the mean free path of the molecules of the gas, Eq. (21) shows that the velocity of free fall, v_0, will be greater than predicted by Eq. (16).

If the Stokes' law term in Eq. (17) is reduced by the factor $(1 + b/pa)$, it is seen that the velocity of rise, v_1, is increased by this same factor. Thus, Eq. (19) for the charge on the drop is modified as follows:

$$q = \frac{6\pi n (v_0 + v_1)}{E} \sqrt{\frac{9nv_0}{2g(d-d')}} \left(1 + \frac{b}{pa}\right)^{-3/2} \tag{22}$$

If now we let e be the correct value of the electronic charge when Stokes' law holds precisely, and if we let e' be the apparent, measured value of the electronic charge, we have then

$$e' = e \left(1 + \frac{b}{pa}\right)^{3/2} \tag{23}$$

Taking the $\frac{2}{3}$ power of both sides of Eq. (23), we have

$$(e')^{2/3} = e^{2/3} \left(1 + \frac{b}{pa}\right) \tag{24}$$

If the apparent electronic charge, e', is calculated using Eq. (19) and a plot is made of $(e')^{2/3}$ versus $1/pa$, a straight line should result if we have made the proper correction to Stokes' law.

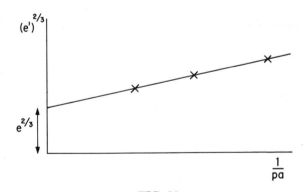

FIG. 10

Method of plotting data to reconcile deficiencies in Stokes' law when applied to small oil-drops.

A plot of data as shown above to correct Stokes' law is given in Fig. 10. The extrapolated intercept gives the value of $(e)^{2/3}$ for $1/pa = 0$, which corresponds to drops which are very large compared to the distance between gas molecules, so that Stokes' law could be expected to hold exactly. This intercept is thus the value of $e^{2/3}$, so that the correct value of the electronic charge is easily computed.

After making this correction, Millikan found the value

$$e = 4.770 \times 10^{-10} \text{ esu}$$

This value began to be doubted in 1928 when values of e from X-ray measurements gave somewhat higher values. This difficulty seems to be settled by the discovery by Kellstrom (in 1935) and others that Millikan had used too small a value for the viscosity of air. Recent determinations of e both by the oil-drop method and by X-rays give values in good agreement, the best modern value being

$$e = 4.8029 \times 10^{-10} \text{ esu} = 1.6021 \times 10^{-19} \text{ coul.}$$

If we use the most recent value of

$$\frac{e}{m} = 1.7589 \times 10^{11} \text{ coul/kg,}$$

the mass of the electron is found to be $m = 9.1086 \times 10^{-31}$ kg. Millikan's classic experiment thus not only confirms the atomicity of electricity, but also provides values of the charge and mass of the electron separately.

1.6 THE PROTON

An ionized hydrogen atom is called a *proton*. We shall see in Sec. 9.4 that the proton is one of the fundamental building blocks of all nuclei. Experimentally it is found that approximately 96,500 coulombs of electricity are required to release one gram of hydrogen electrolytically. Since one gram of hydrogen is a gram-atom, this amount of hydrogen contains 6.02×10^{23} atoms according to Avogadro's Law. Assuming that all protons carry the same charge, the value of this charge is given by

$$q = \frac{96,500}{6.02 \times 10^{23}} = 1.60 \times 10^{-19} \text{ coulomb} = 4.80 \times 10^{-10} \text{ esu}$$

This is identical with the charge of the electron as found by Millikan. However, if a stream of protons in a discharge tube is deflected electromagnetically, it is found that the sign of the proton charge is positive. Thus, the magnitude of the electron charge seems to be fundamental, and at least up to the present time, no experiments on ions or charged particles have uncovered any charge which is not an integral multiple of the magnitude of the electronic charge.

The charge-to-mass ratio of the proton is found to be 2.87×10^{14} esu/gram. Since the charges of the electron and the proton are the same, the proton is seen to be approximately 1840 times as heavy as the electron.

ADDITIONAL READING

Loeb, Leonard B., *Fundamental Processes of Electrical Discharges in Gases.* New York: John Wiley and Sons, 1939. A comprehensive study of gaseous conduction.

Millikan, Robert Andrews, *Electrons (+ and −), Protons, Photons, Neutrons, and Cosmic Rays.* Chicago: University of Chicago Press, 1935. An excellent account of the discovery of the electron and the measurement of the electronic charge by one of the major contributors.

Hoag, J. Barton and S. A. Korff, *Electron and Nuclear Physics.* Princeton, N. J.: D. Van Nostrand Co., 1948 (3rd Ed.). Numerous laboratory experiments are well-described for the student.

PROBLEMS

1. In a typical cathode ray tube (5BP1), electrostatic deflection plates 19 millimeters square and separated a distance of 5 millimeters are located a distance of 25 centimeters from the fluorescent face of the tube. Assume that the electric field between the plates is uniform and the deflection takes place only between the plates. Assume also that all the electrons have the same velocity, acquired by falling through a potential difference of 1500 volts between cathode and anode. Compute the deflection sensitivity of this tube; that is, compute the deflection of the beam at the fluorescent screen for each volt applied to the deflection plates. Look up the actual sensitivity of the 5BP1 tube and compare with your value.

   (*Ans.* 0.333 mm/volt)

2. A voltage of 10 kilovolts is applied to the anode of a cathode ray tube. The distance from the anode to the fluorescent screen is 0.5 meter. The axis of the tube is east-west. The earth's magnetic field is 0.5 gauss directed into the earth at an angle of 70° with the horizontal. Compute the magnitude and direction of the deflection of the electron beam by the earth's magnetic field.

3. Electrostatic deflection plates 2 centimeters apart have applied to them a potential of 3000 volts. A magnetic field of 1000 gauss is parallel to the plates and in such a direction that the electrostatic and magnetic forces on a beam of electrons passing between the plates are in opposite directions. Find the velocity of electrons which will pass between the plates undeflected. ⋅ (This is the principle of the velocity selector often used in mass spectrometers.)   (*Ans.* 1.5×10^8 cm/sec)

4. In a Millikan oil-drop experiment, oil of density 0.880 gm/cm³ is used in air at a temperature of 25°C. The average time for a certain drop to fall 0.269 centimeters is found to be 25.1 seconds. Neglecting the density of air, compute the radius of the drop. Look up needed data in the *Handbook of Physics and Chemistry*.

5. In the experiment described in Problem 4, a voltage of 1180 volts is applied between plates separated 0.845 centimeter. The drop is found to require an average time of 30.2 seconds to traverse 0.269 centimeter. Find how many electrons are on the drop and compute the value of the electronic charge. Neglect any correction to Stokes' law. (*Ans.* 3; 4.91 × 10⁻¹⁰ esu)

6. 1000 volts is applied between the anode and cathode of a plane diode, the separation between the electrodes being 5 millimeters. Assuming that electrons are emitted by the cathode with negligible velocity, compute the velocity with which electrons strike the anode and the time required for the transit of an electron between the two electrodes.

7. If the current between the electrodes of the diode described in Problem 6 is 100 milliamperes, compute the force exerted on the anode by the electron stream. (*Ans.* 1.07 dynes)

8. An electron is accelerated through a potential difference of V volts and then bent into a circular path of radius R meters by a magnetic field of strength B webers/m^2. Derive the following relation:

$$BR = 3.37 \times 10^{-6} \sqrt{V}$$

9. A particle of charge q and mass m suddenly appears in a region where there is a varying electric field given by

$$E_x = E \sin (\omega t - \alpha)$$

Take the origin at the point at which the particle first appears and begin counting time from the instant of the particle's appearance. Show that the position of the particle at later times is given by

$$x = \left(\frac{qE \cos \alpha}{m\omega}\right)t - \frac{qE \sin \alpha}{m\omega^2} - \left(\frac{qE}{m\omega^2}\right) \sin (\omega t - \alpha)$$

10. A cathode ray tube is located in a uniform magnetic field B which is parallel to the axis of the tube. Electrons emerge from the electron-gun structure with a velocity v making an angle θ with the magnetic field. Show that the electrons will next pass through the axis of the tube at a time given by $t = 2\pi m/qB$, and at a distance from the electron-gun given by $d = 2\pi mv \cos \theta/qB$.

11. Sketch the design of an electromagnetic deflection apparatus to measure the charge-to-mass ratio and the velocity of protons with velocities of the order of 10^9 centimeters per second. Compute all design parameters, such as distances and voltages, and adjust your design, if necessary, so that all parameters are reasonable laboratory values.

chapter two

the emission of electrons

Electrons may acquire enough energy to escape the forces at the surface of a metal in various ways. When the energy of an electron is acquired as a result of thermal agitation within the metal, we speak of *thermionic emission*. Similarly, an electron may receive energy from electromagnetic radiation, in which case we have *photoelectric emission*. Both processes are discussed in this chapter. In addition, electrons may be pulled through a metallic surface by a strong electric field, resulting in *field emission*, or by the impacts of electrons or other particles on the surface, leading to *secondary emission*. (Secondary emission is discussed in Sec. 8.2 in connection with the photomultiplier tube used in the detection of radiation.)

2.1. THERMIONIC EMISSION

At the beginning of the twentieth century only a few facts were known about the emission of electricity by hot bodies. For two centuries it was known that air in the vicinity of a hot conductor would itself become conducting. In 1873 Guthrie found that red-hot metals would retain a negative charge but not a positive charge. In 1883 Edison found that an electric current would flow through an evacuated bulb from an incandescent carbon filament to a cool filament only when the hot filament was at a negative potential with respect to the cool filament. In 1899 Thomson measured the charge-to-mass ratio of the negative ions emitted by hot metals and concluded that these ions were, very probably, cathode rays or electrons.

The systematic study of the emission of electricity by hot bodies began with Richardson's researches in 1902 and following years. Consider two electrodes contained in an evacuated bulb, as shown in Fig. 11. If the

filament is heated and a positive potential is applied to the plate, a current
is found to flow through the tube and the external circuit.   If the plate
potential is made negative, no current flows, showing the carriers of electricity emitted by the filament are negative in sign.   In view of Thomson's
work, these charges are known to be electrons.   While the electron flow is
from filament to plate, the reader should continually bear in mind that the
flow of conventional current is from plate to filament inside the tube.

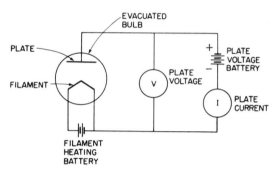

FIG. 11

Schematic of circuit used to study thermionic emission.

There are three variables involved in this phenomenon: the plate voltage, V, the tube current, I, and the temperature of the filament, T.   The
first two quantities are easily measured with meters, and the temperature
of the filament can be determined from the electrical resistance of the
filament or by using an optical pyrometer.   Two special cases will be considered, with either the plate voltage or the filament temperature being
held constant.

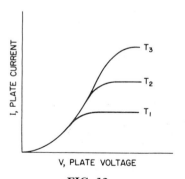

FIG. 12

Variation of plate current with plate
voltage at various constant values of
filament temperature ($T_3 > T_2 > T_1$).

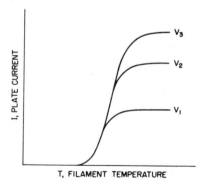

FIG. 13

Variation of plate current with filament
temperature at various constant values
of plate voltage ($V_3 > V_2 > V_1$).

If we keep the filament temperature constant, the variation of plate current with plate voltage is as shown in Fig. 12. Above a certain voltage, which depends on the filament temperature, all the electrons emitted by the filament are collected by the plate. In this case we speak of *voltage saturation*. At higher temperatures, the saturation voltage and corresponding saturation current are higher also.

Let us now consider the effect of maintaining the plate voltage constant while varying the temperature of the filament. The variation or plate current with temperature at various constant plate voltages is shown in Fig. 13. Because of the mutual repulsive forces between the electrons, some electrons will acquire velocities back toward the filament, where they may be re-absorbed. An equilibrium is set up such that the net emission from the filament is just sufficient to supply the plate current, and we say that the plate current is *space-charge limited*. At sufficiently high temperatures, for a given plate voltage, the current remains constant and we speak of *temperature saturation*. In practice, vacuum tubes are always operated with a large space-charge of electrons, so that the current is not limited by the temperature of the filament.

2.2. RICHARDSON'S EQUATIONS OF THERMIONIC EMISSION

In 1902 Richardson worked out a theory of the thermionic emission of electrons by metals which is quite similar to the kinetic theory of vaporization. The electrons inside a metal share the heat energy of the metal. Thus, each electron has a velocity which is continually being changed by collisions with atoms inside the metal. At any temperature, some of the electrons will possess sufficient kinetic energy to overcome the electrostatic forces at the surface of the metal and escape. Since the work done against these surface forces can be represented as $e\phi$, we speak of the electrostatic potential barrier of the surface, ϕ. The quantity $e\phi$ is called the *thermionic work function* of the surface. Since a larger fraction of the electrons in the metal will have the energy required for escape at higher temperatures, we would expect the emission current to increase with the temperature of the emitter, as is shown by Fig. 12.

Richardson's theory deals with the emission current per square centimeter of surface of the emitter. This emission current density is calculated from the saturation current of Fig. 12 by dividing by the area of the emitter, since in this case all the electrons emitted by the hot filament are collected by the plate. The form of the equation obtained depends on the assumption made regarding the dependence of the electron density inside the metal on temperature. If it is assumed that the electron density is independent of temperature, for the emission current density the expression is as follows:

$$i = A T^{1/2} \exp\left(-\frac{e\phi}{kT}\right) \tag{25}$$

In Eq. (25), A is a constant, T is the absolute temperature of the filament, $e\phi$ is the work function of the filament, and k is Boltzmann's constant $(1.38 \times 10^{-23}$ joule/degree). On the other hand, if the electron density is assumed to vary as the $\frac{3}{2}$ power of T, then Richardson obtained the relation

$$i = A T^2 \exp\left(-\frac{e\phi}{kT}\right) \tag{26}$$

In deciding between the two forms of Richardson's equation for the emission current, first take the logarithm of each side of Eq. (25) or (26). Letting n be equal to $\frac{1}{2}$ or 2 in the two cases, we find

$$\ln i = \ln A + n \ln T - \frac{e\phi}{kT} \tag{27}$$

The factor involving $1/T$ completely swamps the factor involving $\ln T$, so that experimentally no choice can be made between the values of $n = \frac{1}{2}$ and $n = 2$. However, Laue, Dushman, and Sommerfeld have shown that the correct quantum mechanical solution of this problem leads to Eq. (26). Furthermore, this theory predicts that the constant A should have the value 120 amp/cm²/deg². In addition, electrons which have sufficient energy to pass through the metal surface may be reflected according to quantum mechanics. (This is somewhat similar to the tunnel effect discussed in Sec. 5.6.) If R is the probability that an electron will be reflected at the metallic surface, then the constant A must be multiplied by the factor $(1 - R)$.

From Richardson's equations it is clear that the lower the value of ϕ for a surface, the greater the emission current density at a given temperature. Values of the work function, $e\phi$, are of the order of a volt or a few volts for clean metallic surfaces freshly prepared in vacuum. Using the effect of surface impurities on the work function is a complicated but very useful art. For instance, a wolfram filament has its work function reduced from 4.52 ev to about 2.6 ev by coating the surface of the filament with a layer of thorium about one atom thick. Wehnelt found that rubbing platinum with sealing wax, for instance, lowers the work function considerably. Many types of Wehnelt filaments are now used. If carbonates are sprayed on filaments, which are then flashed in vacuum, oxides are formed at the surface of the filament, greatly reducing the work function. Some approximate data for various types of filaments are given in Table 1.

TABLE 1

COMPARISON OF THERMIONIC EMISSION CHARACTERISTICS OF VARIOUS COMMONLY USED FILAMENTS

Emitter	Wolfram	Thoriated Wolfram	Wehnelt	Oxide-coated
Temperature °K	2370	1900	1200	1100
Current/cm²/watt	3 ma	100 ma	18 ma	30 ma

As an example of the use of Eq. (26), let us compute the current emitted by a piece of wolfram wire two centimeters long and one millimeter in diameter when kept at a temperature of 2000°K. Neglecting the ends of the wire, the area of emitting surface is

$$\text{Area} = \pi(0.1)(2) = 0.628 \text{ cm}^2$$

Assuming that the value of ϕ for wolfram is 4.52 volts, the exponent in Eq. (26) has the value

$$\frac{e\phi}{kT} = \frac{(1.6 \times 10^{-19} \text{ coul}) \times 4.52 \text{ volts}}{(1.38 \times 10^{-23} \text{ joule/deg}) \times 2000°K} = 26.2$$

Assuming the value of the constant, A, to be 60 amperes per square centimeter, which corresponds to $R = \frac{1}{2}$, the emission current density is then

$$i = 60 \times (2000)^2 \times e^{-26.2} = 1.01 \times 10^{-3} \text{ amp/cm}^2$$

The current emitted by the piece of wire specified is then

$$I = 0.628 \times 1.01 \times 10^{-3} = 0.634 \times 10^{-3} \text{ amp} = 0.634 \text{ ma}$$

2.3. PHOTOELECTRIC EMISSION

The second mechanism by which an electron can acquire enough energy to penetrate the potential barrier at the surface of a metal is by the absorption of electromagnetic radiation, such as visible light. This phenomenon was first observed by Hertz in 1887 during his famous experiments which confirmed Maxwell's electromagnetic theory, but Hertz did not investigate this new effect to any great extent. In Hertz' experiment, an induction coil caused a spark to pass between two metal balls. When a similar receiver was tuned properly, a spark would pass between the balls of the receiver. Hertz noticed that the length of the spark which could be produced at the receiver was increased when light from the transmitter spark was allowed to fall on the balls of the receiver. By letting the visible light be absorbed, Hertz also showed that the effect was produced by ultra-violet light. This peculiar effect of ultraviolet light on metals could have led Hertz to the discovery of the photoelectric effect.

A year later Hallwachs studied this phenomenon and he is usually given credit for the discovery of the photoelectric effect, which is sometimes called the *Hallwachs effect*. Consider the arrangement shown in Fig. 14. If light is allowed to fall on the zinc plate, it is found that the zinc plate loses a negative charge which can be collected by placing a positive potential on the anode. In 1889 Elster and Geitel showed that a transverse magnetic field, perpendicular to the line between the cathode and the anode, decreased the current, and that the carriers of electricity between the zinc plate and the anode must be negative in sign. Since the current persisted even when the tube was evacuated, the gas molecules could not be the carriers of the electricity. Finally, it was shown that the molecules of the zinc were not knocked off and carried over to the anode.

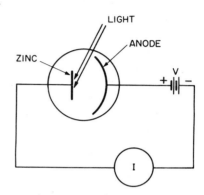

FIG. 14

Schematic of apparatus used to investigate the photoelectric effect.

After Thomson's discovery of the electron in 1897, it was suspected that the carriers of electricity between the zinc and the anode were electrons. In 1900 Lenard measured the charge-to-mass ratio of photoelectric particles by magnetic deflection and found the same value as Thomson had found for the electron. Thus, in some way light must eject electrons from certain metals. In fact, even visible light will produce photoelectrons from some metals. It is interesting to note that if zinc is illuminated with plane polarized light, the photoelectric current increases when the electric vector of the polarized light is rotated so as to have a larger component perpendicular to the zinc surface.

2.4. LAWS OF PHOTOELECTRICITY

Consider a surface in vacuum irradiated by monochromatic light, as in Fig. 14, and let a sufficiently high voltage be applied to the anode to collect all the electrons emitted photoelectrically. We then speak of the *total photoelectric current*. If there is any photoelectric emission at all for the wavelength and surface used, it is found that the total photoelectric current is strictly proportional to the light intensity. This proportionality between total photoelectric current and light intensity holds over a range of intensities varying by a factor of more than 10^8—from intensities too weak for the eye to see up to intensities too strong for the eye to view, such as direct sunlight. This proportionality also holds for light sources emitting a mixture of wavelengths, provided that the relative distribution of energy in the spectrum remains the same as the intensity is varied.

Surfaces are not equally sensitive to various wavelengths of the same intensity. The photoelectric current for various wavelengths of constant intensity is shown for various surfaces in Fig. 15. An important feature

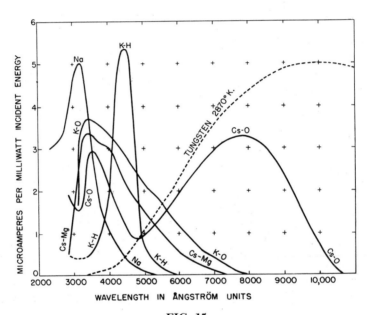

FIG. 15

Photoelectric response of various surfaces as a function of incident wavelength. (The thermal emission of tungsten at 2870°K is also shown.) (From *Procedures in Experimental Physics*, by Strong. Prentice-Hall, 1938.)

of these curves is that the current stops entirely at an upper wavelength limit, called the *threshold wavelength*. For any wavelength longer than the threshold wavelength, no photoelectric current is observed, regardless of the intensity of the incident light.

The threshold wavelength and the variation of current with wavelength depend greatly on the nature of the surface and its manner of preparation. Surfaces of caesium and caesium oxide are quite different, for instance. The preparation of surfaces with desired characteristics is almost an art which must be learned by experience.

Except for the possibly disturbing fact that, for a given surface, light of wavelength less than a certain threshold value must be used to produce any photoelectrons at all, the dependence of the photoelectric current on wavelength and intensity is not at all surprising. Even the shape of the curves of Fig. 15 is no more radical than absorption curves of optical filters, for instance. The break which the photoelectric effect makes with classical physics shows up clearly when the energies of individual photoelectrons are considered.

The energy with which photoelectrons are emitted can be measured in various ways, the best of which involve subjecting the electrons to a retarding electric field or deflecting them with a magnetic field. The standard method is to measure the current collected by the anode of a tube similar to the one shown in Fig. 14 as a function of the anode voltage. Even when the anode is several volts negative, some current flows. This indicates that some electrons are ejected from the cathode with sufficient velocity to allow them to overcome a retarding potential of several volts. The potential, V_s, which completely cuts off all the current, is called the *stopping potential* for that particular surface and illumination.

The velocity of the most energetic electrons, which are just stopped by the stopping potential, can be computed from conservation of energy. [See derivation of Eq. (12).] We have then

$$(\tfrac{1}{2}mv^2)_{\max} = eV_s \tag{28}$$

However, the velocity of these electrons is seldom computed, but instead the energy of the fastest photoelectrons is expressed in terms of electron-volts. That is, if the stopping potential for a particular tube is 2.13 volts, then the most energetic electrons have an energy of 2.13 electron-volts.

If the stopping potential for a given surface irradiated by monochromatic light is measured as a function of the light intensity, a surprising result is obtained: the stopping potential is found to be independent of the light intensity. Thus, the maximum energy of electrons emitted by the surface is not changed by increasing the amount of energy striking the surface per unit time.

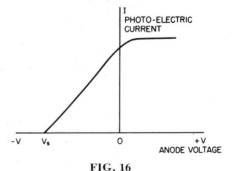

FIG. 16

Variation of total photoelectric current as a function of anode voltage for a given surface and irradiation.

This is clearly unexpected, since a greater incident energy should give more energy to each electron emitted.

However, if the stopping potential is measured for various frequencies of incident monochromatic light, we find the straight line shown in Fig. 17. As in the case of the total photoelectric current, there is a definite threshold frequency, and at lower frequencies absolutely no electrons are emitted. Above the threshold, the stopping potential and thus the maximum energy of the electrons emitted is linear with increasing frequency.

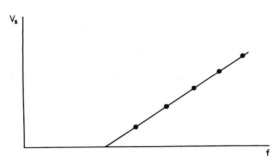

FIG. 17
Variation of stopping potential with frequency of light for a typical photoelectric surface.

To summarize the laws of photoelectricity, we have found the following facts to be true experimentally

1. The total photoelectric current is proportional to the intensity of the light striking the surface.

2. For any surface a threshold of frequency (or wavelength) exists, such that at frequencies below the threshold, no photoelectrons are emitted, no matter how great the intensity.

3. The maximum energy of the photoelectrons is independent of the light intensity.

4. The maximum energy of the photoelectrons is linearly related to the frequency of the light.

While Item 1 is in accord with classical expectations, Item 2 involves a discontinuity which is quite surprising. Item 3 is not at all what one might expect on any classical grounds, while Item 4 is quite unexplained. Clearly, the absorption of light and the emission of photoelectrons must require an explanation completely different from classical electromagnetic theory. Before presenting Einstein's theory of the photoelectric effect, we will discuss some fundamental characteristics of sources of radiant energy.

2.5. SOURCES OF RADIANT ENERGY

For reasons of convenience, the spectrum of electromagnetic radiations is broken up into various ranges, depending on the methods of generating and detecting radiations of various wavelengths. A conventional breakdown of this sort is shown in Fig. 18. However, the only essential differences among these sources of radiant energy is in their wavelength (or frequency). The various ranges overlap, and the division of the spectrum into discrete bands is simply a matter of convenient terminology.

The wavelengths which are involved in photoelectric effects lie almost entirely in the near infrared, visible, and ultraviolet regions of the spectrum. To be concrete, we will be concerned with wavelengths in the range of 1000 to 10,000 angstroms (10^{-5} to 10^{-4} centimeters), with corresponding frequencies ranging from 3×10^{15} to 3×10^{14} cycles per second. The sources of radiation which produce wavelengths of this order may be grouped into three classes: excited gases and vapors, luminescent materials, and thermal radiators. Since the study of thermal radiators led Planck to the idea of the discreteness of energy transfer by radiation, we will confine our present discussion to this type of radiation source.

2.6. BLACK-BODY RADIATION

Thermal radiators are incandescent materials which emit electromagnetic radiations by virtue of their temperature, for example, the sun, the tungsten lamp, and the carbon arc. An idealized thermal radiator is the *black body*, which has the property of absorbing all of the radiation falling on it. It can be shown by a thermodynamic argument that all black bodies also have the same emission characteristic at a given temperature. The *absorptivity* of a real body is defined as the fraction of the radiant energy striking the body which is absorbed by the body; in general, the absorptivity depends on the wavelength used and the temperature of the body. It can be shown that the emissive power of any body at a particular temperature and wavelength is equal to the emissive power of a black body for the same temperature and wavelength multiplied by the absorptivity of the body under those conditions. Thus, if the emissive properties of an ideal black body are known, the emissive properties of any actual body can be easily determined from a knowledge of the body's absorptivity at the particular temperature and wavelength. It is obvious that no other thermal radiator can emit radiation more intensely than a black body of the same temperature.

A black body can be very well approximated by a small hole in the wall of a cavity which is lined with lampblack. Nearly all of the radiation entering the hole will be absorbed by successive reflections inside the cavity, so

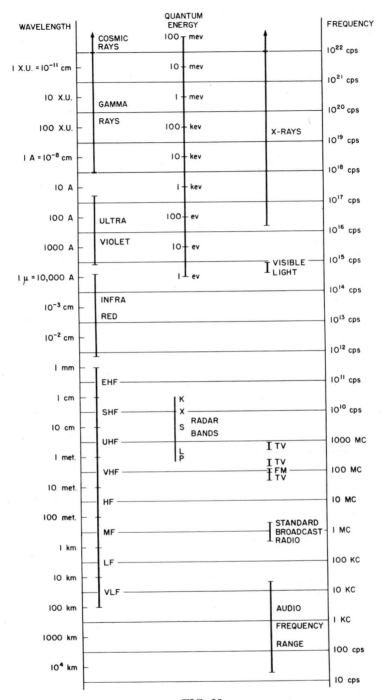

FIG. 18
The electromagnetic spectrum.

36

that the hole almost exactly satisfies the definition of a black body.   If the cavity is maintained at a particular temperature, the radiation emerging from the hole will be very nearly that of a black body.

In 1879 Stefan found experimentally that the emissive power of a black body is proportional to the fourth power of the absolute temperature of the black body.   In 1884 Boltzmann derived this relation from the laws of thermodynamics.   In the form of an equation, the *Stefan-Boltzmann law* becomes

$$E = \sigma T^4$$

$$\sigma = 5.6699 \times 10^{-8} \text{ joule m}^2 \text{ sec}^{-1} \text{ deg}^{-4} \quad (29)$$

This expression for the total rate of emission of radiant energy by a black body will later be derived from Planck's theory of black body radiation.

Investigation of the distribution of energy in the spectrum of a black body also provides useful information.   In this case we are interested in the *monochromatic emissive power* of a black body, E_λ, which is the energy emitted between wavelengths λ and $(\lambda + d\lambda)$. Lummer and Pringsheim carefully measured this spectral distribution in 1899, and typical curves for a black body at various temperatures are shown in Figure 19.   The product of the temperature at which a particular curve of Fig. 19 is measured and the wavelength at which the curve has a maximum, is found to be constant.   This is a special case of *Wien's displacement law*, which may be written as follows:

$$\lambda_{max} T = 2.8976 \times 10^{-3} \text{ meter deg} \quad (30)$$

The task of theory is to fit the curves of Fig. 19 and lead to Eqs. (29) and (30).

By making certain special assumptions concerning the process of absorption and emission, Wien arrived at an expression for E_λ which is given below:

$$E_\lambda = \frac{a}{\lambda^5 \exp \dfrac{b}{\lambda T}} \quad (31)$$

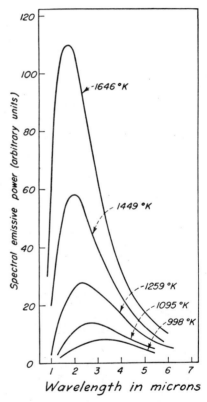

FIG. 19

Relative emission of a black body at different temperatures as a function of wavelength.   (From *Physics*, by Shortley and Williams, vol. 1.   Prentice-Hall, 1950).

Wien's formula holds true for short wavelengths, if the constants a and b are properly chosen, but is ineffective for long wavelengths. In 1900 Rayleigh suggested the application of statistical mechanics to this problem. In terms of the Boltzmann constant, k, (defined later in Sec. 7.1) the Rayleigh-Jeans formula for E_λ is given below:

$$E_\lambda = \frac{2\pi ckT}{\lambda^4} \tag{32}$$

Equation (32) is successful for long wavelengths, but it is clearly not correct in general, since it predicts that the spectral emission per unit wavelength should increase indefinitely at short wavelengths. Since Eq. (32) is accepted as the correct result of classical theory, apparently a radically different theory must be used to get agreement within the whole range of experiment.

2.7. THE PLANCK RADIATION LAW

In 1901, Planck solved the problem of black-body radiation by introducing a completely new concept regarding the possible energies of electrical oscillators. Since at that time the electromagnetic theory of light was well established, it seemed clear that black-body radiation was produced by electrical oscillators in the walls of the isothermal enclosure. He assumed that the energy of an oscillator of frequency f could have only one of the values 0, hf, $2hf$, etc., where h is a constant now known as *Planck's constant*. The classical case could then be found in the limit as h was allowed to approach zero. The first part of the problem is to determine the average energy of a collection of oscillators of frequency f in thermal equilibrium at a temperature T. Next the number of modes of vibration of electromagnetic waves in the frequency range from f to $(f + df)$ must be found. Finally we must compute the monochromatic emissive power E_λ from the energy striking a unit area per unit time per unit wavelength. The result is the Planck radiation law.

Consider a collection of N systems in thermal equilibrium. According to the classical statistical mechanics of Maxwell and Boltzmann, the number N_i of systems having the energy E_i is proportional to $e^{-E_i/kT}$ where e is the base of natural logarithms, and k is the Boltzmann constant defined in Sec. 7.1. Introducing a constant of proportionality C, we can write

$$N_i = CNe^{-E_i/kT} \tag{33}$$

Summing the whole collection we have

$$\Sigma N_i = N = CN \Sigma (e^{-E_i/kT}) \tag{34}$$

Thus, for the constant C we find the value

$$\frac{1}{C} = \Sigma \, (e^{-E_i/kT}) \qquad (35)$$

For any collection in thermal equilibrium, the average energy per system in the collection is given by

$$\bar{E} = \frac{\Sigma \, N_i E_i}{\Sigma \, N_i} = \frac{CN \, \Sigma \, E_i e^{-E_i/kT}}{N} = \frac{\Sigma \, E_i e^{-E_i/kT}}{\Sigma \, e^{-E_i/kT}} \qquad (36)$$

The result given in Eq. (36) is general for any collection of systems in thermal equilibrium, regardless of restrictions which may or may not be imposed on the energies of the individual systems.

Following Planck, we will now restrict the energies of the electrical oscillators in a thermal enclosure to the values

$$E_n = 0, \, hf, \, 2hf, \, \ldots, \, nhf, \, \ldots \qquad (n = \text{integer}) \qquad (37)$$

The average energy of a collection of oscillators of frequency f is

$$\bar{E} = \frac{\displaystyle\sum_{n=0}^{\infty} nhf e^{-nhf/kT}}{\displaystyle\sum_{n=0}^{\infty} e^{-nhf/kT}} \qquad (38)$$

In order to evaluate the summations in Eq. (38), put $x = hf/kT$. We then have

$$\bar{E} = hf \frac{\Sigma \, n e^{-nx}}{\Sigma \, e^{-nx}} \qquad (39)$$

Expanding the summation in the denominator of Eq. (39), we find

$$S = \sum_{0}^{\infty} e^{-nx} = 1 + e^{-x} + e^{-2x} \ldots = \frac{1}{1 - e^{-x}} \qquad (40)$$

Since this summation is absolutely convergent, we can differentiate it, term by term, obtaining

$$\frac{dS}{dx} = -\sum_{0}^{\infty} n e^{-nx} = \frac{-e^{-x}}{(1 - e^{-x})^2} \qquad (41)$$

When we substitute Eq. (40) and (41) into Eq. (39) we find

$$\bar{E} = \frac{hf}{e^{hf/kT} - 1} \qquad (42)$$

Eq. (42) gives the average energy of an oscillator of frequency f, provided the possible energies of such oscillators are quantized according to Eq. (38).

The next problem is the computation of the number of oscillators with frequencies between f and $(f + df)$, or wavelengths between λ and $(\lambda + d\lambda)$. Here we must calculate the number of modes of vibration of the medium, by which we mean the number of standing waves which satisfy certain boundary conditions.

We will begin by considering one-dimensional oscillations on a stretched wire of length L. If we take the X-axis along the wire, and let u be the displacement of any part of the wire, the wave equation then takes the form

$$v^2 \frac{\partial^2 u}{\partial x^2} = \frac{\partial^2 u}{\partial t^2} \tag{43}$$

In Eq. (43), v is the velocity of the wave along the wire. If the wire is fixed at $x = 0$ and $x = L$, $u = 0$ at these points. It is easily seen by substitution of $x = 0$ or $x = L$, that the following function satisfies the boundary conditions:

$$u = A \sin \frac{n\pi x}{L} \cos (\omega_n t) \qquad (n = \text{integer}) \tag{44}$$

When Eq. (44) is substituted into Eq. (43), we find that this is a solution of the wave equation, provided that $\omega_n = n\pi v/L$. Since the frequency is given by

$$f_n = \frac{\omega_n}{2\pi} = \frac{nv}{2L} \tag{45}$$

we find that the number of modes of vibration or standing waves dn in the frequency interval from f to $(f + df)$ is given by

$$dn = \frac{2L}{v} df \tag{46}$$

In the case of vibrations in three dimensions, the wave equation takes the form

$$v^2 \left(\frac{\partial^2 u}{\partial x^2} + \frac{\partial^2 u}{\partial y^2} + \frac{\partial^2 u}{\partial z^2} \right) = \frac{\partial^2 u}{\partial t^2} \tag{47}$$

If the material is a cube of side L, and no displacements are permitted at the faces, then a function which satisfies the boundary conditions is

$$u = A \sin \frac{n_x \pi x}{L} \sin (n_y \pi y/L) \sin (n_z \pi z/L) \cos (\omega t) \tag{48}$$

$(n_x, n_y,$ and n_z are integers)

If we substitute Eq. (48) into Eq. (47), we find that Eq. (48) is a solution of the wave equation, provided that ω satisfies the following relation:

$$\left(\frac{\omega}{v}\right)^2 = \left(\frac{n_x\pi}{L}\right)^2 + \left(\frac{n_y\pi}{L}\right)^2 + \left(\frac{n_z\pi}{L}\right)^2 \qquad (49)$$

Solving Eq. (49) for the frequency $f = \omega/2\pi$, we find

$$f^2 = \left(\frac{v}{2L}\right)^2 (n_x^2 + n_y^2 + n_z^2) \qquad (50)$$

Again we wish to know the number of modes of vibration between f and $(f + df)$.

Consider a network of points in the first octant, each point being determined by a set of values of the integers n_x, n_y and n_z. We can write Eq. (50) in the following form, which is the equation of a sphere:

$$n_x^2 + n_y^2 + n_z^2 = \left(\frac{2Lf}{v}\right)^2 \qquad (51)$$

On the average each point occupies unit volume, since each cubical unit volume has eight points at its corners, but each point serves as a corner for eight unit volumes. The number of points, dN, between R and $(R + dR)$ is then

$$dN = \frac{1}{8} 4\pi R^2 dR = \frac{\pi}{2}\left(\frac{2Lf}{v}\right)^2\left(\frac{2Ldf}{v}\right)$$

$$= 4\pi\left(\frac{L}{v}\right)^3 f^2 df \qquad (52)$$

The number of modes of vibration per unit volume, dn, is then seen to be

$$dn = \frac{dN}{L^3} = \frac{4\pi f^2}{v^3}\, df \qquad (53)$$

The frequency is related to the wavelength λ by the equation $f\lambda = v$. Therefore $df = -v d\lambda/\lambda^2$. From Eq. (53), the number of modes per unit volume between λ and $(\lambda - d\lambda)$ is $-4\pi d\lambda/\lambda^4$. Therefore the number of modes per unit volume between λ and $(\lambda + d\lambda)$ is given by

$$dn = \frac{4\pi d\lambda}{\lambda^4} \qquad (54)$$

In the case of transverse waves there are two modes for each frequency, so that Eq. (54) must be doubled when applied to electromagnetic waves.

We will now consider quantized electromagnetic waves with an average energy given by Eq. (42), and with a number of modes per unit volume twice the value given in Eq. (54). Then the radiant energy per unit volume in the range from λ to $(\lambda + d\lambda)$, ϕ_λ, is given by

$$\phi_\lambda \, d\lambda = \bar{E} \, dn = \frac{8\pi \, d\lambda}{\lambda^4} \frac{hf}{e^{hf/kT} - 1} = \frac{8\pi ch/\lambda^5 \, d\lambda}{e^{hc/\lambda kT} - 1} \tag{55}$$

Now consider N beams of electromagnetic radiation, each of energy density u, so that the total energy density, ϕ, is given by

$$\phi = Nu \tag{56}$$

Consider a surface of unit area. Beams will strike this surface, at random, from all directions. The number, dN_θ, which strike the surface between angles θ and $(\theta + d\theta)$ with the normal to the surface, is given by the following expression:

$$dN_\theta = N \frac{2\pi \sin \theta \, d\theta}{4\pi} = \frac{N}{2} \sin \theta \, d\theta \tag{57}$$

Since the beams travel with the velocity of light, c, the energy per unit time per unit area, dE, due to the beams hitting the surface between angles θ and $(\theta + d\theta)$ is given by

$$dE = (cu \cos \theta) \, dN_\theta = (cu \cos \theta) \left(\frac{N}{2} \sin \theta \, d\theta \right) \tag{58}$$

The total energy per unit time per unit area striking the surface is

$$E = \frac{Ncu}{2} \int_0^{\pi/2} \cos \theta \sin \theta \, d\theta = \frac{Ncu}{4} = \frac{c\phi}{4} \tag{59}$$

The relation given in Eq. (59) between the total energy per unit time per unit area, E, and the total energy density, ϕ, also holds between the corresponding quantities per unit wavelength. Thus, for the monochromatic emissive power or emissivity, E_λ, we have the expression

$$E_\lambda = \frac{c}{4} \phi_\lambda \tag{60}$$

When we combine Eq. (60) with Eq. (55) we obtain

$$E_\lambda = \frac{2\pi hc^2}{\lambda^5} (e^{hc/\lambda kT} - 1)^{-1} \tag{61}$$

Eq. (61) is Planck's radiation law.

Planck's radiation law is successful in predicting the spectral distribution of radiation from a black body over the entire range of experiment. It is not difficult to show that Planck's law reduces to Eq. (31) for short wavelengths and to Eq. (32) for long wavelengths. The Stefan-Boltzmann law can be derived from Eq. (61) by integration over all wavelengths. Then we have

$$E = \int_0^\infty E_\lambda \, d\lambda = 2\pi h c^2 \int_0^\infty \frac{1}{\exp\left(\dfrac{ch}{\lambda k T}\right) - 1} \frac{d\lambda}{\lambda^5} \tag{62}$$

The definite integral in Eq. (62) can be converted into a standard form. The result of the integration is

$$E = \frac{2\pi^5 k^4}{15 c^2 h^3} T^4 \tag{63}$$

Equation (63) is seen to be exactly the same as Eq. (29), and a numerical evaluation of the constant, σ, from Eq. (63) agrees with the experimental value of σ. Finally, the Wien displacement law of Eq. (30) can be derived from Planck's law by differentiating Eq. (61) and equating this derivative to zero.

We see that Planck's formula does reproduce correctly the data on black-body radiation, regardless of the fact that his assumption about the properties of electrical oscillators is arbitrary. If Planck's constant, h, is treated as a constant known from other phenomena (for instance, the photoelectric effect, discussed in the next section), Planck's formula and the deductions from it agree quantitatively with black-body observations, without any adjustable parameters. This remarkable theory was the origin of Einstein's theory of the photoelectric effect, Bohr's theory of atomic spectra, and the varied aspects and effects of quantum theory.

2.8. EINSTEIN'S THEORY OF PHOTOELECTRICITY

Planck's hypothesis that the electrical oscillators involved in black-body radiation emitted radiation in discrete units or quanta, provided the key to the photoelectric effect, too. In 1905, Einstein hypothesized that light was absorbed in quanta, the energy of a quantum of frequency f being hf. If this were true, a given electron at the surface of a metal would receive either all the energy of a given quantum or no energy at all. The energy incident on the surface of a metal would not be spread evenly, but instead, only certain electrons would receive any energy at all.

Let us assume that a certain energy, W, is used up by the electron in overcoming the surface forces as the electron escapes from the metal. If the electron originates below the surface, additional energy may be used up in reaching the surface. For electrons originating at the surface or electrons which lose no energy in reaching the surface, the kinetic energy after escaping the surface will be a maximum. This maximum kinetic energy will be the difference between the energy brought in by the quantum of radiation, hf, and the energy used up at the surface, W. Then we have

$$(\tfrac{1}{2}mv^2)_{\max} = hf - W \tag{64}$$

Returning to Eq. (28), which relates the maximum kinetic energy of photoelectrons to their stopping potential, we have the following equations:

$$eV_s = (\tfrac{1}{2}mv^2)_{\max} = hf - W \tag{65}$$

$$V_s = \frac{h}{e}f - \frac{W}{e} \tag{66}$$

The discussion above and Eqs. (64)–(66) give a clear picture of the mechanism of photoelectric emission of electrons and explain the experimental laws of this phenomenon. We see that if the energy of the incident quantum is less than the energy needed to free an electron from the surface, no emission can take place, regardless of light intensity or the number of quanta which strike the surface per second. The threshold frequency, below which no emission can take place, is seen to be given by W/h. In addition, Eqs. (64)–(66) show that the maximum kinetic energy and the stopping potential are independent of the light intensity, but linearly related to the frequency of the incident light. Thus, the theory accounts for three laws of photoelectricity which could not be explained on classical grounds.

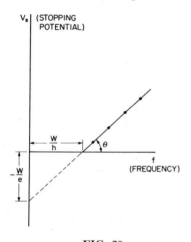

FIG. 20

Plot of stopping potential of photo-electrons vs. frequency of incident light in order to verify Einstein's photoelectric equation.

At the time that Einstein proposed the theory of photoelectric emission given above, the data were not accurate enough to test the equations accurately. Millikan carefully verified Eq. (66), with results similar to those sketched in Fig. 20. From Eq. (39), it is seen that the slope of the straight line obtained when V_s is plotted against f should be given by

$$\tan \theta = \frac{h}{e} \tag{67}$$

The intercepts on the f axis and V_s axis respectively are seen to be W/h and $-W/e$. The quantity W/e is called the *photoelectric work function* of the surface, analogous to the thermionic work function. From a determination of the slope of this curve, Millikan found for h the value 6.55×10^{-27} erg-seconds, which agrees with the value obtained by black-body measurements.

Let us calculate the energy carried by a single quantum or photon of frequency, f, and energy, hf.   This energy is

$$E = hf = h\frac{c}{\lambda} \tag{68}$$

Since, experimentally, wavelengths are commonly measured in angstrom units and a convenient unit of energy is the electron-volt, it will be useful to have an equation relating these quantities.   Remembering that one electron-volt equals 1.60×10^{-19} joule, we have

$$E \text{ (ev)} = \frac{hc/\lambda}{1.60 \times 10^{-19}} = \frac{1}{\lambda}\frac{6.62 \times 10^{-34} \times 3 \times 10^8}{1.60 \times 10^{-19}}$$

After performing the arithmetic indicated, we find the desired relation, first given by Duane and Hunt in 1915, to be

$$E \text{ (ev)} = \frac{12{,}396.44}{\lambda \text{ (A.U.)}} \tag{69}$$

The numerator of Eq. (69) is often remembered as "12,345", which is correct to better than 0.5 percent.

To summarize Einstein's theory of the photoelectric effect, for which he received the Nobel prize in 1921, the key hypothesis is that radiation is absorbed in quanta of energy, hf, with a single electron receiving all the energy of a given quantum.   The application of the principle of conservation of energy leads to Eqs. (64)–(66), which agree both qualitatively and quantitatively with the experimental facts of photoelectricity.

2.9. THERMIONIC AND PHOTOELECTRIC WORK FUNCTIONS

In the theory of thermionic emission, we assumed that an electron must do an amount of work, $e\phi$, in order to escape from the surface.   Similarly, in the case of the photoelectric emission of electrons, we assumed the electron to lose an amount of energy, W, in passing through the surface.   Since the mechanism of escape seems to be the same, regardless of the manner in which the electron acquires its energy, we should expect the thermionic work function, ϕ, and the photoelectric work function, W/e, to be the same for a given surface.

Unfortunately, the hypothesis above is only approximately confirmed, even for clean and newly-prepared metallic surfaces.   Table 2 gives some typical values taken from the text of Hughes and DuBridge (see references at end of chapter).   A complete survey of this field is given in the

TABLE 2

COMPARISON OF THERMIONIC AND PHOTOELECTRIC WORK FUNCTIONS

	Pt	Rh	Ta	Ag	Au
ϕ (volts):	6.27	4.58	4.07	4.08	4.42
W/e (volts):	6.30	4.57	4.05	4.73	4.82

article "Work Functions of the Elements" by Herbert B. Michaelson, *Journal of Applied Physics,* **21,** No. 6, June, 1950, pages 536–540. Possibly additional experimental or theoretical work will clear up these discrepancies satisfactorily.

2.10. PHOTOELECTRIC CELLS AND THEIR APPLICATIONS

A photoelectric cell is usually a two-electrode vacuum tube, containing a photosensitive cathode and an anode maintained at some positive potential.

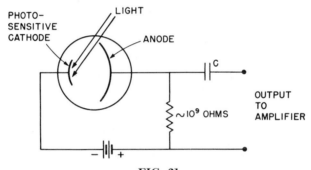

FIG. 21
Typical phototube circuit.

Since the output of the cell is quite small, an amplifier is used to amplify the small photoelectric currents, as shown in Fig. 21. The amount of amplification used depends on the type of application and the device which the circuit is to actuate.

To obtain larger currents from photoelectric cells, they are often filled with a small amount of some monatomic gas, such as argon, at a pressure of a few millimeters of mercury. Gaseous multiplication factors of the order of ten can be obtained through the electron avalanche discussed in connection with cathode rays in Chapter 1. At low voltages there is little or no gas amplification, and the current-voltage characteristic of the cell is the same as if it were evacuated. Fig. 22 shows the typical characteristic curve of such a cell, both with and without a gas filling. Higher voltages applied to the gas phototube lead to a self-sustaining glow discharge, so that high gas amplification factors cannot be obtained.

Phototubes have numerous applications in modern society.   The sound accompanying motion pictures is translated from the sound track on the film into sound by a source of light and a phototube.   Phototubes may be used to count objects such as cars pass-ing a given point, by having the output of the phototube actuate a relay each time the beam of light striking the phototube is interrupted.   The photoelectric effect is also used in the image orthicon tube, which is used as a television camera tube. Phototubes which are sensitive to infra-red may be used for confidential light-beam signalling or to detect hot bodies; an application of this idea during World War II was called a *snooperscope*.   Additional applications of phototubes, such as illumi-nation control, automatic door opening, photoelectric safety devices, and photo-

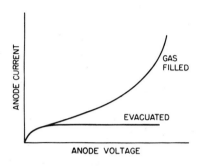

FIG. 22

Typical phototube characteristics, showing increase in current because of gas amplification.

electric controls of industrial processes, are almost limitless.   The inter-ested reader is referred to the book listed at the end of this chapter, by Zworykin and Ramberg, for additional information.

2.11. MISCELLANEOUS PHOTOELECTRIC EFFECTS

When light is passed through certain gases and vapors, particularly vapors of the alkali metals, electrons may be liberated.   The atoms or molecules of the vapor are ionized by light in this process of *photo-ionization,* but the cur-rents produced are very small.   Peaks of current occur at wavelengths which are the natural emission wavelengths of the optical spectrum of the vapor. The reason for this will be clear after the study of Chapter 4, where atomic structure and energy levels are treated.

Photo-ionization also can take place in certain solids, such as selenium and diamond, giving the effect known as *photoconductivity.*   The crystal may be mounted, as shown in Fig. 23, between

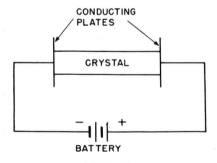

FIG. 23

Arrangement for studying photo-conductivity.

two metal plates at different potentials.   Two effects are observed when the crystal is irradiated with light of the proper wavelength.   Electrons are set free inside the crystal, producing the *primary current*. As the primary current passes through the crystal, the number of free electrons in the crystal is increased, resulting in a lowering of the original electrical resistance of the crystal. (All practical photoconductors are also semi-conductors, possessing large, but not infinite, resistivities.) This reduction in the resistance of the crystal also produces an increase in the current through the crystal. This component of current is called the *secondary current*. The secondary current usually is very much larger than the primary current, completely masking the primary current.

Selenium cells are commonly used as photoconductors, since they have the high sensitivity of approximately one electron per quantum of visible light. Since the sensitivity of such a cell is proportional to the potential difference across it, voltages just below the breakdown voltage of the cell are possible. By way of comparison, for a light flux of one lumen, a typical photoelectric vacuum cell will produce 20 microamperes, a typical gas-filled phototube will produce 80 microamperes, and a selenium photo-conducting cell will produce 260 microamperes. Thallous sulfide is also often used, since it is somewhat more sensitive than selenium, while lead sulfide cells are used in the far infra-red range.

No external source of voltage is needed with *photovoltaic cells*, which produce an electromotive force and current when illuminated unsymmetrically. The *barrier-layer* photovoltaic cell is chiefly used, although wet photovoltaic effects have been known for over a century. The "photox" type of cell consists of a layer of cuprous oxide, approximately 10^{-4} centimeter thick, on copper. Light striking the semiconducting layer of cuprous oxide forces electrons into the copper, which are then passed through a meter which completes the circuit. This type of cell has the advantage of having a spectral response very similar to that of the human eye. "Photronic" cells consist of a thin layer of selenium on a base of iron. This type of cell is most common, since it is less sensitive to temperature changes and is stable over long periods of time. Provided that a meter of low electrical resistance is used, the photovoltaic current produced by this type of cell is almost exactly proportional to the illumination. The sensitivity is relatively large, ranging from 140 to 600 microamperes per lumen for a short-circuited cell. By using a suitable filter, the spectral response of this type of cell can be matched to that of the human eye without losing too much sensitivity. Photovoltaic cells are used mainly for photographic exposure meters and to operate relays, their major advantage being that they are self-contained sources of current.

ADDITIONAL READING

Hughes, Arthur Llewelyn and DuBridge, Lee Alvin, *Photoelectric Phenomena.* New York: McGraw-Hill Book Co., Inc., 1932. A standard and comprehensive account of the subject with a wealth of detail.

Strong, John, *Procedures in Experimental Physics.* Englewood Cliffs, N. J.: Prentice-Hall, Inc., 1938. Practical information necessary for the construction and use of phototubes, thermionic tubes, and radiation instruments.

Zworykin, V. K. and Ramberg, E. G., *Photoelectricity and Its Application.* New York: John Wiley and Sons, 1949. An excellent account of the principles and preparation of photosensitive devices, as well as comprehensive discussion of numerous applications.

Dushman, Saul, "Thermionic Emission," *Reviews of Modern Physics*, October, 1930, **2**, pp. 381–476. Complete survey of this field as of that date.

PROBLEMS

1. The thermionic work-function of molybdenum is 4.20 volts. Compute the temperature to which a filament one millimeter in diameter and five centimeters long must be heated so that the emission current will be 10 milliamperes. (Take $R = \frac{1}{2}$)

2. Treat wolfram as a perfect black body. We will assume that the work done when a charge Q is emitted by the wolfram is $Q\phi$, where ϕ is the work-function of wolfram, so that the rate at which work is done by the emission of charges is $I\phi$ for a current I. Compute the temperature at which the loss of energy due to radiation equals the loss of energy due to the emission of electrons. (3460°K)

3. Plot the following data for a platinum filament coated with barium oxide in such a way as to verify Eqs. (25) and (26), and use your graphs to determine the constants A and ϕ in each equation.
   (*Ans.* 4.17 $\times$ 10⁵ amp/cm²; 1.81 volts; 3.16 amp/cm²; 1.69 volts)

Temperature °K:	700	800	900	1000
Micro-amp/cm²:	0.72	28.8	615	7030

4. Show that Eq. (61) reduces to Eqs. (31) and (32) for short and long wavelengths respectively.

5. Derive Eq. (30) from Eq. (61) and compute the value of the constant.

6. When potassium is irradiated with monochromatic light of various wavelengths, the following stopping potentials are found at each wavelength given:

Wavelength—angstroms:	2000	3000	3000	5000
Stopping potential—volts:	4.11	2.05	1.03	0.41

Plot these data in such a way as to verify Einstein's equation.

7. From the data given in Problem 6 for potassium, find the threshold wavelength in angstroms and the photoelectric work function in volts for potassium.   (*Ans.* 6020 angstroms; 2.06 volts)

8. Light of wavelength 4000 angstroms strikes lithium, which has a photoelectric work-function of 2.13 volts. Find the energy in ergs and electron-volts for the fastest photoelectrons emitted, and find the velocity of these electrons.

9. When light of wavelength 4000 angstroms strikes a certain metal, electrons are emitted. These photoelectrons are bent into circular paths by a magnetic field of strength 3 gauss. The circle of greatest radius is observed to be 1.2 centimeters. For this surface and illumination, compute the stopping potential in volts and the work-function of the metal in volts.

(*Ans.* 1.14 volts; 1.86 volts)

10. The photoelectric threshold of sodium is 6800 angstrom units. Compute the stopping potential of the electron emitted by the sodium when irradiated with the following wavelengths: 4000, 5000, 6000, 7000, 8000 (angstroms).

11. At the earth's surface the radiation from the sun is approximately 1.3 kilowatts per square meter. Treat the sun as a black body and compute its surface temperature. (5670°K)

chapter three

the special theory of relativity

The description of physical events requires the specification of the motions of bodies relative to a frame of reference. Such a frame of reference must include not only the space coordinates of the body, but also a time coordinate. Clearly, the mathematical form of the law of nature may be affected by the particular frame of reference used, and it is important to investigate the effects of various choices. In this chapter it will be shown how the classical ideas of position and time must be modified in order to give theoretical results that agree with electrodynamics. The resulting *special or restricted theory of relativity* is presented at this point because of its many applications to the dynamics of electrons and other high-speed particles.

3.1. THE NEWTONIAN PRINCIPLE OF RELATIVITY

The *classical principle of relativity* may be stated as follows:

> *A law of mechanics which is valid in a given coordinate system is equally valid in a second coordinate system moving with constant velocity relative to the first system.*

We will show that this principle of relativity is satisfied by Newton's first law of motion, which states that the momentum of a particle subject to no forces remains constant. Suppose a particle moves with constant velocity in the first system, thus showing that no force acts on it. Relative to the second system the particle will have a different, but still constant, velocity, so that relative to the second system it also has no forces acting on it, showing that Newton's first law satisfies the principle of relativity. Similarly, no matter how the velocity of the particle may change, the

51

velocities relative to the two systems will always differ by the constant relative velocity of the systems, so that the acceleration of the particle will be the same in either system.   Thus the same force will be assigned by Newton's second law of motion, showing that this law satisfies the principle of relativity.   Finally, since the forces are the same in the two systems, Newton's third law of motion will have the same form in both systems, again satisfying the principle of relativity.

Systems in which Newton's first law of motion holds are called *inertial systems*.   Thus an inertial system is not an accelerated frame of reference. From the above discussion it is seen that inertial systems can differ from one another only by a motion with constant relative velocity.   The Newtonian principle of relativity may be restated in the following form: *All inertial systems are equivalent for the description of nature*.   Therefore, no mechanical experiment can discover an inertial system which is more fundamental than any other.   In the following section we shall see how the laws of optics and electromagnetism apparently violate the classical principle of relativity.   Finally, we shall consider Einstein's modifications of the classical ideas of space and time, which extended the principle of relativity to electromagnetism.

3.2. THE WAVE THEORY OF LIGHT

The wave theory of light was fully investigated and established during the first part of the nineteenth century by the experiments of Young, Fresnel and others.   Since it was difficult for scientists of the nineteenth century to conceive of a wave without a medium to support its vibrations, a medium called the *ether* was postulated for the propagation of light. This belief in an ether was strengthened by Maxwell's electromagnetic theory of light and the experimental verification of this theory by Hertz.

Unfortunately, this electromagnetic ether would have to possess rather peculiar mechanical properties in order to serve as a medium for the transmission of light.   Polarization effects, for instance, show that light is a transverse wave.   Since fluids possess no shear rigidity and therefore transmit only longitudinal waves, the ether must be a rigid body.   However, rigid bodies transmit both longitudinal and transverse waves, while no longitudinal component has been observed in the case of light.   This last difficulty can be removed by assuming an infinitely rigid ether, thus reducing the energy carried away by longitudinal waves to zero, leaving only the transverse waves to be observed.   Such an ether is not at all plausible, since the ether must pervade all space, even transparent material bodies.   The longitudinal wave in a rigid ether may also be removed by a proper choice of the elastic constants of the ether, but such an ether would be unstable and would have to be fixed to a framework at the edge of the universe. We see that in either case the ether would have to be a mechanical monstrosity in order to transmit only a transverse wave.

Disregarding the difficulties with a material ether, light waves should travel with a definite velocity with respect to the ether itself (3×10^{10} centimeters per second in empty space). In general, all waves have a definite velocity with respect to the medium in which they are propagated, regardless of the motion of the source or the detector. Thus, the velocity of light waves relative to material bodies should depend on the velocities of the bodies through the ether. As an example, water waves of a given wavelength have a certain velocity relative to the water. To an observer on a moving ship, the apparent velocity of the water waves is greater if the ship is moving into the waves and less if the ship is moving in the same direction as the waves. If the velocity of the waves relative to the water is known, measuring the apparent velocity of waves with respect to the ship in the two opposite directions would make it possible for the velocity of the ship through the water to be calculated.

Similarly, the velocity of the earth through the ether should be derivable from measurements on electromagnetic waves through the ether. A number of ingenious experiments were performed during the last part of the nineteenth century, but all were unsuccessful in measuring the earth's velocity relative to the ether. We will discuss in detail only the most famous of these experiments, which was carried out over a number of years by Michelson and Morley.

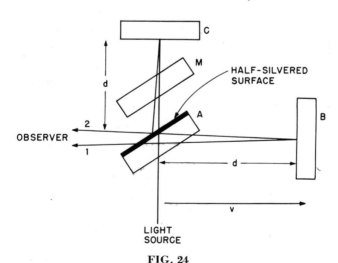

FIG. 24

Diagram of the Michelson interferometer used to measure the earth's velocity through the ether.

3.3. THE MICHELSON-MORLEY EXPERIMENT

This experiment was first performed in 1881 by Michelson alone and later repeated in 1887 by Michelson and Morley. The apparatus which they used is the *Michelson interferometer*, which is shown schematically in Fig. 24. Monochromatic light from the source travels to the partially-silvered mirror at A, where some of the light is transmitted toward mirror C and some is reflected towards mirror B. After reflection from mirrors B and C, some of the light reaches the detector, where the two beams of light recombine. The compensating plate, M, which is cut from the same piece of glass as mirror A, is introduced to compensate the light travelling to mirror C for the extra passages of light from mirror B through the half-silvered mirror A. The light which reaches the detector may interfere either constructively or destructively, depending on the paths travelled by the two beams.

Let us consider the earth to be moving with a velocity, v, relative to the ether in a direction parallel to AB. It is evident that the times required for the beams of light to travel the distances ABA and ACA will be unequal; we will now compute this difference. If we let the velocity of light relative to the ether be c, then the velocity of a wave travelling from A to B is $(c - v)$ relative to the apparatus. Similarly, from B to A, the velocity of light relative to the apparatus is $(c + v)$. Thus, the time for the round trip, ABA, is

$$t_1 = \frac{d}{c - v} + \frac{d}{c + v} = \frac{2cd}{c^2 - v^2} \tag{70}$$

Since the velocity of the earth in its orbit around the sun is approximately 30 kilometers per second, while the velocity of light is 300,000 kilometers per second, we see that v is small compared to c. Expanding Eq. (70) by the use of the binomial theorem, we have

$$t_1 = \frac{2(d/c)}{1 - (v/c)^2} = 2\frac{d}{c}\left(1 + \frac{v^2}{c^2} \ldots\right) \tag{71}$$

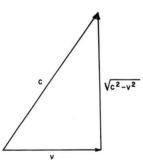

FIG. 25
Composition of velocities for ray making the round-trip ACA.

In order to reach mirror C, a wave starting from A must be aimed at a point slightly beyond C, since C will move a small distance during the time required for the wave to travel from A to C. The same should be done for the wave moving from C to A. The velocity of the wave relative to the apparatus is the vector difference between the velocity of the wave relative to the ether, c, and the velocity of the apparatus through the ether, v, as shown in Fig. 25. (This is similar to the problem of rowing straight across a swift river.) The time required for the round trip ACA is seen to be

$$t_2 = \frac{2d}{\sqrt{(c^2 - v^2)}} = \frac{2(d/c)}{\sqrt{(1 - v^2/c^2)}} = 2\frac{d}{c}\left(1 + \frac{1}{2}\frac{v^2}{c^2}\cdots\right) \qquad (72)$$

Thus, while the two waves were originally in phase when they reached A from the source, they are now out of phase, since the wave travelling to B took slightly longer to return to A. This time difference is given by

$$\Delta t = t_1 - t_2 = \frac{dv^2}{c^3} \qquad (73)$$

If the whole apparatus is now rotated to a second position at right angles to the first position, paths ABA and ACA will interchange their roles. The total time difference will be twice as much as that given by Eq. (73). Since the waves travel with a velocity c, the path difference introduced by rotating the equipment 90° will be

$$\Delta P = 2c\,\Delta t = \frac{2dv^2}{c^2} \qquad (74)$$

Thus, when the apparatus is rotated from the first position to the second position, the fringe pattern observed at the detector should shift a number of fringes given by

$$\Delta F = \frac{\Delta P}{\lambda} = \frac{2dv^2}{c^2\lambda} \qquad (75)$$

Even if the direction of the earth's motion through the ether is not known, continuous observation of the fringe pattern as the equipment is slowly rotated should show that it eventually passes through two positions similar to positions one and two above. A given fringe will oscillate about its average position with a maximum range of variation given by Eq. (75).

Let us assume that the earth's velocity through the ether is approximately the same as its orbital velocity, so that $v/c = 10^{-4}$. By using repeated reflections, Michelson and Morley achieved effective path lengths, d, of the order of 10 meters. For a wavelength of 5000 angstrom units we should then expect a maximum fringe shift as follows:

$$\Delta F = \frac{2 \times 11 \times 10^2 \times (10^{-4})^2}{5 \times 10^{-5}} = 0.4 \text{ fringes}$$

So great a fringe shift is clearly well within the range of observation, so according to the theory presented above we could measure the fringe shift and use Eq. (75) to compute the earth's velocity through the ether.

Experimentally however, Michelson and Morley found fringe shifts which were only a very small fraction of the expected amount. Their

measurements were made at various times of the day and night, as well
as at different seasons of the year, so that it would be certain that at
least one of the measurements would be made when the earth had a high
velocity through the ether.   Many others repeated the experiment and
found the same null result, which is now accepted as experimentally true.
Apparently, then, optical experiments cannot be used to determine the
earth's velocity through the ether, even though the theory of the Michelson-
Morley experiment seems to be a logical deduction from the wave theory
of light, using classical kinematics in the calculation.

3.4. OTHER EXPERIMENTS TO MEASURE ETHER DRIFT

Although Michelson and Morley were unsuccessful in their attempt to
measure the velocity of the earth through the ether by essentially optical
methods, it might be possible to devise a successful electromagnetic experiment.   In 1902 Trouton and Noble performed an experiment of this sort.
The plates of a condenser were suspended by fine wires and charged
through fine wires dipped into mercury, so that an electric field existed
between the plates of the condenser.   If the earth is moving through the
ether, then there should be relative motion between this electric field and
the ether.

Suppose that the angle between the direction of the velocity of the
earth through the ether and the direction of the electric field between the
condenser plates is θ.   Then this moving electric field will induce a magnetic
field, B, which is proportional to sin θ.   Since the energy per unit volume of
a magnetic field in empty space is $B^2/2\mu_0$, the condenser should rotate to
make θ zero, thus minimizing the induced magnetic energy.   No such
turning effect was found.   Other electromagnetic experiments were equally
unsuccessful in detecting the motion of the earth through the ether.

In 1958 Townes, Cedarholm, Bland, and Havens reported an extremely
accurate experiment designed to measure the earth's velocity through the
ether.   The experiment consisted of comparing the frequencies of two
masers (masers are discussed in more detail in Chapter 7) with their
beams of ammonia molecules travelling in opposite directions.   If the
velocity of a maser through the ether is v and the thermal velocity of an
ammonia molecule is u, it can be shown that the fractional shift in frequency due to the Doppler effect is $\pm uv/c^2$, depending on the directions of
u and v.   If the frequencies of two masers are compared and then the
whole apparatus is rotated through 180°, the fractional shift in frequency
should be $4uv/c^2$.

In this experiment u was about 0.6 km/sec and the frequency was
about 2.4×10^{10} cps.   If v is taken as the earth's orbital velocity of

30 km/sec, the expected change in frequency would be about 20 cps.   No variation greater than 1/50 cps was found, indicating that any velocity of the earth relative to the ether is less than 1/1000 of the earth's orbital velocity.

3.5. POSSIBLE SOLUTIONS TO THE DILEMMA

There are various possible explanations for the apparent impossibility of measuring the earth's velocity through the ether by optical or electro-magnetic experiments.   One may assume that the ether is dragged along with the earth like a viscous fluid, so that the ether is at rest relative to the surface of the earth.   This would yield the null results found.   However, the ether near the earth would have a motion relative to the ether in interstellar space, and this motion would deflect light rays from the stars in the same way that a wind would deflect sound waves.   The correct amount of deflection for any plausible motion of the ether has not been determined, so this is not a satisfactory solution to the dilemma.

Another possibility is that light emitted by a moving source has the velocity of the source added to the normal velocity of light.   If this were true, the light in the Michelson-Morley experiment would always have the same velocity relative to the interferometer, and a null result would be expected.   However, all other waves have a definite velocity in the medium, which is unaffected by the motion of the source of the waves. This is not an acceptable solution to the problem, since it violates the wave theory of light.

Fitzgerald and Lorentz suggested that a null result would be found in all optical and electromagnetic experiments, provided that all lengths contracted in the proportion $\sqrt{(1 - v^2/c^2)}$ in the directions of their motions through the ether.   Either the contraction itself, or the forces and torques associated with the contraction, would then be just sufficient to cancel the desired effect.   This is seen from Eqs. (70) and (72) in the case of the Michelson-Morley experiment.   While Lorentz showed that this *Lorentz-Fitzgerald contraction* was plausible according to electrody-namics, he was unable to show that it was a logical deduction from the theory.

Since none of the electromagnetic experiments was able to yield a value of the earth's velocity through the ether, or even to demonstrate that the earth is moving through "space," some of the basic physical laws from which we made our deductions were wrong.   Einstein came to the conclusion that the traditional ideas of kinematics were wrong, and that it was impossible to determine our "absolute motion" through space. Since the only motion which is physically measurable is motion relative to material bodies, we must confine ourselves to such motions, at least in physics. Einstein's revisions of kinematics, as applied to reference systems moving with constant velocity with respect to each other, predict exactly the null results found for all experiments which attempt to measure absolute velocities of the earth through the ether. In addition, this special theory of relativity predicted a number of other unusual effects involving the fundamental quantities of length, mass, and time.

3.6. THE POSTULATES OF THE SPECIAL THEORY OF RELATIVITY

In 1905 Einstein revised the classical ideas of space and time by asserting that absolute motion is meaningless. Defining an *inertial system,* as before, as a frame of reference in which Newton's first law of motion holds, consider inertial systems which differ only in that they are moving with constant velocity with respect to one another. Einstein's basic postulates then take the following form:

1. There is no preferred inertial system. Physical laws and principles must have the same mathematical form when expressed in the coordinates of any inertial system.
2. All observers measure the same value for the velocity of light, regardless of the inertial system in which a particular observer is situated.

All of the deductions of the theory of special relativity come from these two postulates. Since they are postulates, they are not provable or even necessarily self-evident. As in the case of any physical theory, certain basic postulates are set up, and the theory is retained only as long as deductions from these postulates continue to agree with experimental observation. However, we will try to explain and justify these basic postulates of special relativity in the subsequent paragraphs.

The first postulate extends the classical principle of relativity to include optics and electromagnetism as well as mechanics. It is indeed hard to imagine that any particular reference system chosen by man should have the unique property of describing nature. Let us consider two observers, O and O', located in two reference systems, S and S', which move with respect to each other with a constant relative velocity. Each observer makes observations in his own system on a particular event; that is, O uses coordinates $xyzt$ to describe the event, and O' uses coordinates $x'y'z't'$ to describe the same event. An alternative is to consider a single observer, O, located in S, who may use either the coordinates of S or the coordinates of S' as he finds convenient. The first postulate then states that if a particular physical law has the form $P = QR$ relative to system S, it must also have the form $P' = Q'R'$ relative to S'. This is the meaning of the postulate that all physical laws must have the same mathematical form in the coordinates of any inertial system. The phrase *relativistically invariant* is commonly used to refer to this property of nature and of the laws describing nature.

The second postulate is really a corollary of the first, if it is assumed to be a physical law in some inertial system that the velocity of light is a constant. Of course, it is strongly suggested by the negative results of attempts to measure a variation of the apparent velocity of light with the variation of motion of the reference system, the earth. This is the physical law which we will use as a test of the mathematical form of our kinematical equations.

3.7. TRANSFORMATIONS OF COORDINATES

Since we are assuming that the difficulty with the classical theory, which led to incorrect ideas of absolute motion through space, lay in our ideas of space and time, let us review kinematics. Consider transforming from coordinates $xyzt$ of system S to coordinates $x'y'z't'$ of system S', which moves with respect to system S with velocity v. For simplicity, we will let S' have a velocity v down the positive x-axis of system S, as shown in Fig. 26. For convenience in terminology, we shall sometimes refer to

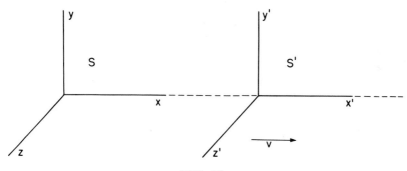

FIG. 26

Diagram illustrating transformation of coordinates between two systems which move with respect to one another.

system S as being at rest and system S' as being the "moving system," but the two systems are clearly equivalent according to our first postulate. An observer at rest in S' is fully justified in considering himself to be at rest while system S moves down his negative x'-axis with velocity $-v$.

If we begin counting time at the instant that the two origins are coincident, then we have the following equations connecting positions measured in S' and S respectively:

$$x' = x - vt, \qquad y' = y$$
$$z' = z, \qquad\qquad t' = t \tag{76}$$

In Eq. (76), the classical idea that a single time scale suffices for all frames of reference, since there seems to be no kinematical reason for supposing that time depends on the motion of the frame of reference, has been shown explicitly. The equations connecting velocity components of a particle as measured in S' and S would similarly be written down by a person acquainted with kinematics as follows:

$$v'_x = v_x - v \qquad v'_y = v_y \qquad v'_z = v_z \tag{77}$$

Equations (76) and (77) are known as the Galilean or Newtonian transformation equations or *transforms*. By using these equations, we can transform from measurements made in S to those in S', or vice versa. We will now investigate whether or not these transforms satisfy the postulates of special relativity as given above.

Maxwell's equations are the fundamental equations of electromagnetism (including optics, of course). If now we express these equations in terms of the coordinates, $xyzt$, of S, we find the equations to have their usual form. However, if we transform Maxwell's equations into the coordinates and velocity components of S', using Eqs. (76) and (77), we find that the form of the equations is changed. This violates the first postulate of special relativity, so that the classical transforms appear to need revision. Since this violation of the first postulate is laborious to demonstrate, we will demonstrate instead a violation of the second postulate. Consider a light photon moving with velocity c along the x-axis of S. According to Eq. (77), the velocity, c', of this photon in the system S' would be $c' = c - v$. Observers in the two systems would thus measure different values for the velocity of light, which is a violation of the second postulate of special relativity. The classical transforms again fail to satisfy our postulates; in the following section we will develop the correct set of transforms.

3.8. THE LORENTZ-EINSTEIN TRANSFORMATION EQUATIONS

We will now consider the problem of transforming from one frame of reference to another frame which moves with constant velocity with respect to the first. We will look for a set of transforms which will satisfy the postulates of special relativity, if such a set exists. Clearly, any set of transforms which we do find, must reduce to the classical transforms at

ordinary velocities, since the classical transforms have been highly successful in most applications. In view of the null result of the Michelson-
Morley experiment, we should expect differences between the relativistic
and classical transforms in cases where the velocities involved are comparable to the velocity of light.

Consider the systems S and S', as shown in Fig. 26, with the axes
parallel, and with S' moving down the positive x-axis of S with velocity v.
As before, we will begin counting time from the instant that the two
origins are coincident. At this instant we have $t = t' = 0$, and $x = x' = 0$.
In order to preserve the left-right symmetry of each coordinate system
with its x-axis or x'-axis respectively, we must have $y' = y$ and $z' = z$.

The position of the origin, O', of S' is described relative to S by the
equation

$$x - vt = 0 \tag{78}$$

Relative to S' itself, the position of the origin O' is given by

$$x' = 0 \tag{79}$$

The transformation equations must certainly be linear, so that one event
in S corresponds to one event in S'. Since Eqs. (78) and (79) describe
the motion of the same point, O', they must be equivalent. Assuming a
linear relationship, we have

$$x' = k(x - vt) \tag{80}$$

where k is a constant of proportionality. If we apply similar reasoning
to the description of the motion of the origin, O, of the system S, we have

$$x = k(x' + vt') \tag{81}$$

The same constant, k, is used in both Eqs. (80) and (81), since, according to the first postulate, nothing distinguishes S and S' from one another
except the sign of their relative velocity.

Substituting x' from Eq. (80) into (81), we have

$$x = k^2(x - vt) + kvt' \tag{82}$$

Solving Eq. (82) for t', we find

$$t' = kt + \left(\frac{1 - k^2}{kv}\right)x \tag{83}$$

Gathering together our tentative hypotheses regarding the form of the
correct relativistic transformation equations, we will try the following
set of transforms:

$$x' = k(x - vt), \qquad y' = y$$

$$z' = z, \qquad t' = kt + \left(\frac{1 - k^2}{kv}\right)x \tag{84}$$

Our problem is to show that a particular choice of the constant k, allows Eq. (84) to satisfy the second postulate of special relativity.

Assume that at $t = 0$ a spherical electromagnetic wave leaves the origins of S and S', which are coincident at that instant. According to the second postulate, the velocity, c, of this wave is the same in all directions in either frame of reference. The position of the wave-front at any time is given by either of the equivalent equations

$$x^2 + y^2 + z^2 = c^2 t^2 \tag{85}$$

$$x'^2 + y'^2 + z'^2 = c^2 t'^2 \tag{86}$$

Substituting the tentative transforms of Eq. (84) into Eq. (86), we have

$$k^2(x^2 - 2xvt + v^2 t^2) + y^2 + z^2$$
$$= c^2 k^2 t^2 + \frac{2c^2 tx(1 - k^2)}{v} + \frac{c^2 x^2 (1 - k^2)^2}{k^2 v^2} \tag{87}$$

We must now choose k such that Eq. (87) reduces to Eq. (85), since each of these equations represents the position of the wave-front as measured in S. Equating the coefficients of the terms in xt in order to eliminate this term, we have

$$-2k^2 v = \frac{2c^2(1 - k^2)}{v} \tag{88}$$

Solving Eq. (88) for k^2, we have

$$k^2 = \frac{1}{1 - (v^2/c^2)} \tag{89}$$

Since Eq. (81) must reduce to the classical form given by Eq. (76) for the case of small velocities, we must take the positive square root of Eq. (89). For k we find the value

$$k = \frac{1}{\sqrt{1 - (v^2/c^2)}} \tag{90}$$

Returning to Eq. (87), we must now show that the terms in x^2 and t^2 have the same coefficients as the corresponding terms in Eq. (85). Collecting terms in x^2, the coefficient of this term is

$$k^2 - \frac{c^2(1 - k^2)^2}{k^2 v^2} = k^2 + (1 - k^2) = 1 \tag{91}$$

Similarly, the coefficient of the terms involving t^2 is

$$c^2 k^2 - k^2 v^2 = c^2 k^2 \left(1 - \frac{v^2}{c^2}\right) = c^2 \tag{92}$$

Eqs. (91) and (92) show that with the value of k^2 given by Eq. (89), a spherical wave expanding with velocity c in S', transforms into a spherical wave expanding with the same velocity in S. The transformation equations assumed in Eq. (84) are seen to satisfy the second postulate of special relativity, if k is properly chosen.

Returning to Eq. (84), a correct set of transformation equations satisfying the second postulate of relativity is

$$x' = k(x - vt), \qquad y' = y, \qquad z' = z$$

$$t' = k\left(t - \frac{vx}{c^2}\right)$$

$$k = \frac{1}{\sqrt{1 - (v^2/c^2)}} = \frac{1}{\sqrt{1 - \beta^2}}$$

$$\beta = \frac{v}{c} \tag{93}$$

Since the only difference between S and S' is in the signs of their relative velocities, the inverse relations are

$$x = k(x' + vt'), \qquad y = y'$$

$$z = z', \qquad t = k\left(t' + \frac{vx'}{c^2}\right) \tag{94}$$

It is easily seen that for the case of small velocities Eqs. (93) and (94) reduce to the classical form given by Eq. (76).

Consider now the meaning of Eqs. (93) and (94). These equations provide us with a means of translating times and positions measured in S into times and positions measured in S'. We see that events which are regarded as simultaneous in S are not necessarily observed as simultaneous in S'. Space and time differences between events depend on the particular frame of reference used, and events can only be said to be simultaneous or to occur at the same place in terms of a given frame of reference.

The next problem is to determine the way in which velocity components are transformed. One of Einstein's contributions to the transformation equations was to recognize that the time coordinate of each frame of reference must be used in computing velocities in that system. Thus, the x-component of velocity of a particle in S is dx/dt, while the x'-component of velocity of a particle in S' is dx'/dt'. Writing the differentials of x' and t' from Eq. (93), we have

$$dx' = k(dx - v\,dt) \tag{95}$$

$$dt' = k\left(dt - \frac{v\,dx}{c^2}\right) \tag{96}$$

Taking the ratio, dx'/dt', from Eqs. (95) and (96), we have

$$\frac{dx'}{dt'} = \frac{dx - v\,dt}{dt - v\,dx/c^2} = \frac{dx/dt - v}{1 - (v/c^2)dx/dt} \tag{97}$$

Replacing the derivatives by the velocity components v_x and v'_x respectively, and using the notation $\beta = v/c$, Eq. (97) can be written thus:

$$v'_x = \frac{v_x - v}{1 - (\beta/c)v_x} \tag{98}$$

We will now follow the same procedure for the y-components of velocity; that is, we will compute dy'/dt' from Eq. (93), and then replace the derivatives by v_y and v'_y. The result is

$$v'_y = \frac{dy'}{dt'} = \frac{dy}{k\left(dt - \dfrac{v\,dx}{c^2}\right)} = \frac{\dfrac{dy}{dt}}{k\left[1 - \dfrac{v}{c^2}\dfrac{dx}{dt}\right]}$$

$$v'_y = \frac{v_y\sqrt{1 - \beta^2}}{1 - (\beta/c)v_x} \tag{99}$$

Computing the z-component velocities in the same way, we will put down the velocity transformation equations of special relativity.

$$v'_x = \frac{v_x - v}{1 - (\beta/c)v_x}$$

$$v'_y = \frac{v_y\sqrt{1 - \beta^2}}{1 - (\beta/c)v_x} \tag{100}$$

$$v'_z = \frac{v_z\sqrt{1 - \beta^2}}{1 - (\beta/c)v_x}$$

Since the only difference between S and S' is in the signs of their relative velocities, the inverse relations to Eq. (100) are found by replacing v by $-v$ in Eq. (100). The result is

$$v_x = \frac{v'_x + v}{1 + (\beta/c)v'_x}$$

$$v_y = \frac{v'_y\sqrt{1 - \beta^2}}{1 + (\beta/c)v'_x} \tag{101}$$

$$v_z = \frac{v'_z\sqrt{1 - \beta^2}}{1 + (\beta/c)v'_x}$$

Equations (100) and (101) for the transformation of velocity components from one frame of reference to another moving with constant velocity with respect to the first, should not be confused with the usual rules for adding velocities measured in the same system. An example may clarify this point. Consider two electrons which are emitted by a filament which is stationary in the laboratory. Let electron No. 1 have a velocity 0.8c to the right and electron No. 2 have velocity 0.9c to the left, both velocities being parallel to the x-axis, as shown in Fig. 27. Their relative velocity in the laboratory coordinates is then 1.7c, as usual, and relativity plays no part in the calculation.

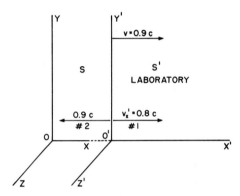

FIG. 27
Example of the application of the relativistic velocity transforms.

Let us now compute the velocity of No. 1 as seen by an observer travelling with No. 2. The frame of reference in which the observer is at rest, S, is thus attached to electron No. 2. The laboratory becomes the moving frame, S', with a velocity $v = 0.9c$ down the positive x-axis of frame S. Relative to frame S', electron No. 1 has a velocity $v'_x = 0.8c$. Using Eq. (101), the velocity of electron No. 1 relative to frame S and thus relative to electron No. 2 is given by

$$v_x = \frac{v'_x + v}{1 + (\beta/c)v'_x} = \frac{0.8c + 0.9c}{1 + (0.9/c)0.8c} = 0.988c$$

Similarly, if we had computed the velocity of electron No. 2 relative to an observer travelling with electron No. 1, we would have found the same value as above, but with a negative sign.

It is interesting to note that an alternative form for Eq. (101) is as follows:

$$\tanh^{-1}\frac{v_x}{c} = \tanh^{-1}\frac{v'_x}{c} + \tanh^{-1}\frac{v}{c} \qquad (102)$$

Thus, if we call $\tanh^{-1}(u/c)$ the *rapidity* of the velocity u, then the usual Newtonian rule for the addition of velocities is obeyed relativistically by the rapidities of the motion.

It is easy to show that the velocity transforms given by Eq. (100) and (101) satisfy the second postulate of special relativity. Consider a photon travelling with velocity $v_x = c$ down the positive x-axis. From Eq. (100), the velocity of the same photon in S' is given by

$$v_x' = \frac{v_x - v}{1 - (\beta/c)v_x} = \frac{c - v}{1 - (\beta/c)c} = \frac{c - v}{1 - \beta} = c\frac{(1 - \beta)}{1 - \beta} = c$$

Thus, regardless of the relative velocity of the two systems, each observer will obtain the same value for the velocity of light. It should also be evident that Eq. (100) reduces to Eq. (77) for small velocities, so that the relativity transforms yield the classical transforms as a limiting case.

The last and most important question is whether or not the transformation equations of Eqs. (93)–(94) and Eqs. (100)–(101) satisfy the first postulate. Even before Einstein's theory of special relativity, Lorentz had investigated this problem and shown in 1904 that these transforms do preserve the form of Maxwell's equations unchanged as we transform from system S to system S'. The analytical proof will not be given here. We see then that the *Lorentz-Einstein transforms* satisfy both the postulates of special relativity and reduce satisfactorily to the classical transforms in the limiting case of small velocities compared to the velocity of light. We will next determine the effect of these modified transformation equations on physical theories and measurements.

3.9. RELATIVISTIC KINEMATICS

Since the relativistic transformation equations just developed are somewhat more complicated than the classical equations, it might be suspected that length and time measurements might also be modified. In this section we will study this problem and find that the Lorentz-Einstein transforms do imply a dependence of length and time measurements on the relative motion of the observer and the object.

Consider a rigid measuring rod which has a length L_0, in any system in which it is at rest, as measured by an observer also at rest in the same system. Let the rod be at rest in system S', so that it moves with the velocity, v, relative to an observer at rest in system S. In either system, the length of the rod will be determined by noting the positions of the two ends of the rod at a given time, and then subtracting one position from the other to compute the length. Let the observer in S observe the positions of the ends of the moving rod at a time t, finding values x_a and

x_b. According to Eq. (93) the positions of the ends of the rod in S' are related to the corresponding coordinates in S by the equations

$$x_a' = k(x_a - vt)$$
$$x_b' = k(x_b - vt) \tag{103}$$

Subtracting one equation of Eq. (103) from the other we have

$$x_b' - x_a' = k(x_b - x_a) \tag{104}$$

Now by definition the measured length in S is $L = x_b - x_a$, while the measured length of the rod in S' is $L_0 = x_b' - x_a'$. We can therefore write Eq. (104) in the form

$$L_0 = kL \tag{105}$$

Solving Eq. (105) for L and inserting the explicit form of k, we have

$$L = L_0 \sqrt{\left(1 - \frac{v^2}{c^2}\right)} \tag{106}$$

From Eq. (106) we see that the length of the rod is measured to be smaller than its rest-length, L_0, if the rod moves with respect to the observer. This is the famous *contraction of moving lengths*, which is a kinematical consequence of the Lorentz-Einstein transforms.

It should be noted that the contraction of moving lengths in the direction of their motion past an observer is exactly the same as that postulated empirically by Lorentz and Fitzgerald to explain the null result of the Michelson-Morley experiment. However, this contraction now appears as a logical deduction from certain rather attractive and basic postulates concerning the mathematical expression of physical laws, rather than as an ad hoc postulate to explain a particular experimental result. Unfortunately, this contraction is too small to be observed directly with ordinary laboratory velocities, so the null result of the Michelson-Morley experiment must be considered as a confirmation of this deduction of special relativity.

Consider a clock which is fixed at a point, x', in S' and therefore moves with the velocity, v, relative to an observer in S. The time coordinate measured by an observer in S will be related to the time coordinate as measured by an observer in S' by Eq. (94). If two successive readings are made, the corresponding times will be related as follows:

$$t_1 = k\left(t_1' + \frac{vx'}{c^2}\right)$$
$$t_2 = k\left(t_2' + \frac{vx'}{c^2}\right) \tag{107}$$

The relation between time intervals measured in S and S' respectively is found by subtracting one equation of Eq. (107) from the other. We then have

$$t_2 - t_1 = k(t_2' - t_1') = \frac{t_2' - t_1'}{\sqrt{1 - v^2/c^2}} \tag{108}$$

From Eq. (108) we see that a particular time interval measured in S is greater than the corresponding time interval measured in S'. An observer in S concludes that the clock located at rest in S' runs slow, since the clock in S' indicates a smaller time interval between events. Conversely, to an observer in S', a clock fixed in S seems to run slow by exactly the same amount. This effect is the *slowing down of moving clocks*, which predicts that a clock moving with respect to an observer will run slow compared to the observer's own clock.

In Chapter 4 we will see that atoms emit characteristic frequencies. According to Eq. (108), moving atoms should emit slightly lower frequencies than similar atoms at rest with respect to the observer. This frequency shift will be superimposed on any shift due to the ordinary Doppler effect which may occur. In 1938 Ives and Stilwell verified Eq. (108) by making observations on the frequencies emitted by hydrogen atoms moving at high speeds.

Additional verification of Eq. (108) is provided by observations on the life-times of unstable particles, such as mesons, which are discussed in Chapter 11. A given type of meson has a definite mean life in a system in which the meson is at rest. If the meson moves with respect to the observer, its measured lifetime will be increased by the factor k defined in Eq. 93. Therefore, the lifetime of an unstable particle should always be quoted in terms of the frame of reference in which the particle is at rest.

The question might now be raised as to whether or not a moving rod is "really" shortened by its motion and a moving clock "really" slowed down. The answer, of course, is that motion has no effect on the properties of a measuring rod or clock. However, the "real" length of a rod plays no part in physical theory; only measured quantities are of interest. This means that an observer must assign a shorter length to a rod moving relative to him than he would assign to the same rod if it were at rest in his frame of reference. Similarly, an observer must assign a shorter time interval between events in a system moving relative to him. The test of a theory is its agreement with experimental observations, and some deductions of the theory cannot be discarded merely because they seem paradoxical. Unfortunately, every-day velocities are exceedingly small compared to the velocity of light, so that the classical approximation intuitively seems correct.   However, intuition need not be entirely correct, and the deductions of special relativity must be accepted on the basis of experimental verification.

3.10. RELATIVISTIC DYNAMICS

If the fundamental law of dynamics is Newton's second law in the form $F = ma$, this law of motion does not preserve its form when transformed according to Eqs. (93) and (94).   Our problem is to find a new form of the law of motion which will transform properly and will reduce to the classical form as a low-speed approximation.   This requires more knowledge of mathematical analysis than is expected of readers of this book, so we will derive the variation of mass with velocity by considering a special case and then will state the relativistic law of motion.

Consider two identical particles, 1 and 2, moving along the x'-axis with velocities u' and $-u'$ respectively, as measured in system S'.   The

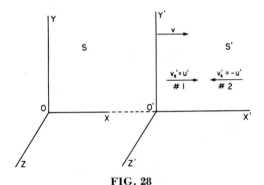

FIG. 28

Collision of two identical masses moving with equal but oppositely directed velocities in S'.

situation is shown in Fig. 28.   If the masses of the particles are the same when they are at rest in S', they will still be equal when they move with velocities u' and $-u'$ respectively with respect to S'.   This is necessary to preserve the isotropic characteristics of system S', since the effect of a given speed, u', on the mass of a particle must be independent of direction in S'.

Now let the two particles collide inelastically and stick together in S', like two putty balls.   Since their masses are equal just before collision, their momenta before collision will be equal but oppositely directed.   We see that after the collision the two particles will be at rest in S' and will there-

70

2 = most# 70

70

70

e# 70

70

tion# 70

70

arles,# 70

fore move with respect to system S with the velocity, v, of system S' with respect to S.

The same collision is described quite differently by an observer at rest in system S. Before collision the respective velocities of the two particles, relative to S, are found from Eq. (101) to be

$$u_1 = \frac{u' + v}{1 + \dfrac{u'v}{c^2}} \tag{109}$$

$$u_2 = \frac{-u' + v}{1 - \dfrac{u'v}{c^2}} \tag{110}$$

Since the speeds of the two particles are different relative to S, we must assume that their masses relative to S, m_1 and m_2, may be different also. We will assume, however, that relative to S both mass and momentum are conserved in the collision. Since the coalesced masses move together with the velocity of the system S' after collision, conservation of momentum gives us the equation

$$m_1 u_1 + m_2 u_2 = (m_1 + m_2)v \tag{111}$$

Substituting the velocities of the particles from Eqs. (109)–(110)

$$(m_1 + m_2)v = m_1 \frac{u' + v}{1 + \dfrac{u'v}{c^2}} + m_2 \frac{-u' + v}{1 - \dfrac{u'v}{c^2}} \tag{112}$$

If we now collect terms in m_1 and m_2 in Eq. (112) and solve for the ratio m_1/m_2, we find

$$\frac{m_1}{m_2} = \frac{1 + \dfrac{u'v}{c^2}}{1 - \dfrac{u'v}{c^2}} \tag{113}$$

For convenience, let $x = u'v/c^2$. Then Eq. (113) takes the form

$$\frac{m_1}{m_2} = \frac{1 + x}{1 - x} \tag{114}$$

In terms of the substitution, x, Eqs. (109) and (110) take the form

$$u_1 = \frac{u' + v}{1 + x} \tag{115}$$

$$u_2 = \frac{-u' + v}{1 - x} \tag{116}$$

Squaring Eq. (115) and (116), we have

$$u_1^2 = \frac{u'^2 + v^2 + 2c^2 x}{(1 + x)^2} \tag{117}$$

$$u_2^2 = \frac{u'^2 + v^2 - 2c^2 x}{(1 - x)^2} \tag{118}$$

Subtracting c^2 from each side of Eq. (117)–(118), we have

$$u_1^2 - c^2 = \frac{u'^2 + v^2 - c^2 - c^2 x^2}{(1 + x)^2} \tag{119}$$

$$u_2^2 - c^2 = \frac{u'^2 + v^2 - c^2 - c^2 x^2}{(1 - x)^2} \tag{120}$$

$$\frac{u_2^2 - c^2}{u_1^2 - c^2} = \frac{(1 + x)^2}{(1 - x)^2} \tag{121}$$

Comparing Eq. (121) with (114), we find the following value for the ratio of the masses of the particles before collision

$$\frac{m_1}{m_2} = \frac{\sqrt{u_2^2 - c^2}}{\sqrt{u_1^2 - c^2}} = \frac{\sqrt{1 - (u_2^2/c^2)}}{\sqrt{1 - (u_1^2/c^2)}} \tag{122}$$

Equation (122) confirms our suspicion that the velocities of the particles would affect their masses.

Suppose now that we make $u' = v$, so that particle 2 is at rest in S before collision, since $u_2 = 0$ according to Eq. (110). As measured in S for this case, Eq. (122) gives the following relation between the masses of the two particles:

$$m_1 = \frac{m_2}{\sqrt{1 - (u_1^2/c^2)}} \tag{123}$$

The interpretation of Eq. (123) is that the mass m_1, of a particle moving with a velocity u_1, relative to S, is different from the mass of an identical particle m_2, which is at rest in S. Since this relationship is valid for the velocities and masses before collision, the fact of the later collision is obviously immaterial, so that the relationship holds in general for moving bodies. Usually the mass of a body at rest is symbolized by m_0 and its mass while moving with velocity u, by m. Equation (123) then takes the conventional form

$$m = \frac{m_0}{\sqrt{1 - (u^2/c^2)}} = \frac{m_0}{\sqrt{1 - \beta^2}} \tag{124}$$

Equation (124) has been extensively verified in the case of high-speed electrons and today even with heavier particles, so there remains no doubt of its experimental correctness.

A more rigorous deduction of Eq. (124) is provided by finding a law of motion which is relativistically invariant and which will reduce to Newton's second law of motion as an approximation. It is found that the momentum of a particle is analogous to its classical form, namely,

$$p = mv = \frac{m_0 v}{\sqrt{1 - v^2/c^2}} \tag{125}$$

The basic law of motion then takes the form

$$F = \frac{dp}{dt} = \frac{d}{dt}\left(\frac{m_0 v}{\sqrt{1 - v^2/c^2}}\right) \tag{126}$$

It is easily seen that, for small velocities, Eqs. (125)–(126) reduce to the classical forms.

3.11. RELATIVISTIC ENERGY

We define the increase in the kinetic energy of a body as the work done by the forces acting on the body, in accord with the classical definition. If a body is accelerated from rest to some final velocity, u, its kinetic energy increases by an amount given by

$$\Delta T = \int F \, dx = \int \frac{dp}{dt} \, dx \tag{127}$$

Using the value of the momentum from Eq. (125) and expanding the integrand in Eq. (127), we have

$$\Delta T = \int_{v=0}^{v=u} \frac{d}{dt}\left[\frac{m_0 v}{\sqrt{1 - v^2/c^2}}\right] dx$$

$$\Delta T = \int_{v=0}^{v=u} \left[\frac{m_0 (dv/dt)}{\sqrt{1 - v^2/c^2}} + \frac{m_0 v (dv/dt)(v/c^2)}{(1 - v^2/c^2)^{3/2}}\right] dx \tag{128}$$

The differentials can be combined by noting the following relation:

$$\frac{dv}{dt} \, dx = dv \, \frac{dx}{dt} = v \, dv \tag{129}$$

The increase in kinetic energy now becomes

$$\Delta T = \int_0^u \frac{m_0 v \, dv}{\sqrt{1 - v^2/c^2}} + \int_0^u \frac{m_0 v^3 \, dv}{c^2 (1 - v^2/c^2)^{3/2}} \tag{130}$$

Writing Eq. (130) in terms of $\beta = v/c$, we have

$$\Delta T = m_0 c^2 \int_0^{\beta = u/c} \frac{\beta d\beta}{\sqrt{1 - \beta^2}} + m_0 c^2 \int_0^{\beta = u/c} \frac{\beta^3 d\beta}{(1 - \beta^2)^{3/2}} \qquad (131)$$

The integrals occurring in Eq. (131) are both standard forms, as follows:

$$\int \frac{x \, dx}{\sqrt{1 - x^2}} = -\sqrt{1 - x^2} \qquad (132)$$

$$\int \frac{x^3 \, dx}{(1 - x^2)^{3/2}} = \frac{x^2}{\sqrt{1 - x^2}} + 2\sqrt{1 - x^2} \qquad (133)$$

Using the results of Eqs. (132)–(133), Eq. (131) becomes

$$\Delta T = m_0 c^2 \left[-\sqrt{1 - \beta^2} + 1 + \frac{\beta^2}{\sqrt{1 - \beta^2}} + 2\sqrt{1 - \beta^2} - 2 \right] \qquad (134)$$

Combining terms in Eq. (134), we finally obtain the following value for the increase in kinetic energy of the particle

$$\Delta T = m_0 c^2 \left[\frac{1}{\sqrt{1 - \beta^2}} - 1 \right] \qquad (135)$$

It seems reasonable to define the kinetic energy of a body as zero when its velocity is zero, as is also done in classical mechanics. With this definition, the kinetic energy of a body moving with a velocity, u, takes the form

$$T = m_0 c^2 \left[\frac{1}{\sqrt{1 - u^2/c^2}} - 1 \right] \qquad (136)$$

Superficially, Eq. (136) seems radically different from the classical expression for the kinetic energy of a body, but we find that, for small velocities, Eq. (108) reduces to the classical form. Expanding the radical in Eq. (136) by means of the binomial theorem, we have

$$T = m_0 c^2 \left[1 + \frac{1}{2} \frac{u^2}{c^2} + \frac{3}{8} \frac{u^4}{c^4} \cdots - 1 \right]$$

$$T = \frac{1}{2} m_0 u^2 + \frac{3}{8} \frac{m_0 u^4}{c^2} \cdots \qquad (137)$$

Thus, for sufficiently small velocities the relativistic kinetic energy reduces to $\frac{1}{2} mu^2$, which is the classical expression.

If we combine Eqs. (124) and (136), we can write the kinetic energy in the form

$$T = (m - m_0)c^2 \tag{138}$$

Thus, accompanying an amount of kinetic energy, there is a corresponding increase in mass given by

$$\Delta m = T/c^2 \tag{139}$$

This suggests the hypothesis that *all* forms of energy might be associated with an equivalent amount of mass. Although we have not proved this in general, the relation between the amount of mass and energy would be similar to Eq. (139). In that case, even the rest-mass of a particle would represent a type of internal or intrinsic energy, which we may call the rest-mass energy of the particle. Let us assume that with every mass m, there is associated an amount of energy E, and vice versa, the relation between the two quantities being as follows:

$$E = mc^2 \tag{140}$$

Equation (140) is the famous Einstein mass-energy relation, which is undoubtedly the most important result of the restricted or special theory of relativity.

If we follow up this point of view, the total energy of a body, U, will be the sum of its kinetic energy and its rest-mass energy. We can write then

$$U = T + m_0c^2 = mc^2 = \frac{m_0c^2}{(1 - v^2/c^2)^{1/2}} \tag{141}$$

For the momentum of a particle we can write the equivalent forms

$$p = mv = \left(\frac{U}{c^2}\right)v = \frac{\beta U}{c} \tag{142}$$

If we eliminate v between Eqs. (141) and (142), we find the following useful relation between the total energy and the momentum of a particle:

$$U^2 = (pc)^2 + (m_0c^2)^2 \tag{143}$$

If we eliminate U between Eqs. (141) and (143), we find the following relation between the momentum and the kinetic energy of a particle:

$$pc = (T^2 + 2m_0c^2T)^{1/2} \tag{144}$$

Mass and energy no longer appear as distinct entities, but rather as analogous to the two faces of a coin. The separate laws of conservation of mass and energy are now to be replaced by a single conservation law, by which the sum of mass and energy are conserved. In applying this new principle of conservation of mass-and-energy, Eq. (140) is to be used when necessary to convert from one form to the other.

The equivalence of mass and energy is on a firm footing, experimentally. For instance, gamma-rays are high frequency electro-magnetic waves similar to X-rays, and yet it is found that sometimes the gamma-ray will disappear, leaving in its place two material particles, a positive and a negative electron. Clearly, since two masses are being created out of energy, each of mass m_0, this process of *pair formation* cannot take place unless the gamma-ray energy is at least equal to $2m_0c^2$. This is found to be true. Furthermore, after subtracting this amount of energy from the incident energy of the gamma-ray, the remainder appears as kinetic energy shared by the two particles. An even more striking example of the conversion of mass into energy according to Eq. (140) is provided by the many nuclear reactions in which there is a gain or loss of mass, with the corresponding absorption or emission of energy. The most spectacular experiment of this kind is the explosion of a so-called "atomic bomb," in which fission processes lead to a large-scale conversion of mass into energy. It may safely be said that many nuclear phenomena would be inexplicable without the principle of the equivalence of mass and energy deduced from the theory of special relativity.

3.12. SUMMARY OF SPECIAL RELATIVITY

Since various optical and electromagnetic experiments seemed to deny the existence of an "absolute space" or ether, Einstein critically examined the classical ideas of space and time in 1905. Since there appeared to be no preferred inertial system, Einstein stated the following postulates:

1. Physical laws must have the same form when expressed in the coordinates of any inertial system.
2. Observers in all inertial systems find the same value for the velocity of light.

In order to satisfy these postulates, it was found that a new set of transformation equations was needed. This purely mathematical exercise had been done by Lorentz in 1904 for Maxwell's electromagnetic equations. The applications of the Lorentz-Einstein transforms to measurements of length, time, and mass then came simply as logical deductions, which have been confirmed by experiment. The equivalence of mass and energy is strongly suggested by the theory, although not proven in general, and is confirmed experimentally.

The main logical value of the theory is its insistence that physical laws must be indifferent to coordinate transformations between inertial systems. Experimentally, the results of the theory have proved to be accurate in many aspects of atomic and nuclear physics, so that a discrepancy in a single experiment should not force us to begin again with a completely new theory. Instead, it would be advisable to try to make small modifications within the basic structure of the present theory. The principle of relativity will undoubtedly be retained until a violent disagreement with experiment is found.

3.13. GENERAL RELATIVITY

In the theory of special relativity we have limited ourselves to inertial frames of reference, all of which move with constant velocity with respect to one another. This theory successfully accounted for the facts of electrodynamics and kinematics, but did not include gravitational effects. We would like to generalize the principle of relativity so as to cover accelerated reference systems and the law of gravitation. The result is the *general theory of relativity*. Since this theory requires the use of tensor analysis, only a brief discussion of it can be given here.

To a person in an accelerated elevator, the acceleration of the elevator produces effects on objects inside the elevator which are identical with those produced by the force of gravity. No mechanical experiments performed by the observer inside the elevator could tell him whether the acceleration of bodies inside the elevator was due to a gravitational force or to the acceleration of the elevator. Einstein therefore postulated the *principle of equivalence* in 1916, which states that there is no difference at any given point between an acceleration produced by a gravitational force and that produced by accelerating the observer's frame of reference. Thus, there is no difference between an inertial frame of reference with a gravitational field superimposed and a non-inertial frame of reference.

We see that at any point it is possible to transform away a gravitational field by properly choosing a frame of reference. If we choose the correct frame of reference, the laws of nature can be expressed without reference to forces. All frames of reference become equally suitable for the formulation of physical laws.

Einstein found that physical laws could be expressed in a form which was *covariant* to very general transformations of coordinates. (An equation is said to be covariant if it remains valid because its terms transform according to identical transformation laws, even though the terms are not invariant.) Of course, the predictions of the theory agree with Newton's law of gravitation, which is known to be highly successful. The general theory of relativity, however, does yield three predictions differing from classical mechanics, which provide tests of the accuracy of the new theory. These are described on the following page.

1. The motion of a particle in a strong gravitational field is slightly different from the classical orbit. In our solar system, only the planet Mercury is affected sufficiently for the difference to be observable. The theory of relativity predicts that the elliptical orbit of Mercury should precess about the sun at a rate of 43 seconds of arc per century. This discrepancy had already been discovered by astronomers during the nineteenth century, and the agreement with Einstein's theory is quite satisfactory.

2. A light ray passing through a strong gravitational field will be deviated slightly. This can be observed during eclipses of the sun, when light from a fixed star just grazes the sun. The theory of relativity predicts a deflection of such a light ray of 1.75 seconds of arc, which is at the limit of experimental error. Experimentally the result is at least not in disagreement with the relativity theory.

3. Physical processes should proceed more slowly in regions where the gravitational field is strong, as compared to the same processes in regions of weak gravitational fields. Thus, an atom on the sun should emit a slightly lower frequency than a similar atom on the earth. This very small *red-shift* is superimposed on frequency shifts owing to the Doppler effect. These shifts are much larger, making verification of this prediction difficult. Observations on the companion to Sirius, which is an extremely dense star, show satisfactory agreement between the theory of relativity and experiment.

It is seen that the predictions of the general theory of relativity differ only minutely from classical predictions and that the differences are difficult to measure. It can be said, however, that in no case is the theory of relativity contradicted by experiment. Even if small discrepancies are found, it is likely that small modifications in the theory will be made, so as to achieve agreement with experiment, while retaining the basic generality of the theory. The principle of relativity seems to have a secure place among the great, all-embracing theories of nature, and in the future its main applications may be to problems of cosmology and the universe.

ADDITIONAL READING

Einstein, Albert, translated by Robert W. Lawson, *Relativity*. New York: Crown Publishers, 1931. A lucid and non-mathematical treatment of the ideas of special and general relativity by the composer of the theory.

Lindsay, Robert Bruce and Henry Margenau, *Foundations of Physics*. New York: John Wiley and Sons, 1936. A complete discussion of the theoretical and philosophical aspects of the principle of relativity, with some mathematical details.

Bergmann, Peter Gabriel, *Introduction to the Theory of Relativity*. Englewood Cliffs, N. J.: Prentice-Hall, Inc., 1942. A thorough treatment of the mathematical methods and the physical aspects of the theory of relativity.

Einstein and others, *The Principle of Relativity*. New York: Dover Publications, Inc. Reprints of original papers on relativity (in translation), with notes by A. Sommerfeld.

PROBLEMS

1. Find the velocity and mass of an electron which has been accelerated through a potential difference of 100 kilovolts. (1.64×10^8 m/sec; 10.9×10^{-31} kg)

2. For speeds approaching the speed of light, it is convenient to define the small quantity $x = 1 - \beta$. For x sufficiently small, show that Eq. (124) can be written

$$\frac{m}{m_0} = \frac{1 + (x/4)}{\sqrt{2x}}$$

3. A particle of mass m_0, is accelerated from rest by a constant force F. Use the abbreviation $R = Fx/m_0 c^2$, and show that after the particle has moved a distance x, its velocity is given by

$$\frac{v}{c} = \frac{(R^2 + 2R)^{1/2}}{1 + R}$$

Show that the above relation reduces to the classical expression for the case of slow speeds.

4. Use the notation of problem 3, and show that the time for the particle to travel a distance x is

$$t = \left(\frac{2m_0 x}{F}\right)^{1/2} + \frac{x^2}{c^2}$$

Show that the above expression yields the classical value for the time as the non-relativistic limit.

5. Two different types of particles are accelerated through the same potential difference, V, and subsequently deflected by the same uniform magnetic field, B. Let particles of mass m and charge q travel in a path of radius r in the magnetic field, while particles of mass M and charge Q travel in a path of radius R. Show that the accelerating voltage is

$$V = 2c^2 \left[\frac{M/Q - (m/q)(R/r)^2}{(R/r)^2 - 1}\right]$$

6. Refer to Problem 5. The radius of curvature of a proton beam is 12 times as great as the radius of curvature of a beam of positrons (positive electrons). Show that the accelerating voltage is 12.2×10^6 volts.

7. The lifetime of a beam of μ-mesons moving with respect to the observer with a speed 90% of that light is measured to be 5.00×10^{-6} sec. Compute the lifetime of a μ-meson in a system in which it is at rest. (2.18×10^{-6} sec)

8. Compute the energy released in ft lb and in kwhr when one pound of mass is completely converted into energy.

9. Compute the rest-mass energy of an electron in joules, and in mev. (8.18×10^{-14} joules; 0.511 mev)

10. When a gamma-ray of energy 10 mev is annihilated, an electron and a positron (positive electron) are formed, each with the same energy. Compute the energy and velocity of each particle.

11. Repeat problem 10 for a gamma-ray of energy 1.00 mev.

12. Derive Eq. (102). $\left(\text{Hint: } \tanh (A - B) = \dfrac{\tanh A - \tanh B}{1 - \tanh A \tanh B} \right).$

13. Compute the contraction in the length of a freight train 2 miles long when travelling at 90 miles per hour.

14. An electron is bent into a circular path by a magnetic field. Show that the relation between the radius of the path in centimeters, magnetic field strength in gauss, and energy of the electron in mev is as follows:

$$Br = \frac{10,000}{3} \sqrt{(T^2 + 1.02T)}$$

15. An electron is bent into a circle of radius 50 cm by a magnetic field of strength 200 gauss. Find the mass of this electron in terms of its rest-mass. (*Ans.* 5.96 m_0)

16. A singly-charged particle has a kinetic energy much greater than its rest-mass energy. Show that

$$T \text{ (mev)} = 300 \, Br \text{ (webers/m}^2 \times \text{meters)}$$

part two

atoms and molecules

chapter four

atomic spectra and
the Bohr-Rutherford theory

In this chapter we will describe the spectra emitted by atoms and discuss the search for an atomic model which would explain the regularity of these spectra. The Bohr-Rutherford theory of atomic hydrogen will be treated and shown to be quite successful. However, we will see that the mathematical scheme of this theory is inadequate for treating more complex atoms, and the useful residue of the theory will be found to be atomic energy levels and associated emission frequencies. In the following chapter we will describe the mathematical apparatus of quantum mechanics, which has been successful in computing atomic energy levels.

4.1. SPECTRAL SERIES

Accurate determination of the wavelengths of light emitted by the various elements became possible about 1880 with the development of the interferometer by Michelson and the construction of good ruled gratings by Rowland. In either case, the directly measured quantity is the wavelength, which is usually expressed in one of the following units:

$$1 \text{ angstrom unit (abbreviated A)} = 10^{-10} \text{ meter}$$

$$1 \text{ micron (abbreviated } \mu) = 10^{-6} \text{ meter}$$

$$1 \text{ millimicron (abbreviated m}\mu) = 10^{-9} \text{ meter}$$

Wavelengths from approximately 4000 A to 7500 A are visible to the human eye, while the regions of shorter and longer wavelengths are called respectively the *ultra-violet* and *infra-red*. In the present chapter we will be concerned with wavelengths not differing by more than a factor of ten from visible wavelengths, although there is no clear-cut boundary to the region of optical spectra.

Although the wavelength is the quantity directly measured spectroscopically, the frequency of the radiation is more useful in theoretical work, as might be suspected from the theory of black-body radiation or the photoelectric effect. Since the velocity of light, c, is known, the frequency, f, is to be computed from the measured wavelength using the relation

$$f = \frac{c}{\lambda} \tag{145}$$

However, optical frequencies are quite large and, in addition, the value of the frequency computed from Eq. (145) will contain any errors in the value of c, so that it is customary to use the *wave-number*, f, defined as follows:

$$\bar{f} = \frac{1}{\lambda} \tag{146}$$

The wave-number thus measures the number of waves per unit length. For instance, for the case of yellow light of wavelength 6000 A, $\bar{f} = \frac{1}{6000}$ per angstrom = 1,666,700 per meter.

The wavelengths of light emitted by a given element depend on the type of excitation. The spectrum produced by a spark is usually greatly different from an arc or flame spectrum. However, each type of excitation gives a spectrum of discrete lines, with wavelengths characteristic of that particular element. By comparison with acoustics and vibrating strings, it might be supposed that the various wavelengths or frequencies emitted by a given element would bear some harmonic relationship to one another. Nothing quite so simple is found, but various consistencies have been discovered.

The first spectral series was discovered by Balmer in 1885. He showed that the nine lines then known in the spectrum of atomic hydrogen could all be expressed by the simple formula

$$\lambda = 3646 \, \frac{n^2}{n^2 - 4} = \frac{3646}{1 - 4/n^2} \tag{147}$$

In Eq. (147), n takes on successively the values 3, 4, 5, . . . , in computing the wavelengths in angstroms of the 1st, 2nd, 3rd . . . , lines of the spectrum of hydrogen. The agreement between the wavelengths computed from Balmer's formula and the measured values is close. Furthermore, the formula correctly predicts that all the lines of this series should lie between the limits of 6562 A, for which n equals 3, and 3646 A, for which n equals infinity.

After this first spectral series was announced, numerous investigators soon found other series. Since regularities in series are found to be more

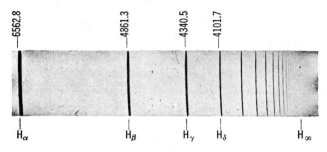

FIG. 29
The Balmer series of hydrogen.   (From Molecular Spectra and Molecular Structure, vol. I by Herzberg, Prentice-Hall, 1939.)

simply expressed in terms of wave-numbers rather than wavelengths, we shall rewrite Eq. (147) as follows:

$$\bar{f} = \frac{1}{\lambda} = \frac{1}{3646}\left(1 - \frac{4}{n^2}\right) = 1.097 \times 10^{-3}\left(\frac{1}{2^2} - \frac{1}{n^2}\right) \qquad (148)$$

Other series are found for hydrogen, all of the same general form as Eq. (148). Expressing $\bar{f}$ in waves per meter instead of waves per angstrom, all of the series can be computed from the single equation below

$$\bar{f} = 10{,}967{,}800\left(\frac{1}{m^2} - \frac{1}{n^2}\right) \qquad (149)$$

(where $n = m + 1, m + 2, m + 3$, etc).

The Lyman series in the ultra-violet is obtained by taking m equal to one; the successive lines in this series are then found by computing $\bar{f}$ for $n = 2, 3, 4, \ldots$, etc. The Balmer series in the visible region is obtained by taking $m = 2$, and then letting n take on all higher values. Similarly, the Paschen series in the infra-red is found by taking $m = 3$, the Brackett series by taking $m = 4$, and the Pfund series by taking $m = 5$. We will later see that the major triumph of the Bohr theory is the correct prediction of Eq. (149), thus accounting for the spectral series of hydrogen.

By 1890 Rydberg had found that the series of many elements could be written in the form below:

$$\bar{f} = \bar{f}_0 - \frac{R}{(n + a)^2} \qquad (150)$$

In Eq. (150), $\bar{f}_0$ and a are constants which vary from series to series. For a given series, the *running integer*, n, takes on successive integral values in yielding the successive wave-numbers of the series. R is called the *Rydberg constant* and it has approximately the value 10,970,000 per meter for all series, the slight differences being due to differences in the atomic weights of the elements. As n takes on large values, the lines of the series become very close together. The short-wavelength *limit* of the series is obtained for infinite n, while the lowest value of n gives the longest wavelength, which is called the *head* of the series. These features are shown in Fig. 29 for the Balmer series of hydrogen.

For the various series of a given element, Rydberg found an even more general and powerful relation. This principle, known as the *Ritz combination principle*, states that the wave-number of each spectral line can be represented as the difference between two numbers, which are called *spectral terms*. In the form of an equation, we have

$$\bar{f} = T_m - T_n \tag{151}$$

Rydberg found empirically that each term was of the form

$$T_n = \frac{R}{(n + a)^2} \tag{152}$$

Even more important, each element has a relatively small number of term values from which a large number of spectral lines can be computed. The first step in the analysis of a spectrum is to find the term values which will yield the observed wave-numbers of the various series of the element in the most economical manner. The term values themselves then become of primary interest. The great simplicity and generality of this scheme suggest that some general mechanism must be involved in the emission of light. Our next problem is to find the mechanism which can correctly predict spectroscopic term values, and thus, emitted wavelengths.

4.2. ATOMIC MODELS

Before we can consider theoretically the problem of the emission of spectra, we must first discuss the structure of atoms. Any theory of atomic structure must also agree with a number of facts not connected with spectroscopy. If the atom is to be constructed from charged particles, it must contain equal numbers of positive and negative charges, since atoms are known to be electrically neutral. After Thomson's discovery of the electron in 1897, it seemed clear that the negative charges were electrons, while the positive charges might be protons. The problem is to choose an arrangement of charges in correct numbers in such a way that the model can account successfully for a number of different phenomena, including spectroscopy.

By 1911 two arrangements of positive and negative charges were under consideration. Thomson's model consisted of a sphere of positive electricity in which electrons were embedded like plums in a pudding. The vibrations of the electrons about their positions of equilibrium would result in the emission of radiation in a way similar to a radio antenna. While this model was partially successful in accounting for the facts of spectroscopy, it had one major difficulty according to classical electro-magnetism. Earnshaw's theorem states that no system of charged particles can be in static equilibrium under the action of electrostatic forces alone. Thus, classically, the matrix of positive charges would fly apart. If Thomson's model of the atom is to be used, this difficulty must be over-come or, perhaps, ignored.

Rutherford's model of the atom is similar to the solar system. All of the positive charge and nearly all of the mass of the atom is concentrated at the center, called the *nucleus*, while the electrons rotate about the nucleus in various orbits, just as the planets revolve about the sun. While this model avoids the stability difficulty of Thomson's model, it too has a problem with stability. Classically an accelerated charge emits radia-tion, as in the case of current flowing in a radio antenna. Since the elec-trons in Rutherford's model of the atom are subject to centripetal accelera-tions in their motions about the nucleus, such an atom would continually radiate energy. Since this radiation of energy must come at the expense of the electrostatic potential energy of the atom, the electrons would spiral in toward the nucleus and in a very short time the atom would collapse. However, atoms are not observed to radiate energy under all conditions, nor are they observed to collapse, so this is a severe difficulty for the Rutherford model of the atom.

Disregarding temporarily the stability problems mentioned in connec-tion with both models of the atom proposed above, we will consider the nuclear physics experiments of Geiger and Marsden which provided a test between the two theories. A few facts from nuclear physics must first be considered, which will be treated in more detail in later chapters. Radio-active elements emit various radiations, among them *alpha-particles*. Alpha-particles are found to be helium ions, with a positive charge twice the magnitude of the electronic charge and nearly the mass of a neutral helium atom. Their velocities are of the order of 10^9 centimeters per second, so the energy of an alpha-particle is several mev. When an alpha-particle strikes a screen covered with zinc sulphide or some other fluorescent material, a small flash of light is emitted by a crystal of the zinc sulphide each time an alpha-particle strikes the screen. If the flashes of light are observed in darkness with a low-power microscope, each individual alpha-particle registers its presence and position on the screen by a single flash of light.   With this method we can not only count numbers of particles, but also find how they are distributed in space.

Let a beam of alpha-particles from a radioactive element be collimated into a narrow beam by narrow slits made of lead, as shown in Fig. 30.

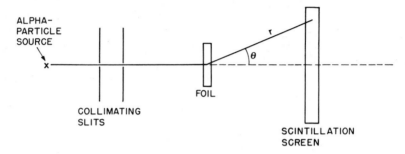

FIG. 30
Schematic diagram of arrangement for observing the scattering of alpha-particles.

Before the thin foil of metal is put in place, the flashes of light on the zinc sulphide screen will cover a region equal to the size of the slit.   If a thin foil of metal is now interposed in the alpha-particle beam, the area over which flashes are seen is found to be increased.   Apparently some of the alpha-particles in the collimated beam are deflected by the atoms in the metallic foil, perhaps as a result of the electrostatic forces between the positively-charged alpha-particles and the charges making up the atoms.

It is possible to compute the amount of deflection to be expected for a beam of alpha-particles passing through a thin foil according to either Thomson's or Rutherford's model of the atom.   Since the results are quite different, this may prove to be a crucial test of the two theories.

If we use Thomson's model of the atom, we will let N_0 be the total number of alpha-particles arriving at $\theta = 0$ and let θ_{av} be the average deflection of the beam.   It is found by calculation that the number of alpha-particles N, deflected through an angle greater than θ, is given by

$$N = N_0 \exp \frac{-\theta^2}{\theta_{av}^2} \tag{153}$$

Since the average deflection, θ_{av}, is found experimentally to be of the order of a degree, Thomson's model predicts that only an infinitesimal number of alpha-particles will be deflected through angles over a few degrees.   However, in 1909 Geiger and Marsden showed that approximately one alpha-particle in 8000 was deflected more than 90°. This relatively large number of particles scattered through angles more than a few degrees cannot be accounted for by Thomson's theory.

We will now use Rutherford's model and compute the deflection expected for a beam of alpha-particles. We will use polar coordinates to describe the motion of the alpha-particle and will treat the scattering nucleus as fixed. Since electrons are so light, they can be ignored in calculating the deflection of an alpha-particle. When the alpha-particle is far from the nucleus we will call its velocity v_0. If there were no deflection, the alpha-particle would pass the nucleus at a minimum distance, p, as shown in Fig. 31. The mass of the alpha-particle is m and its charge is $+2e$. The charge on the nucleus is $+eZ$.

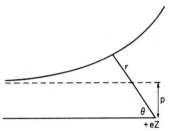

FIG. 31
Trajectory of an alpha-particle in the vicinity of a nucleus of charge $+ eZ$.

By conservation of energy we then have

$$\tfrac{1}{2}\, mv_0^2 = \frac{(2e)(Ze)}{r} + \frac{m}{2}\left[\left(\frac{dr}{dt}\right)^2 + \left(r\,\frac{d\theta}{dt}\right)^2\right] \qquad (154)$$

By conservation of angular momentum about the nucleus we have

$$mv_0 p = mr^2\,\frac{d\theta}{dt} \qquad (155)$$

If we eliminate $d\theta/dt$ between Eqs. (154) and (155) and solve for dr/dt, we find

$$\frac{dr}{dt} = \pm v_0 \sqrt{1 - \frac{4Ze^2}{mv_0^2 r} - \frac{p^2}{r^2}} \qquad (156)$$

Since r is decreasing as the alpha-particle approaches the nucleus, we must take the minus sign in Eq. (156). If we let $k = 2Ze^2/mv_0^2$ in Eq. (156) and compute $d\theta/dr$, we find

$$\frac{d\theta}{dr} = \frac{d\theta/dt}{dr/dt} = \frac{pv_0/r^2}{-v_0[1 - (2k/r) - (p^2/r^2)]^{1/2}}$$

$$\frac{d\theta}{dr} = \frac{-p}{r(r^2 - 2kr - p^2)^{1/2}} \qquad (157)$$

Integrating Eq. (157) to find the equation of the orbit, we find

$$\theta = -p\int \frac{dr}{r(r^2 - 2kr - p^2)^{1/2}} = -\sin^{-1}\left[\frac{-kr - p^2}{r(k^2 + p^2)^{1/2}}\right] + C \qquad (158)$$

We can evaluate the constant of integration, C, in Eq. (158) by the condition that $\theta = 0$ when r is infinite. We then find

$$C = \sin^{-1}\left[\frac{-k}{(k^2 + p^2)^{1/2}}\right] \qquad (159)$$

The equation of the trajectory now takes the form

$$\theta = \sin^{-1}\left[\frac{-k}{(k^2 + p^2)^{1/2}}\right] - \sin^{-1}\left[\frac{-kr - p^2}{r(k^2 + p^2)^{1/2}}\right] \qquad (160)$$

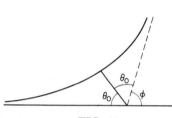

At the point of closest approach of the alpha-particle to the nucleus, r and θ have the values r_0 and θ_0, as shown in Fig. 32. At this point $dr/dt = 0$, and from Eq. (156) we find the following:

$$1 - \frac{2k}{r_0} - \frac{p^2}{r_0^2} = 0 \qquad (161)$$

FIG. 32
Relation between polar angle θ_0 of alpha-particle trajectory and angle of scattering ϕ.

Solving Eq. (161) for r_0 we find

$$r_0 = k \pm (k^2 + p^2)^{1/2} \qquad (162)$$

We must take the positive sign in Eq. (162), since r is always positive. When we substitute r_0 from Eq. (162) into Eq. (160) and simplify, we find

$$\theta_0 = \sin^{-1}\left[\frac{-k}{(k^2 + p^2)^{1/2}}\right] - \sin^{-1}(-1) = \frac{\pi}{2} + \sin^{-1}\left[\frac{-k}{(k^2 + p^2)^{1/2}}\right] \qquad (163)$$

Evidently the same change in θ occurs during the second half of the trajectory in which the alpha-particle moves away from the nucleus. The total deflection of the alpha-particle from its original direction we will call ϕ. As is shown in Fig. 32, ϕ is related to θ_0 in the following way:

$$\phi = \pi - 2\theta_0 = -2\sin^{-1}\left[\frac{-k}{(k^2 + p^2)^{1/2}}\right] = 2\sin^{-1}\left[\frac{k}{(k^2 + p^2)^{1/2}}\right] \qquad (164)$$

From Eq. (164) it is easily seen that $\tan(\phi/2) = k/p$. Therefore, for p we can write the expression

$$p = k \cot \frac{\phi}{2} \qquad (165)$$

Let N alpha-particles approach a unit area of the target. The number which will have a value of p between p and $(p + dp)$, as shown in Fig. 33, is then

$$dN = N\, 2\pi p\, dp \qquad (166)$$

These dN atoms will be deflected through an angle between ϕ and $(\phi + d\phi)$. If we differentiate Eq. (165) we find

$$dp = \frac{k \, \csc^2(\phi/2)}{2} \, d\phi \tag{167}$$

At a distance R from the scatterer, these dN atoms will cover an area given by

$$dA = (2\pi R \sin \phi)R \, d\phi = 2\pi R^2 \sin \phi \, d\phi$$

The number per unit area of the scintillation screen, $N\phi$, which have been scattered through angles between ϕ and $(\phi + d\phi)$ is then given by the expression

$$N_\phi = \frac{dN}{dA} = \frac{N(2\pi p \, dp)}{2\pi R^2 \sin \phi \, d\phi}$$

$$= \frac{2\pi N \, k \cot(\phi/2) \, \dfrac{k \, \csc^2(\phi/2)}{2} \, d\phi}{2\pi R^2 \sin \phi \, d\phi} \tag{168}$$

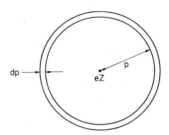

FIG. 33

Annular ring of radius p and width dp about a target nucleus.

If we write all angles in terms of $\phi/2$ and replace k by its value defined above, Eq. (168) takes the form

$$N_\phi = N \frac{Z^2 e^4 \csc^4(\phi/2)}{m^2 v_0^2 R^2} = N \frac{Z^2 e^4 \csc^4(\phi/2)}{4E^2 R^2} \tag{169}$$

In the right-hand expression of Eq. (169) we have put

$$E = \frac{m}{2} v_0^2$$

where E is the initial kinetic energy of the alpha particle. A striking feature of Eq. (169) is that it predicts appreciable scattering of alpha-particles through large angles, which the Thomson theory was unable to do.

Geiger and Marsden checked Eq. (169) factor by factor in 1913 by letting a single factor vary at a time, such as the angle of scattering, alpha-particle energy, etc. In each case Eq. (169) was verified quantitatively, which decisively decides in favor of Rutherford's model of the atom in favor of Thomson's. In the next section it will be seen that this model of the atom is also successful in predicting the optical spectrum of atomic hydrogen.

Before leaving the study of alpha-particle scattering, it is of special interest to note that Geiger and Marsden found that the number of charges on the nucleus, Z, was approximately equal to the atomic number of the element used in the foil. Experiments on the scattering of X-rays, which are discussed later, show that the number of electrons associated with an atom is also approximately equal to the atomic number of the element. We will thus take as the model of an atom a nucleus with a charge equal to the atomic number of the element multiplied by the electronic charge, and revolving about this nucleus we will have a number of electrons equal also to the atomic number of the element.

4.3. BOHR'S THEORY OF ONE-ELECTRON ATOMS

As described above, Rutherford's model of the atom seems to be correct in explaining the deflection of alpha-particles by atoms. The application of this model to the theoretical explanation of the optical spectra of one-electron atoms was made by Bohr in 1913. This successful application gives us additional confidence in the Rutherford model of the atom.

We will consider only the case of a single electron revolving about a nucleus with a charge Ze. Examples of such one-electron systems are atomic hydrogen, for which $Z = 1$, ionized helium, for which $Z = 2$, and doubly ionized lithium, for which $Z = 3$. The theory will be presented for an electron revolving about the nucleus in a circular orbit of radius, r, as shown in Fig. 34. The electron has a speed, v. The extension of the theory to include elliptical orbits and relativistic effects was made by Sommerfeld, but nothing strikingly different is found, although these extensions do help to explain the detailed, fine structure of spectral series.

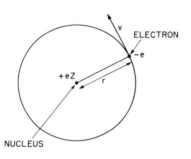

FIG. 34

Electron traveling in a circular orbit about a fixed nucleus of charge $+ eZ$.

Bohr overcame the classical difficulty of the collapse of the atom through continuous radiation by postulating that certain orbits could violate this classical principle. For a single electron the first postulate takes the form

  I. The electron can exist only in certain stable orbits, and in these orbits the electron does not radiate energy. The stable circular orbits satisfy the quantum condition

$$mvr = \frac{nh}{2\pi} \qquad (170)$$

(where $n = 1, 2, 3, \ldots$).

In the quantum condition imposed on stable circular orbits by Eq. (170), m is the mass of the electron, v the electron's speed, r is the radius of the orbit corresponding to a particular value of the *quantum number*, n, and h is Planck's constant, which has already appeared in the theory of black-body radiation and the photoelectric effect. Each value of n leads to a different stable or *allowed* orbit. While this postulate is admittedly contrived to avoid the classical difficulties of the Rutherford atom, its validity must be judged by the comparison of the results of the theory with the facts of spectroscopy.

Bohr's second postulate provides the connection between the atomic model and spectral series emitted by a particular atom. Since the theory of black-body radiation and the photoelectric effect show that radiant energy is transferred in units called quanta, each of energy, hf, the following postulate is suggested:

II. When the energy of an atom changes from a value, W_1, to a lower value, W_2, the difference in energy is emitted as a quantum of radiation, of frequency given by

$$hf = W_1 - W_2 \qquad (171)$$

The relation shown in Eq. (171) is known as the *Einstein frequency condition*. Conversely absorption of a quantum of energy hf raises the energy of the atom from the value W_2 to a higher value, W_1, given by Eq. (171).

We will now apply the usual laws of dynamics and electrostatics to the stable orbits satisfying Eq. (170). Our main interest will be in the energy of each of the stable orbits, since the application of Eq. (171) to various energy changes will allow us to compute the various frequencies emitted by the one-electron atom we are considering. At present we will consider the nucleus to be fixed, but later a correction for the motion of the nucleus will be made.

The force which holds the electron in the circular path of Fig. 34 is the electrostatic force of attraction between the electron and the nucleus, which is given by Coulomb's law as $K'e(eZ)/r^2$. In MKS units, K' has a value very close to 9×10^9 when the charges are measured in coulombs and their separation in meters. The force between the charges is then expressed in newtons. The gravitational force between the electron and the nucleus is negligible, as shown in Problem 1 of this chapter. For a circular orbit the acceleration is entirely centripetal and given by v^2/r. When we apply Newton's law of motion to this situation, we find

$$F = K' \frac{e^2 Z}{r^2} = ma = \frac{mv^2}{r} \qquad (172)$$

If we solve Eq. (170) for the velocity of an electron in an allowed orbit, we find

$$v = \frac{nh}{2\pi mr} \tag{173}$$

Substituting the value of v from Eq. (173) in Eq. (172) and solving for the radius of an allowed orbit for some particular quantum number, n, we have

$$r = \frac{n^2 h^2}{4\pi^2 m e^2 K' Z} \tag{174}$$

Since the only quantities in Eq. 174 which vary from orbit to orbit or from element to element are n and Z, let us compute the value of the remaining constant factor. We have

$$\frac{h^2}{4\pi^2 m e^2 K'} = \frac{(6.62 \times 10^{-34})^2}{4\pi^2 \times 9.11 \times 10^{-31} \times (1.60 \times 10^{-19})^2 \times 9.00 \times 10^9}$$
$$= 5.23 \times 10^{-11} \text{ meter}$$

Thus for the radii of the allowed orbits we can write

$$r = \frac{n^2}{Z} (5.23 \times 10^{-11} \text{ meter}) \tag{175}$$

Now the density of solid hydrogen is 0.076 grams per cubic centimeter, so that one gram of atomic hydrogen occupies 13.2 cubic centimeters. Since a gram of hydrogen consists of approximately 6×10^{23} hydrogen atoms, the number of atoms per cubic centimeter is approximately 0.456×10^{23}. The average separation of the hydrogen atoms in solid hydrogen is therefore seen to be

$$d = \frac{1}{(0.456 \times 10^{23})^{1/3}} = 2.8 \times 10^{-8} \text{ cm}$$

Similarly, the density of lithium is 0.534 grams per cubic centimeter, and a similar calculation shows that the average distance between atoms of solid lithium is also approximately 2.8×10^{-8} centimeter. If we assume that the atoms in a solid are packed as closely as possible, then the radius of an atom is approximately 1.4×10^{-8} centimeter. Returning to Eq. (175), if we assume that the radius of an allowed electron orbit determines the effective radius of an atom, we find the allowed radii predicted by the Bohr theory are at least of the correct order of magnitude.

Let us now find the energy of the atom when the electron is in one of the allowed orbits. From Eq. (172) we have

$$mv^2 = K' \frac{e^2 Z}{r} \tag{176}$$

Thus, the kinetic energy of the electron is

$$T = \tfrac{1}{2}\, mv^2 = K'\, \frac{e^2 Z}{2r} \tag{177}$$

As the nucleus is assumed to be at rest, all of the kinetic energy of the atom is possessed by the electron. At present it will be convenient to leave the kinetic energy in the form of Eq. (177), although by the use of Eq. (174), r could be eliminated, giving the kinetic energy in terms of n, Z, and certain physical constants. This will be done after we obtain an expression for the potential energy of the atom.

The potential energy of a system is the energy stored in the system by virtue of its position or configuration. Regarding the nucleus as fixed, the potential energy of the atom changes when the electron is moved from one position to another. The difference in potential energy between two positions of the electron is equal to the work done against the forces acting in moving the electron from the first position to the second. Since the force between an electron and a nucleus is zero when the electron is very far from the nucleus, the potential energy of the atom is conventionally taken to be zero when the electron and the nucleus are separated by an infinite distance. Using this convention, the potential energy of the atom, when the electron is located a distance, r, from the nucleus, is equal to the work done in bringing the electron up to this point starting at infinity.

From the above discussion, it is seen that the potential energy of a one-electron atom is given by

$$V = \int_{\infty}^{r} F\, dr = \int_{\infty}^{r} K'\, \frac{e^2 Z}{r^2} = -K'\, \frac{e^2 Z}{r} \tag{178}$$

The significance of the minus sign in Eq. (178) is that work can be taken out of the system as the electron approaches the nucleus. Thus, the closer the electron is to the nucleus, the lower is the potential energy of the atom.

The total energy of the atom is the sum of its kinetic and potential energies. From Eqs. (177) and (178) we have

$$W = T + V = \tfrac{1}{2} K'\, \frac{e^2 Z}{r} - K'\, \frac{e^2 Z}{r} = -\tfrac{1}{2} K'\, \frac{e^2 Z}{r} \tag{179}$$

When we susbtitute the value of r from Eq. (174) in Eq. (179), we have for the energy, W_n, of the atom when the electron is in the nth allowed orbit, the value

$$W_n = -\frac{2\pi^2 m e^4 Z^2\, K'^2}{n^2 h^2} \tag{180}$$

The energy of the atom must be one of the values given by Eq. (180) for an integral value of n, and no other energy value can satisfy Bohr's first postulate. Since all of the allowed energy values are negative, the lowest algebraic value of the energy of the atom is found for $n = 1$. Since the most stable state of a system is its state of lowest energy, the orbit for $n = 1$ is the normal or *ground state* of the atom. The atom is normally in its lowest state, and energy must be acquired by the atom through collisions or by other means before the electron is raised to an *excited state*, for which n is greater than one. Finally, let us recall that the potential energy of the atom was taken to be zero when the electron was separated ·an infinite distance from the nucleus. Since this situation corresponds physically to ionization of the atom, the numerical value of the energy of the lowest state is just equal to the energy required to ionize the atom. We shall return to this point later.

Now that we have computed the possible energy values of a one-electron atom, we can let the energy change from one allowed value to another. Using the second Bohr postulate we can calculate the frequency of radiation emitted during such a transition. This clearly requires the atom to have been raised to an excited state by some process before the transition takes place, since the emission of radiation requires the energy of the atom to decrease. Let the atom change from the energy state, for which $n = j$, to the lower energy state, for which $n = k$. According to Eq. (171), the frequency of the quantum of radiation emitted is given by

$$hf = W_j - W_k = \frac{-2\pi^2 m e^4 Z^2 K'^2}{j^2 h^2} - \frac{-2\pi^2 m e^4 Z^2 K'^2}{k^2 h^2} \qquad (181)$$

Solving Eq. (181) for the frequency, f, we find

$$f = \frac{2\pi^2 m e^4 Z^2 K'^2}{h^3} (1/k^2 - 1/j^2) \qquad (182)$$

For the wave-number of the emitted radiation we find

$$\bar{f} = \frac{f}{c} = \frac{2\pi^2 m e^4 Z^2 K'^2}{c h^3} (1/k^2 - 1/j^2) \qquad (183)$$

Since the quantum numbers, j and k, are both integers, Eq. (183) is seen to be the same in form as Eq. (149), which was the empirical formula which predicted the various series of atomic hydrogen.

The constant factor not involving Z, j, or k in Eq. (183) is easily found to have the value

$$R = \frac{2\pi^2 m e^4 K'^2}{c h^3} = 1.09737 \times 10^7 \text{ per meter} \qquad (184)$$

(When the effect of the motion of the nucleus is included by using the reduced-mass theorem proved in Section 4.5, the value of R for atomic hydrogen is found to be 1.09678×10^7 per meter.) In terms of the new constant, R, we can write Eq. (183) in the simpler form

$$\bar{f} = RZ^2 \left[\frac{1}{k^2} - \frac{1}{j^2} \right] \tag{185}$$

One asset of the Bohr Theory is that it gives not only the form of the empirical equations for the spectra of hydrogen, but also a very good value for the Rydberg constant. For hydrogen we take $Z = 1$, and Eq. (185) reduces exactly to Eq. (149). The spectrum of ionized helium is obtained by taking $Z = 2$, the spectrum of doubly ionized lithium is obtained by taking $Z = 3$, and the spectrum of triply ionized beryllium is obtained by taking $Z = 4$. The various spectra of ions with a single electron have been observed and agree with the predictions of the theory given here. In predicting the spectra of one-electron systems the theory has been highly successful, but unfortunately we shall see later that this theory cannot be extended successfully to systems containing more than two particles, such as the normal helium atom or the hydrogen molecule.

4.4. ENERGY LEVELS

Referring to Eq. (175), it is seen that the radii of successive allowed orbits increase as the square of the quantum number n. For this reason, only a few orbits can be drawn to scale in a diagram of reasonable size. However, from Eq. (180) we see that all the energy values lie between the lowest value, for $n = 1$, and the value zero, for $n = \infty$, which corresponds to ionization, so that the complete range of energy values can conveniently be represented on a diagram.

Let us calculate the value of the constant factor in Eq. (180). We have

$$K'^2 \frac{2\pi^2 m e^4}{h^2} = 2.17 \times 10^{-18} \text{ joules} = 13.58 \text{ electron-volts}$$

The energy of the nth allowed orbit then takes the form

$$W_n = \frac{-13.58 Z^2}{n^2} \tag{186}$$

A few of the energy values of hydrogen are plotted in Fig. 35 in the form of a potential energy diagram. A hydrogen atom is usually in the normal or ground state, with $n = 1$, but a collision or other process may raise the energy of the atom to some higher level, with a correspondingly high value of n. When the atom drops back to a lower energy level, which is not necessarily the ground state, the difference in energy is emitted as a quantum of radiation. After one or more transitions, the atom eventually returns to its normal state.

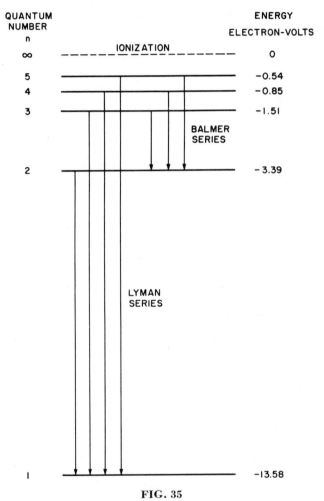

FIG. 35

Energy-level diagram of atomic hydrogen, showing a few transitions.

The wavelength of the radiation emitted during a given transition could be found by first computing the frequency from Eq. (171) and then computing the wavelength from Eq. (145). However, we already have derived the Duane-Hunt relation in connection with the photoelectric effect. Equation (69) gives the relation between the wavelength of an absorbed quantum of radiation and the energy of this quantum in electron-volts. Exactly the same reasoning applies to the converse effect, where radiation is emitted corresponding to a decrease in energy. Thus, we have the following relation between the wavelength emitted (in angstroms) and the decrease in energy of the atom (in electron-volts):

$$\lambda =' \frac{12,396.44}{\Delta W} \tag{187}$$

For any energy transition, ΔW, we can compute the corresponding wavelength of radiation emitted from Eq. (187)

When an electron is raised to the second quantum state, with $n = 2$, it can only return directly to the ground state, and the first member of the Lyman series is emitted, as shown in Fig. 35. However, when an electron is raised to the state for which $n = 3$, two alternative return paths exist. The electron can return directly to the ground state, with the accompanying emission of the second member of the Lyman series, or the electron can return in two transitions, with the emission of the first line of the Balmer series in cascade with the first line of the Lyman series. An inspection of Fig. 35 will show the various possibilities when an electron is raised to a given excited state. Clearly, many atoms combine to yield the entire spectrum of hydrogen, since a given atom emits only one or a few quanta in returning to the ground state.

In the emission of a quantum, we speak of the higher energy state as the *initial state* and the lower energy state as the *final state*. All lines of a given spectral series share a common final state, while the various lines differ in their initial states. All of the members of the Lyman series are emitted when electrons drop from some excited state to the lowest or ground state. The Balmer series is emitted by electrons dropping from various excited states down to the second quantum state. Similarly, the Paschen series is emitted during transitions ending on the third quantum state, the Brackett series by transitions ending on the fourth quantum state, and so forth. In passing it might be noted that the spectral series which is produced by transitions to the ground state is usually called the *principal series* of that element.

A crucial test of the validity of the energy levels assigned is that the energy levels must be internally consistent. For instance, the third quantum state of hydrogen is seen in Fig. 35 to be the initial state for the second line of the Lyman series, the initial state for the first line of the Balmer series, and the final state for the Paschen series. The fact that this one value of an energy level yields correct wavelengths in three different spectral series gives one confidence in the correctness of this energy level.   Proceeding in this way, the various assignments of energy levels of an element are checked.   This may be a long and tedious process, of course, but the spectra of most elements have been analyzed and the energy levels of the corresponding elements determined.

One mechanism by which atoms may be raised to excited states is bombardment by electrons.   Since the energy of the bombarding electrons may be controlled, this provides an electrical method for observing and measuring the energy levels of elements.   Consider an arrangement as shown in Fig. 36.   Electrons emitted by the filament are accelerated to the potential of the accelerating grid and then pass into the gas-filled space between the grid and the anode.   If the gas atoms are given enough energy by the impact of the electrons, they may emit their characteristic wavelengths or even be ionized.

The energy required to raise an atom from its ground state to a given excited state is called the *excitation potential* of that state.   Franck and Hertz made the first direct observation of an excitation potential in 1914. They bombarded mercury vapor with electrons and found that the electrons had to have energies at least as great as 4.9 electron-volts in order to excite the strong line at 2536 angstroms.   According to Eq. (187), this line corresponds to an energy transition of 4.88 electron-volts.   Thus, it is very likely that the bombarding electrons have raised mercury atoms to their first excited state by collision.   When each atom returns to its ground state, the wavelength 2536 angstroms is emitted.   Many experiments similar in principle to this have been performed to measure excita-

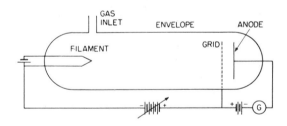

FIG. 36
Apparatus for determining the excitation potentials of gases.

tion potentials directly, and the results are in agreement with energy levels determined spectroscopically.   However, spectroscopic values of energy levels are usually more precise than electrical values, so that the electrical experiments' main use is the confirmation of the existence of energy levels for atoms.

If the bombarding electron knocks an atomic electron completely free of the atom, the atom is said to be *ionized*.   As the energy of the bombarding electrons in the arrangement of Fig. 36 is raised, the current conducted by the gas suddenly rises at the *ionization potential* of the gas. At this point, the electrons have just enough energy to raise an atomic electron from its ground state to the state of ionization. This gives directly the numerical value of the ground state of the gas. According to the Bohr theory of atomic spectra, the short-wavelength convergence limit of the principal series of an element is produced when an electron suffers a transition from zero energy down to the ground state. Converting this wavelength limit into electron-volts by the use of Eq. (187), we get a spectroscopic value of the ground-state energy of the element. Values of ground-state energies measured electrically compare well with spectroscopic values, again confirming the existence of atomic energy levels.

No matter what model of the atom is eventually accepted as most nearly correct, energy levels are assured of a permanent and important place in atomic theory. Energy levels are derived directly from experimental values of wavelengths or from excitation potentials measured by electron bombardment and do not depend on any particular model of atomic structure. It is the task of theory to devise a scheme for computing these energy levels, which then occupy a central position in atomic theory.

4.5. MOTION OF THE NUCLEUS AND REDUCED MASS

In Bohr's theory of the one-electron atom, up to this point we have neglected the motion of the nucleus. We shall now proceed to prove a general theorem of dynamics which applies to any pair of particles with an interacting force along the line joining the particles, and which depends only on the separation of the particles. Examples of such *central forces* are the well-known gravitational, electrostatic, magnetostatic and elastic

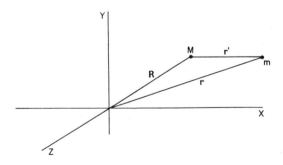

FIG. 37

Motion of particles m (electron) and M (nucleus) relative to an inertial system, XYZ.

forces. Even though both particles are free to move, we shall see that we may consider one particle to be fixed provided we correct the mass of the other particle suitably.

Take fixed axes, XYZ, to describe the motions of the two particles, m and M, as shown in Fig. 37. The respective positions of the two particles are described by the vectors, r and R, drawn from the origin. (Vectors will be symbolized by boldface type.) The position vector of m with respect to M is given by

$$r' = r - R \tag{188}$$

In our analysis of the one-electron atom we have dealt only with functions of r', neglecting the motion of the nucleus. Since the nucleus, represented by the mass M here, may move, it is not a suitable origin for an inertial system. Newton's second law of motion will apply only with respect to an inertial system, so that r and R must be used in computing accelerations, in place of r'.

We shall assume that the force between the two particles is along the line joining them and depends only on their separation. Thus, the force acting on m is of the form

$$F_m = f(r')r' \tag{189}$$

In Eq. (189), $f(r')$ may be any arbitrary, scalar function of $|r'|$. The equation of motion of m relative to the inertial axes, XYZ, is thus:

$$m \frac{d^2r}{dt^2} = f(r')r' \tag{190}$$

According to Newton's third law of motion, the force on M is equal to that on m, but oppositely directed. The equation of motion of M relative to the inertial axes, XYZ, is

$$M \frac{d^2R}{dt^2} = -f(r')r' \tag{191}$$

Solving Eqs. (190) and (191) for the accelerations of the two particles relative to XYZ, we have

$$\frac{d^2r}{dt^2} = \frac{1}{m} f(r')r' \tag{192}$$

$$\frac{d^2R}{dt^2} = -\frac{1}{M} f(r')r' \tag{193}$$

Subtracting (193) from (192), we have

$$\frac{d^2r}{dt^2} - \frac{d^2R}{dt^2} = \left(\frac{1}{m} + \frac{1}{M}\right) f(r')r' \tag{194}$$

However, if we differentiate (188) twice, we find

$$\frac{d^2\boldsymbol{r}'}{dt^2} = \frac{d^2\boldsymbol{r}}{dt^2} - \frac{d^2\boldsymbol{R}}{dt^2} \tag{195}$$

Comparing (194) and (195), we find

$$\frac{d^2\boldsymbol{r}'}{dt^2} = \left(\frac{1}{m} + \frac{1}{M}\right)f(r')\boldsymbol{r}' \tag{196}$$

Defining the reduced mass, μ, of the two particles by the equation

$$\frac{1}{\mu} = \frac{1}{m} + \frac{1}{M} \tag{197}$$

In terms of the reduced mass, we can now write Eq. (196) in the form

$$\mu \frac{d^2\boldsymbol{r}'}{dt^2} = f(r')\boldsymbol{r}' \tag{198}$$

Comparing Eqs. (190) and (198), we see that the equation of motion of m relative to M, as given by Eq. (198), has exactly the same form as the equation of motion of m relative to the inertial axes XYZ, provided only that we replace m by μ. This theorem often considerably simplifies the analysis of the motions of bodies.

We can now correct the Bohr theory for the actual motion of the nucleus by replacing m by μ. For instance, the correct form of the Rydberg constant in Eq. (184) is

$$R = \frac{2\pi^2 e^4 \mu K'^2}{ch^3} = \frac{2\pi^2 e^4 m K'^2}{\left(1 + \dfrac{m}{M}\right)ch^3} \tag{199}$$

If we define R_0 as the value of the Rydberg constant for a nucleus of infinite mass, in which case the nucleus would remain strictly motionless, we then have for the Rydberg constant for an atom with a nucleus of mass, M, the value

$$R = \frac{R_0}{1 + \dfrac{m}{M}} \tag{200}$$

The slight variation of R with nuclear mass makes the energy levels of various one-electron systems somewhat different. For instance, the first line of the Balmer series of hydrogen is 1.79 angstroms greater than the corresponding line emitted by deuterium, since the mass of a deuterium nucleus is twice that of a hydrogen nucleus. This difference in wavelength can easily be detected without elaborate equipment. Similar differences are found between certain hydrogen wavelengths and the corresponding wavelengths of ionized helium.

4.6. EXTENSION OF THE BOHR THEORY TO MORE COMPLICATED ATOMS

So far our treatment of the Bohr theory has been limited to systems consisting of a nucleus and a single electron rotating about the nucleus. The next problem is to apply this theory to more complicated systems. The second postulate given by Eq. (171) is found to be effective in predicting the frequency of a quantum of radiation emitted when an atom changes its energy state. This postulate can be retained unchanged in discussing all atomic systems. This is not surprising, since this postulate was strongly suggested by the theories of black body radiation and of photoelectricity, in which radiation was emitted or absorbed in discrete quanta. Regardless of the theoretical scheme used to calculate energy levels and allowed energy transitions, the accuracy of the second postulate in predicting emitted frequencies seems to be beyond question.

The situation is different, however, in the case of the actual Bohr model of the atom or the quantization rules for allowed orbits. Although the first postulate seems rather artificial and is not strengthened by evidence from other fields of physics, its application to the theory of one-electron atoms is quite successful. However, the Bohr theory fails to give correct results whenever a rapidly varying electric field affects the electron under consideration. The examples below will help to make the meaning of this statement clear.

One of the simplest extensions of the theory is to the spectrum of the normal helium atom. In this case, two electrons circle about the nucleus, so that each electron is affected by the rapidly varying field of the other. Another relatively simple problem is the hydrogen molecule ion, H_2^+, which consists of two protons sharing a single electron, which is subject to the varying electric fields of the two protons. In both of these cases the Bohr theory yields results which definitely disagree with experiment. In the case of dispersion of light, the electrons in the atoms of the dispersive medium are subject to the rapidly varying electromagnetic field of the light waves, and again the Bohr theory is unsuccessful. Finally, in the case of the band spectra of diatomic molecules, the Bohr theory leads to the quantum number, n, while experimentally, n should be replaced by $(n + \frac{1}{2})$.

In addition to the incorrect predictions described above, the Bohr theory is not entirely satisfactory in two more particulars. Semi-classical and rather artificial arguments lead to rules for the intensities of spectral lines emitted, but the expectations are only partially confirmed by experiment. Furthermore, in order to explain the fine structure of energy levels and resulting spectral lines, the electron must have a rotational spin and a resulting magnetic moment. The Bohr theory is unable to account for this electron spin.

In view of the limited success of the Bohr theory, which is mainly useful in the case of one-electron systems only, it appears likely that some more general scheme must be developed to compute atomic energy levels. In the following chapter the radically different theory, called *quantum mechanics* or *wave mechanics*, is presented. Quantum mechanics has been outstandingly successful in solving problems involving atomic energy levels and atomic and molecular structure.

ADDITIONAL READING

Robertson, John Kellock, *Introduction to Physical Optics*. Princeton, N. J.: D. Van Nostrand Co., 1954 (4th Ed.). A clear presentation of various facts concerning atomic and molecular spectra.

Bohr, Niels, *The Theory of Spectra and Atomic Constitution*. Cambridge University Press, 1924 (2nd Ed.). Well-written and relatively non-mathematical treatment of the theory of spectra as of 1922.

White, Harvey Elliott, *Introduction to Atomic Spectra*. New York: McGraw-Hill Book Co., Inc., 1934. A complete and thorough exposition of the subject.

Herzberg, Gerhard, *Atomic Spectra and Atomic Structure*. Englewood Cliffs, N. J.: Prentice-Hall, Inc., 1937 and Dover Publications, 1944. An excellent treatise.

Beyer, Robert T. (editor), *Foundations of Nuclear Physics*. Dover Publications, 1949. Facsimiles of thirteen fundamental papers are presented, including Rutherford's paper on the scattering of alpha-particles. It also has an extensive bibliography.

PROBLEMS

1. Show that the gravitational force between an electron and a proton in the Bohr theory could safely be neglected by calculating the ratio of the electrostatic force to the gravitational force between these two particles.
   Ans. (2.4×10^{39})

2. Electrons accelerated through 13.00 volts strike hydrogen gas. Compute the wavelengths of all spectral lines which could be observed.

3. The short-lived element, positronium, consists of an electron revolving about a positron. The electron and positron are identical except for the sign of their charges, and each has a mass 1/1840 of the proton's mass. Compute the three longest wavelengths emitted by positronium in the series corresponding to the Lyman series of hydrogen.

(*Ans.* 2430, 2070, and 1920 angstroms)

4. An alpha-particle of energy 5 mev is aimed directly at a thorium nucleus ($Z = 90$). Compute the distance of closest approach of the alpha-particle to the nucleus.

5. Compute the first five wavelengths of the Paschen series of hydrogen.

(*Ans.* 18750, 12820, 10940 10050, 9530 angstroms)

6. Show that to convert from electron-volts to wave-numbers per centimeter we multiply by 8080.

7. The ionization potential of lithium is 5.38 volts. The first five wavelengths of the principal series of lithium, which corresponds to the Lyman series of hydrogen, are found to be as follows: 6709, 3233, 2741, 2563, 2475 angstroms. Construct an energy level diagram for lithium in electron-volts and wavelengths.   (*Ans.* .35, .55, .83, 1.55, 3.53, 5.38 ev)

8. A student measures the wavelength of the first line of the Balmer series of hydrogen to be 6563 angstroms and the difference between this line and the corresponding line of deuterium to be 1.80 angstroms. From these data compute the ratio of the mass of the deuterium nucleus to the mass of the hydrogen nucleus.   (*Ans.* 2.03)

9. Find the excitation potential needed to bring out the first line of the Balmer series of hydrogen (6563 angstroms) by electron bombardment.

10. All alpha-particles aimed within a circle of radius p about a nucleus will be deflected through the angle ϕ of Eq. (165) or through a greater angle. If there are n nuclei per unit volume in a foil of thickness t, show that the fraction of alpha-particles which will be deflected through an angle ϕ or greater is given by $\pi p^2 nt$.

chapter five

quantum mechanics

In the discussion of the Bohr theory in the last chapter we saw that, while this theory was quite successful in explaining the main features of the spectra of one-electron atoms, it failed when extended to more complicated systems. We will now present the elements of *quantum mechanics*, which has successfully attacked the more difficult problems of atomic theory. Instead of grafting rather artificial postulates onto the body of classical mechanics, quantum mechanics will be presented as a fundamental and general theory founded on certain basic postulates. We will see that deductions from these basic postulates provide an empirically successful explanation of atomic structure as well as explaining the main features of the periodic table of the elements.

Since quantum mechanics employs mathematical operators extensively, we will discuss briefly the mathematics of operators first. In this way, the physical ideas of quantum mechanics will not be obscured by purely mathematical difficulties. The basic postulates of quantum mechanics will then be stated and discussed. Finally, applications of the theory will be made to the quantization of angular momentum, the spectra of one-electron systems, the tunnel effect, and the periodic table of the elements.

5.1. MATHEMATICAL PRELIMINARIES

A mathematical *operator* is an abbreviated way of representing a mathematical operation, usually on some function. For instance, we can represent the process of adding five by the addition operator, $A = 5+$. With this definition, the meaning of A operating on the function x^2 is as follows:

$$A x^2 = 5 + x^2 \qquad (201)$$

107

A more familiar operator is the *differential operator*, defined by $D = d/dx$. The meaning of D operating on the function x^2 is

$$Dx^2 = \frac{d}{dx}(x^2) = 2x \qquad (202)$$

Other operators can be easily devised. We can represent multiplication by a constant, c, with the operator C. Then if C operates on the function x^2, we have

$$Cx^2 = cx^2 \qquad (203)$$

Another useful operator is X, representing multiplication of a function by the variable x. If the operator X acts on the function x^2, we have

$$Xx^2 = x^3 \qquad (204)$$

Following the convention used in expressing successive differentiations, if two or more operators act on a function, the operator nearest the function is applied first, then the next nearest, and so forth. As an example, let the operators A and D, as defined above, operate on the function x^2. We have

$$ADx^2 = A(2x) = 5 + 2x \qquad (205)$$
$$DAx^2 = D(5 + x^2) = 2x \qquad (206)$$

Comparing Eqs. (205) and (206), we see that the result of the operators A and D operating on the function x^2 depends on the order in which the operators are applied. In general, the result of the operation of several operators on a function does depend on their order of operation. However, if the order of two operators is immaterial, these operators are said to *commute*. An example of two commuting operators is the pair $D = d/dx$ and $Y = y$. Letting this pair of operators act on the function x^2, we have

$$DYx^2 = D(yx^2) = 2xy \qquad (207)$$
$$YDx^2 = Y(2x) = 2xy \qquad (208)$$

This property of commutation of operators will turn out to be important in connection with the simultaneous measurements of physical quantities and will be discussed in connection with the Heisenberg uncertainty principle in Sec. 5.4.

If an operator is raised to some positive, integral power, say the nth power, by definition this operator is to be applied n times successively. For instance, the operator D^2 operating on the function x^2 has the following value:

$$D^2x^2 = DDx^2 = D(2x) = 2 \qquad (209)$$

In general we can write

$$D^n = \left(\frac{d}{dx}\right)^n = \frac{d^n}{dx^n} \qquad (210)$$

Similarly, X^n means multiplication by x^n and so forth for other operators which can be constructed. Using various powers of the operators C, D, and X, a wide variety of more complex operators can be constructed.

Every operator requires a function upon which to "feed," which is called the *operand*. In the examples above the function x^2 was the operand in each case. In theories of nature we are concerned only with *well-behaved functions*. By this we mean functions which are continuous and single-valued, and which vanish appropriately at infinity. These behavior conditions will be treated more exactly later. This requirement of good behavior will have the effect of a boundary condition which must be satisfied by the functions appearing in physical theories.

While it is not true in general for all operators and operands, application of an operator to a given operand may be equivalent to multiplying the operand by a constant. As an example, consider the operator d^2/dx^2 operating on the function sin $(3x)$. We have

$$\frac{d^2}{dx^2} \sin 3x = -9 \sin 3x \tag{211}$$

Here we see that operating with d^2/dx^2 on the operand sin $3x$ is equivalent to multiplying the operand by the constant, -9. For the general case of an operator, P, acting on a function, u, we can write

$$Pu = cu \tag{212}$$

When a relation such as is given by Eq. (212) holds, we say that c is an *eigenvalue* (characteristic value) of the operator P, belonging to the *eigenfunction* (characteristic function) u. In the example of Eq. (211), -9 is the eigenvalue of the operator d^2/dx^2 belonging to the eigenfunction sin $3x$. Summing up, an eigenfunction of an operator is a well-behaved function with this property: operating on the function with the operator is equivalent to multiplying the function by a constant, called the eigenvalue.

The central mathematical problem in quantum mechanics is the determination of the eigenvalues of a given operator, with the requirement that the corresponding eigenfunctions must be well-behaved. In general, a given operator will possess only certain eigenfunctions which are well-behaved and only certain corresponding eigenvalues will be produced. As an example of the general approach, let us determine the eigenvalues of the operator d^2/dx^2 which yield well-behaved eigenfunctions. Equation (212) then takes the form

$$\frac{d^2u}{dx^2} = cu = j^2u \tag{213}$$

Here we have used j^2 for the eigenvalue c for convenience. The general solution of Eq. (213) is easily seen to be the following for positive values of j^2

$$u = A \exp (jx) + B \exp (-jx) \qquad (214)$$

Since the function given by Eq. (214) does not remain finite at infinity, it is not a well-behaved function. Therefore, the operator d^2/dx^2 has no positive eigenvalues which yield well-behaved functions.

Now consider the case when the eigenvalues are negative. Equation (212) takes the form

$$\frac{d^2u}{dx^2} = cu = -k^2u \qquad (215)$$

The general solution of Eq. (215) is seen to be

$$u = C \sin kx + D \cos kx \qquad (216)$$

Since the function in Eq. (216) is well-behaved, we see that any negative number, $-k^2$, is an eigenvalue of the operator d^2/dx^2. For any particular value of $-k^2$, the corresponding eigenfunction is given by Eq. (216). This sort of analysis must be carried through for each operator for which we wish to find the well-behaved eigenfunctions and corresponding eigenvalues.

5.2. SPECIFICATION OF PHYSICAL STATES

The task of a physical theory is to yield values of observable quantities after certain mathematical manipulations of the elements of calculation have been performed. Position, energy, momentum and velocity are examples of *observables*, the measurement of which yields a number. No theory, however, contains only observables, but must instead include postulates, ideas and *constructs*. The electron, for instance, is a construct based on inferences from a number of experiments, rather than on direct observation, and it does not have the same experimental status as a laboratory workbench, for example. Thus, the elements of calculation do not necessarily have to be the results of direct experience.

In describing various branches of physics, various elements of calculation and constructs are used. By the *state* of a system we will mean a function of certain variables from which information concerning observable quantities can be obtained. In classical mechanics the state of a system is specified by a knowledge of the positions, velocities, and momenta of all the particles making up the system. It happens in this case that the elements of calculation are themselves observables with which we have direct

experimental contact.   Because so many fields of physics have been successfully attacked with this mechanical approach, the definition of states in
terms of positions, velocities, and momenta has come to be considered the
only correct specification.

A little thought will show that not all branches of physics use mechanical
quantities to define physical states.   In thermodynamics the state of a
system is much more conveniently specified by pressure, volume, and
temperature, which are themselves observables, rather than in terms of
mechanical quantities which are really constructs in this case.   Similarly,
in electrodynamics the use of mechanical elements of calculation leads,
incorrectly, to the ether, so that it is now customary to specify the state of
an electromagnetic field by a knowledge of the electric and magnetic field
intensities at all points in space.

Thus, we see that various entities can be used to represent physical
experience in terms of a theoretical formulation, the choice often being
made on the basis of simplicity.   Furthermore, the elements of calculation
do not have to be the same as the elements of observation, although this is
usually the case in classical physics.   In the next section we will see that
the elements of calculation in quantum mechanics may be far removed from
direct experience.

5.3. POSTULATES OF QUANTUM MECHANICS

In stating the postulates of quantum mechanics, we will use the variables
x,y,z.   It will be seen later that these variables are the same as the coordinates in the classical analogue of the system under consideration, so that
transformations to other coordinate systems, such as spherical and cylindrical coordinates, may be made.   This must be the case, of course, so that
quantum mechanics may include classical mechanics as a special case for
large bodies, in the same way that special relativity includes classical
dynamics as a special case for small velocities.

The functions appearing in quantum mechanical problems are not
restricted to real functions, but may involve the pure imaginary number,
$i = \sqrt{-1}$.   Consider a function, F, which may be resolved into real and
imaginary parts in the form $F = (u + iv)$, where u and v are real functions.
We *define* the *complex conjugate* of F, F^*, by the relation $F^* = (u - iv)$.
In nearly all cases, however, it is not necessary to write F in the form
$(u + iv)$.   Instead one can obtain F^* from F by replacing i by $-i$ wher-
ever i appears in F.   Consider the following relation:

$$F^*F = F^2 = (u - iv)(u + iv) = u^2 + v^2 \tag{217}$$

Thus, F^2 is a real function, even though F itself may be complex.

We will now state a set of basic postulates which provide the basis for
the various deductions of quantum mechanical equations. As in the case
of other scientific theories, certain postulates must be made, which themselves are not deducible from experiment or from more basic principles,
and their success is justified by the agreement of the consequences of the
postulates with experiment. After stating the basic postulates of quantum
mechanics, we will proceed to discuss them in some detail.

    I. The state of a system is defined by a *state function*, $\phi(x,y,z)$, which
must everywhere be single-valued and continuous, and which must
vanish in such a way that the following integral over the complete
range of the variables has a finite value:

$$\int \phi^* \phi \, dx \, dy \, dz$$

    II. To every observable quantity, p, corresponds an operator, P.

    III. The only possible experimental values of the observable, p, are
the eigenvalues of its corresponding operator, P, which generate
well-behaved eigenfunctions.

    IV. When a system is in a state represented by the state function,
$\phi(x,y,z)$, the mean value of a series of measurements on the observable, p, whose corresponding operator is P, will be given by

$$p_{av} = \frac{\int \phi^* P \phi \, dx \, dy \, dz}{\int \phi^* \phi \, dx \, dy \, dz} \tag{218}$$

The integrals in Eq. (218) are to be taken over all space, or the
region for which ϕ is meaningful.

The first postulate introduces the mathematical construct, $\phi(x,y,z)$,
which specifies the states of systems. We see that the state function is
not itself an observable, but is related to experience through the fourth
postulate.

The requirement of good behavior imposed on state functions and eigenfunctions of observables plays the part of a boundary condition, which
allows only certain eigenvalues. In the classical case of the vibrations of a
stretched wire, only certain wavelengths can exist as standing waves,
because of the boundary condition that there must be a node at each end
where the wire is clamped. Similarly, only certain eigenvalues will generate well-behaved eigenfunctions, so that only certain experimental values
of the corresponding observable will be possible.

There is nothing in the fundamental postulates which tells us how to
write down the operator corresponding to each observable of interest. In
fact, different schemes of quantum mechanics can be developed, depending
on how the appropriate operators are chosen. The difficulty is somewhat

similar to applying the laws of dynamics to a new phenomenon—a judicious guess or trial-and-error may give us the correct functional form of the force. Similarly, the operators which are to be used in quantum mechanics might be found empirically or by intelligent speculation.

We will follow the scheme of Schrodinger in assigning appropriate operators to observable quantities, since this is the scheme which is most commonly used. The observable must first be expressed in its classical form in terms of the rectangular coordinates (x,y,z) and the rectangular components of momentum (p_x,p_y,p_z). Then Schrodinger's prescription to find the corresponding quantum mechanical operator is to make the following replacements in the classical expression:

$$
\begin{array}{cc}
\textit{Classical} & \\
\textit{Quantity} & \textit{Replacement} \\
x & x \\
y & y \\
z & z \\
p_x & \dfrac{h}{2\pi i}\dfrac{\partial}{\partial x} \\
p_y & \dfrac{h}{2\pi i}\dfrac{\partial}{\partial y} \quad i = \sqrt{-1} \\
p_z & \dfrac{h}{2\pi i}\dfrac{\partial}{\partial z}
\end{array}
\tag{219}
$$

The justification for the construction of operators according to the scheme of Eq. (219) may be considered to be the empirical success of this scheme. However, after the original work of Schrodinger, Dirac and von Neumann showed how to generalize quantum mechanics so that the operators of Eq. (219) are derived from more fundamental postulates.

As an example of the construction of a Schrodinger operator, consider a mass, m, suspended by a spring which obeys Hooke's law in the form $F = kx$. If the mass is moved away from its equilibrium position and allowed to oscillate, the classical expression for the energy of the system in terms of the displacement of the mass, x, and its velocity, v, is given by

$$
W = T + V = \tfrac{1}{2}mv^2 + \tfrac{1}{2}kx^2
\tag{220}
$$

Since the momentum is given in terms of the velocity by the relation $p = mv$, we can write the energy of the oscillating mass in the *Hamiltonian form* in terms of position and momentum as follows:

$$
H = T + V = \frac{p^2}{2m} + \frac{kx^2}{2}
\tag{221}
$$

Making the replacements listed in Eq. (219), we find for the operator which will yield the possible energy values of this system the form

$$H_{op} = -\frac{h^2}{8\pi^2 m}\frac{d^2}{dx^2} + \frac{kx^2}{2} \tag{222}$$

The eigenvalues of the operator given in Eq. (222) are then the observable values of the energy of the simple oscillator described above.

A very important problem is that of a particle of mass, m, moving in a potential field given by $V(x,y,z)$. For instance, in the Bohr theory of one-electron atoms, the potential was of the form $-e^2 Z/r$. In this case, the energy of the particle is given by

$$W = T + V = \frac{m}{2}(v_x^2 + v_y^2 + v_z^2) + V(x,y,z) \tag{223}$$

Each momentum component is related to the corresponding velocity component by an equation of the form $p_x = mv_x$. Writing the energy of the particle in terms of the momentum components, we find

$$H = T + V = \frac{1}{2m}(p_x^2 + p_y^2 + p_z^2) + V(x,y,z) \tag{224}$$

If we now make the replacements of Eq. (219), we find

$$H_{op} = -\frac{h^2}{8\pi^2 m}\left(\frac{\partial^2}{\partial x^2} + \frac{\partial^2}{\partial y^2} + \frac{\partial^2}{\partial z^2}\right) + V(x,y,z) \tag{225}$$

In terms of the Laplacian operator, ∇^2, we can write Eq. (225) in the form

$$H_{op} = -\frac{h^2}{8\pi^2 m}\nabla^2 + V \tag{226}$$

The eigenvalues of the operator given by Eq. (225) or Eq. (226) are the only possible values of the energy of a particle moving in the given potential field. Later we will apply this to the problem of the one-electron atom.

Summarizing the Schrodinger method for obtaining quantum mechanical operators, we take the following steps:

1. Express the observable in its classical form in terms of the rectangular coordinates x,y,z and the components of momentum p_x, p_y, p_z.

2. Make the replacements of Eq. (219).

3. Transform, if desired, to curvilinear coordinates, such as spherical or cylindrical coordinates. (While this scheme is not unique, it has been highly successful and is the method most often used.)

The third postulate is easy to apply, in principle. After the correct operator for a given observable has been found by the method outlined above or in some other way, the operator is allowed to operate on an arbitrary function. The eigenvalues of the operator which generate well-behaved eigenfunctions in the sense of the first postulate are then found. These are the possible experimental values of the observable under consideration. As an example, if we use the operator developed for the case of a particle in a potential field, $V(x,y,z)$, Eq. (226), we find for the nth eigenfunction, ψ_n, the equation

$$\left[-\frac{h^2}{8\pi^2 m} \nabla^2 + V(x,y,z) \right] \psi_n = E_n \psi_n \tag{227}$$

The subscript, n, is used to indicate the fact that in general each eigenvalue, E_n, generates a different eigenfunction, ψ_n. If we allow the operator in Eq. (227) to operate on the function ψ_n and put the resulting equation in the form of a standard differential equation, we find

$$\nabla^2 \psi_n + \frac{8\pi^2 m}{h^2} (E_n - V)\psi_n = 0 \tag{228}$$

Equation (228), which yields the energy values of a particle, is called the *Schrodinger equation*. Since energy values are often of the greatest interest, this is perhaps the most important equation in quantum mechanics.

Mathematically the problem becomes that of determining which constants, E_n, yield well-behaved eigenfunctions, ψ_n. Unfortunately, however, among the problems of the greatest physical interest this is usually of considerable mathematical difficulty. Several examples will be worked out, but the reader should refer to texts dealing with quantum mechanics for the details of more complicated problems.

The fourth postulate of quantum mechanics gives the expected mean value or average of a series of measurements on some observable of a system in a state represented by the state function, $\phi(x,y,z)$. This postulate provides the link between states and experience. It is implicit in the last statement, as indeed in all theories of nature, that identical experimental procedures applied to identical systems lead to identical states. For this reason, the mean value postulate may be interpreted in two ways: p_{av} may be the mean of successive measurements on the same system in a given state, or p_{av} may be the mean of a number of simultaneous measurements on identical systems all in the given state. Usually the second meaning is the one used in quantum mechanics, since ordinarily measurements are made of a collection of atoms all in the same state.

If the system is known to be in a *pure energy state*, so that its energy is known to be a particular energy eigenvalue, it will be shown in Problem 10 that the state-function of the system equals the corresponding energy eigenfunction. The mean value theorem can then be used to find the average value of a series of measurements on some other observable, such as position or momentum, of the system which is known to be in a pure energy state. By way of contrast, if a system is in a *mixed energy state*, there is a finite probability that the system will have each of several energy eigenvalues, the sum of the various probabilities adding up to unity, since the system must have some particular energy eigenvalue at any instant. For a mixed state, the state-function is represented as a series in the corresponding eigenfunctions of the energy. Similar remarks apply to pure and mixed states of other observables, such as position and momentum.

The state-function itself has a useful physical interpretation in the case of a particle. Remembering that $\phi(x,y,z)$ may be a complex function which has the complex conjugate, $\phi^*(x,y,z)$, it can be shown that the probability of finding the particle within the volume element, $dxdydz$, is given by $\phi^*\phi\ dx\ dy\ dz$. Since it is certain that the particle is somewhere, the integral of this expression over all space must be unity. This is achieved by adjusting the arbitrary constants in $\phi(x,y,z)$, since the solutions of linear differential equations always contain arbitrary constants. When this has been done so that the total probability of finding the particle somewhere is unity, the resulting state-function is said to be *normalized to unity*. This is usually done before using the state-function in the mean value postulate, so that the value of the denominator in Eq. (218) is unity, which is a simplification.

The application of the fourth postulate to energy states, including radiant energy, leads to probabilities for transitions from one such state to another. If the transition probability between two states is zero, then such a transition is not observed. This leads naturally to *selection rules* for allowed transitions. In particular, the probability of a transition resulting in the emission of radiation characteristic of an oscillating electric dipole (similar to the radiation from a straight radio antenna), has been investigated. The result is that the transition probability is zero unless the frequency emitted is related to the energies of the initial and final states, E_1 and E_2, according to the relation given in Eq. (171). Thus, the frequency condition which was introduced as a postulate in the Bohr theory now appears as a deduction from the basic postulates of quantum mechanics.

5.4. THE HEISENBERG UNCERTAINTY PRINCIPLE

Consider the problem of finding the position and momentum of a particle. Classically, we could find these quantities from two photographs of the particle at successive times. However, in the case of the electron, for instance, we know from the photoelectric effect that the illumination used would transfer energy to the electron, changing the situation which we are trying to determine exactly, since the energy gained by the electron from the illumination would change either its momentum or position or both. A consideration of various possible experiments of this sort leads to the conclusion that the very act of measurement introduces changes in the quantities which we wish to measure. The result is that there is a loss in accuracy in one observable or the other. This principle of the impossibility of the simultaneous measurement of position and momentum with high accuracy was announced by Heisenberg in 1927, and is known as the *Heisenberg uncertainty principle*.

It is a perfectly definite problem to investigate according to quantum mechanics the fluctuations in measurements, using the mean value postulate as a beginning point. To be specific, given the state of a system we can calculate the *dispersion* of a series of measurements of a given observable, where the dispersion is defined as the average of the squares of the differences between the individual observations and the average of the observations. The square-root of the dispersion is called the *deviation* of the series of measurements, and we will use this as the measure of the accuracy of a series of measurements.

The quantum mechanical result is that only observables whose corresponding operators commute (in the sense that the order of x and d/dy is immaterial) can be measured simultaneously with indefinitely high accuracy in both cases. If the operators of two observables do not commute, there will always be some lower limit to the errors of measurement, and this lower limit is independent of the particular measuring process used. In the case of the simultaneous measurement of position, x, and momentum, p, the product of the deviations of the two quantities satisfies the inequality

$$\Delta x \, \Delta p \geq \frac{h}{4\pi} \tag{229}$$

Thus, if we wish to know the position of a particle with mathematical exactitude, so that $\Delta x = 0$, then we can obtain no information whatsoever regarding the momentum of the particle, since $\Delta p = \infty$. It is interesting to note that Eq. (229) applies to any pair of observables which are classically called *canonically conjugate*, such as energy and time, or the z-component of angular momentum and azimuthal angle.

The question now arises as to whether or not Eq. (229) is merely a careful statement of the effect of measurements on the state of a system. The answer is *no*. It is true that the mere act of making a measurement on the system does affect the state of the system, which introduces uncertainty into the results. However, the uncertainty calculated according to quantum mechanics does not depend on a measurement actually being made and takes no account of the choice of the apparatus used or the skill of the experimenter. The uncertainty of Eq. (229) is inherent in the quantum mechanical description of nature; experimental difficulties may make the observed uncertainty even greater than this amount, but Eq. (229) sets a fundamental limit to our knowledge, which experimental ingenuity cannot overcome, since quantum mechanics is basically statistical in nature.

5.5. QUANTIZATION OF LINEAR AND ANGULAR MOMENTUM

In this section we will determine the possible values of the linear and angular momentum of a particle. Consider the linear momentum of the particle, p_x. According to the Schrodinger replacements of Eq. (219), the operator corresponding to this observable is $(h/2\pi i)(d/dx)$. Allowing this operator to act on a function, ψ, we have the equation

$$\frac{h}{2\pi i}\frac{d\psi}{dx} = p\psi \tag{230}$$

The observable values of p_x are then the values of p which produce well-behaved eigenfunctions, ψ. By direct substitution it is easily seen that the solution of Eq. (230) is given by

$$\psi = A e^{2\pi pxi/h} = B \cos (2\pi px/h) + C \sin (2\pi px/h) \tag{231}$$

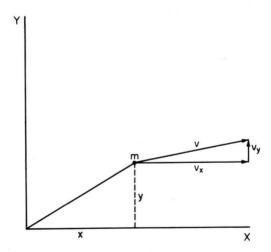

FIG. 38

Velocity components of a particle moving in the XY-plane, which are used in computing the particle's Z-component of angular momentum.

In Eq. (231), A, B, and C are constants. As long as x is confined to a finite range, ψ is a well-behaved function for all values of the constant p, and for all values of the constants. Thus, any value of the linear momentum, positive or negative, is possible. This is a case of *continuous eigenvalues*, and quantum mechanics introduces no quantization.

Next consider the particle to be moving in the xy-plane, as shown in Fig. 38. Its moment of momentum or angular momentum about the z-axis, m_z, is given classically by the products of the momentum components of the particle multiplied by their lever arms. We then have the equation

$$m_z = x(mv_y) - y(mv_x) = xp_y - yp_x \qquad (232)$$

After making the replacements of Eq. (219), we find the following form for the angular momentum operator, M_z:

$$M_z = \frac{h}{2\pi i}\left(x\frac{\partial}{\partial y} - y\frac{\partial}{\partial x}\right) \qquad (233)$$

The observable values of the z-component of angular momentum are then the eigenvalues, m_n, in the equation

$$\frac{h}{2\pi i}\left(x\frac{\partial \psi_n}{\partial y} - y\frac{\partial \psi_n}{\partial x}\right) = m_n\psi_n \qquad (234)$$

In Eq. (234) the subscript, n, is used to indicate that each eigenvalue, m_n, may generate a different eigenfunction, ψ_n.

In order to solve the differential equation of Eq. (234) more easily, let us transform to polar coordinates, r and θ. Referring to Fig. 39, x and y are given in terms of r and θ by the following equations:

$$x = r\cos\theta$$

$$y = r\sin\theta \qquad (235)$$

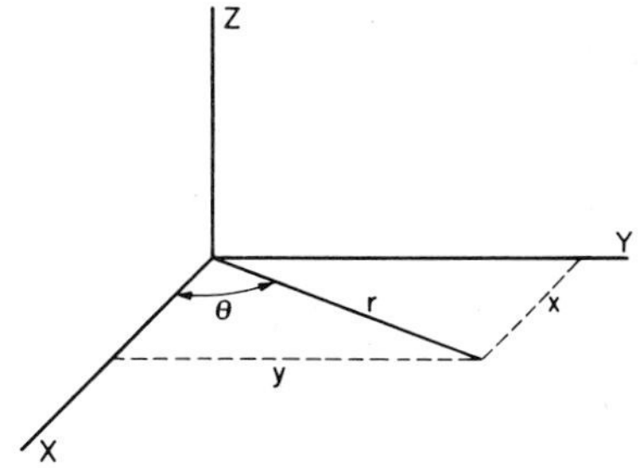

FIG. 39

Transformation from rectangular components, x and y, to polar coordinates, r and θ.

Anticipating the result, consider the derivative of ψ with respect to θ. Using the chain-rule for implicit differentiation, we find

$$\frac{\partial \psi}{\partial \theta} = \frac{\partial \psi}{\partial x}\frac{\partial x}{\partial \theta} + \frac{\partial \psi}{\partial y}\frac{\partial y}{\partial \theta} \qquad (236)$$

Using the values of x and y from Eq. (235) in computing the derivatives involved in Eq. (236), we obtain

$$\frac{\partial \psi}{\partial \theta} = \frac{\partial \psi}{\partial x}\,(-\,r\,\sin\,\theta) + \frac{\partial \psi}{\partial y}\,(r\,\cos\,\theta) = x\,\frac{\partial \psi}{\partial y} - y\,\frac{\partial \psi}{\partial x} \qquad (237)$$

Thus, Eq. (234) takes the following simple form in polar coordinates:

$$\frac{h}{2\pi i}\,\frac{\partial \psi_n}{\partial \theta} = m_n \psi_n \qquad (238)$$

As in the case of the linear momentum, the solution of Eq. (238) is evidently of the form

$$\psi_n = A\,e^{2\pi i m_n \theta / h} = B\,\cos\,(2\pi m_n \theta / h) + C\,\sin\,(2\pi m_n \theta / h) \qquad (239)$$

Clearly, the eigenfunctions given by Eq. (239) are continuous and finite for any real values of m_n. However, for a function of an angle to be single-valued, we require that the function have the same value for $(\theta + 2\pi)$ as it does for θ, since physically both of these angles represent the same direction in space. Since the period of the sine and cosine is 2π radians, increasing the argument of such a function by $2\pi n$ radians, where n is any integer, keeps the value of the function the same. Therefore, in order to make the eigenfunctions of Eq. (239) single-valued, m_n must satisfy the following condition:

$$\frac{2\pi m_n \theta}{h} + 2\pi n = \frac{2\pi m_n (\theta + 2\pi)}{h} \qquad (240)$$

When we solve Eq. (240) for m_n we find the following expression:

$$m_n = \frac{nh}{2\pi} \qquad (n = 0,\,\pm 1,\,\pm 2\,\ldots) \qquad (241)$$

These values of m_n are then the only values which yield well-behaved eigenfunctions for the angular momentum.

The only possible values of the angular momentum about the z-axis are those given in Eq. (241). In this case, the requirement that the eigenfunctions be single-valued has introduced quantization, so that discrete eigenvalues are found. Returning to the first Bohr postulate given by Eq. (170), we see that the angular momentum of the electron when it is in a circular orbit is exactly mvr. Thus, the quantization of angular momentum which appeared as a basic postulate in the Bohr theory now appears as a deduction from quantum mechanics.

5.6. THE TUNNEL EFFECT

Consider a particle of energy E. It cannot classically overcome a potential energy greater than E. For example, a proton travelling with energy E in a region where the potential energy, V, is zero cannot pass through a region where V is greater than E, but is reflected. Similarly a particle projected upward from the surface of the earth with an energy E cannot exceed a height given by $E = mgh$. In this section we will see that according to quantum mechanics a particle will have a finite and non-zero probability of passing through a potential barrier of height V, even when V is greater than E. This effect is called the *tunnel effect*.

We will consider a particle of energy E travelling to the right and striking a barrier of height V and width a. As is shown in Fig. 40, the edges of the barrier are at $x = 0$ and $x = a$. We will further assume that V is greater than E, so that classically the particle would be reflected by the barrier. We must solve the Schrodinger equation given by Eq. (228) in each of the three regions shown in Fig. 40 and join the solutions smoothly at the edges of the barrier. We will then find that there is a finite probability that the particle will emerge to the right of the barrier, showing that it somehow penetrated the barrier. This purely quantum mechanical effect will be used in Sec. 7.6 to explain the inversion spectrum of ammonia.

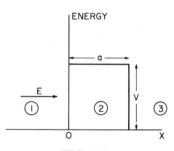

FIG. 40

Particle of energy E incident on a potential barrier of height V greater than E.

In each of the three regions it happens that the eigenfunctions are well-behaved, provided that the particle is confined to a finite region, so that there is no quantization of the energy. Therefore, we will omit the subscripts in Eq. (228). In region 1,

$V = 0$, so that Eq. (228) reduces to the form

$$\frac{d^2\psi_1}{dx^2} + \frac{8\pi^2 mE}{h^2}\,\psi_1 = 0 \tag{242}$$

If we let $c_1^2 = 8\pi^2 mE/h^2$, the solution of Eq. (242) is easily seen to be

$$\psi_1 = A_1 e^{ic_1 x} + B_1 e^{-ic_1 x} \tag{243}$$

In region 2, Eq. (228) takes the form

$$\frac{d^2\psi_2}{dx^2} + \frac{8\pi^2 m}{h^2}\,(E - V)\psi_2 = 0 \tag{244}$$

Since in this case V is greater than E, we will let

$$c_2^2 = (8\pi^2 m/h^2)(V - E)$$

The solution of Eq. (244) is seen to be

$$\psi_2 = A_2 e^{c_2 x} + B_2 e^{-c_2 x} \tag{245}$$

In region 3, the Schrodinger equation has the same form as Eq. (242), so that if we let

$$c_3^2 = 8\pi^2 mE/h^2$$

the solution in region 3 is given by

$$\psi_3 = A_3 e^{ic_3 x} + B_3 e^{-ic_3 x} \tag{246}$$

We must now interpret the eigenfunctions in each region and find out how they join at $x = 0$ and $x = a$.

Consider a pure energy state with an eigenfunction proportional to e^{ix}. For the one-dimensional case the operator corresponding to the x-component of momentum is $(h/2\pi i)(d/dx)$. The numerator in the mean-value theorem of Eq. (218) now takes the form

$$\int \phi^* P \phi \, dx \, dy \, dz = \int e^{-ix} \frac{h}{2\pi i} \frac{d}{dx} e^{ix} \, dx = \int \frac{h}{2\pi i} dx \tag{247}$$

Thus, we see that the energy eigenfunction e^{ix} represents a particle with positive momentum, which means it moves to the right in Fig. 40. Similarly the energy eigenfunction e^{-ix} means a particle moving to the left in Fig. 40.

We can now analyze the eigenfunctions for each of the regions 1, 2, and 3. In region 1, the first term in the eigenfunction given in Eq. (243) represents a particle incident on the barrier from the left, and the second term represents a particle travelling to the left and therefore reflected by the barrier. In region 2, the first term in Eq. (245) represents a particle travelling to the right inside the barrier, and the second term represents a particle travelling to the left inside the barrier. In region 3, the first term in Eq. (246) represents a particle travelling to the right on the right-hand side of the barrier, and the second term represents a particle travelling to the left on the right of the barrier and therefore incident on the barrier from the right. Since we are treating the case of particles incident on the barrier from the left, we must set $B_3 = 0$ in Eq. (246). If we find that A_3 is not zero, we will know that the particle has penetrated the barrier, even through classically this is not possible.

A comparison of Eq. (242) with Eq. (244) shows that there is a finite discontinuity in $d^2\psi/dx^2$ at $x = 0$. If we treat $d\psi/dx$ as the integral of

$d^2\psi/dx^2$, we see that $d\psi/dx$ is continuous at $x = 0$. This ensures that ψ itself will be continuous at $x = 0$. An exactly similar analysis applies at $x = a$, where we go from region 2 to region 3. We see that that at each edge of the barrier, ψ and its first derivative must join smoothly.

Let us put $c_1 = c_3 = c$. At $x = 0$ we then have

$$\psi_1 = \psi_2 \qquad \text{so, } A_1 + B_1 = A_2 + B_2$$

$$\frac{\psi_1}{dx} = \frac{\psi_2}{dx} \qquad \text{so, } ic(A_1 - B_1) = c_2(A_2 - B_2) \qquad (248)$$

Similarly at $x = a$ we have the conditions

$$\psi_2 = \psi_3 \qquad \text{so, } A_2e^{c_2a} + B_2e^{-c_2a} = A_3e^{ica}$$

$$\frac{\psi_2}{dx} = \frac{\psi_3}{dx} \qquad \text{so, } c_2(A_2e^{c_2a} - B_2e^{-c_2a}) = icA_3e^{ica} \qquad (249)$$

The four relations among the coefficients given by Eq. (248)–(249) allow us to eliminate B_1, A_2, and B_2. When we do this, we find

$$A_1 = \tfrac{1}{2}A_3e^{ica}\left[e^{c_2a} + e^{-c_2a} + \frac{i(c_2/c - c/c_2)}{2}(e^{c_2a} - e^{-c_2a}) \right] \qquad (250)$$

From Eq. (250) we see that A_3 is not zero, so that there is a probability of finding the particle to the right of the barrier. The situation is somewhat similar to the passage of a wave through an absorbing layer.

As was discussed in Sec. 5.3, the probability of finding a particle within a particular volume element is proportional to the square of the state-function. In the present case we define the *transmission coefficient*, T, as follows:

$$T = \left| \frac{A_3}{A_1} \right|^2 \qquad (251)$$

The transmission coefficient gives the relative probability of the particle passing through the barrier. In the case where c_2a is several times greater than one, e^{-c_2a} becomes negligible relative to other terms in Eq. (250). In this case T reduces to the form

$$T = \frac{4e^{-2c_2a}}{1 + \tfrac{1}{4}(c_2/c - c/c_2)^2} \qquad (252)$$

In Eq. (252), e^{-2c_2a} is called the *transparency factor*. Clearly, unless c_2a is very large, which means a wide and high barrier, there will always be a probability that the particle will pass through the barrier.

5.7. QUANTUM THEORY OF THE ONE-ELECTRON ATOM

The quantum mechanical solution of the problem of the one-electron atom is important, not only because this is the simplest type of atom, but because the theory of multi-electron systems is based on the solution of the one-electron problem. We shall state the Schrodinger equation for this problem in spherical coordinates, separate this equation into three equations each involving only one variable, and show how quantization is introduced. The energy levels found by this method will be discussed only briefly, since they are the same as those we have already considered in the case of the Bohr theory. Finally, we will see how Dirac's relativistic theory of the one-electron system modifies the results.

The Schrodinger equation for the case of a particle moving in a potential field, $V(x,y,z)$, has already been obtained in Eq. (228). We will consider an electron of charge, $-e$, attracted to a nucleus of charge, eZ, so that in this case the potential energy function takes the form

$$V = -K' \frac{e^2 Z}{r} \tag{253}$$

We will ignore the motion of the nucleus, but the results can be corrected for this motion by using the reduced mass of the system, μ, as was discussed in connection with the Bohr theory. Equation (228) then takes the form

$$\nabla^2 \psi_n + \frac{8\pi^2 \mu}{h^2} \left(E_n + K' \frac{e^2 Z}{r} \right) \psi_n = 0 \tag{254}$$

Our main concern will be to find the values of E_n which make the corresponding eigenfunctions, ψ_n, well-behaved, since we are mainly interested in the possible energy values of this system.

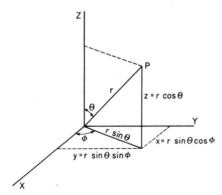

Because of the presence in the potential energy term of r, the separation between the electron and the nucleus, it will be convenient to use spherical polar coordinates, as shown in Fig. 41. The relations between the Cartesian coordinates, xyz, and the spherical coordinates, $r\theta\phi$, are as follows:

FIG. 41
Transformation from rectangular coordinates, xyz, to spherical coordinates, $r\theta\phi$.

$$x = r \sin \theta \cos \phi$$
$$y = r \sin \theta \sin \phi \tag{255}$$
$$z = r \cos \theta$$

The transformation of Eq. (254) from rectangular to spherical coordinates using Eq. (255) is tedious but straightforward. The result is as follows:

$$\frac{1}{r^2}\left[\frac{\partial}{\partial r}\left(r^2\frac{\partial\psi_n}{\partial r}\right) + \frac{1}{\sin\theta}\frac{\partial}{\partial\theta}\left(\sin\theta\frac{\partial\psi_n}{\partial\theta}\right) + \frac{1}{\sin^2\theta}\frac{\partial^2\psi_n}{\partial\phi^2}\right]$$
$$+ \left(\frac{8\pi^2\mu}{h^2}\right)\left(E_n + K'\frac{e^2Z}{r}\right)\psi_n = 0 \quad (256)$$

In order to solve Eq. (256), we shall assume that ψ_n can be written as the product of three functions, each depending on one variable only. Thus,

$$\psi_n(r,\theta,\phi) = R(r)T(\theta)F(\phi) \quad (257)$$

Substituting Eq. (257) into (256), we find

$$\frac{1}{r^2}\left[TF\frac{d}{dr}\left(r^2\frac{dR}{dr}\right) + \frac{RF}{\sin\theta}\frac{d}{d\theta}\left(\sin\theta\frac{dT}{d\theta}\right) + \frac{RT}{\sin^2\theta}\frac{d^2F}{d\phi^2}\right]$$
$$+ \left(\frac{8\pi^2\mu}{h^2}\right)\left(E_n + K'\frac{e^2Z}{r}\right)RTF = 0 \quad (258)$$

Multiplying Eq. (258) through term by term by the factor $r^2\sin^2\theta/RTF$, we find

$$\frac{\sin^2\theta}{R}\frac{d}{dr}\left(r^2\frac{dR}{dr}\right) + \frac{\sin\theta}{T}\frac{d}{d\theta}\left(\sin\theta\frac{dT}{d\theta}\right) + \frac{1}{F}\frac{d^2F}{d\phi^2}$$
$$+ \left(\frac{8\pi^2\mu}{h^2}\right)\left(E_n + K'\frac{e^2Z}{r}\right)r^2\sin^2\theta = 0 \quad (259)$$

Solving Eq. (259) for the third term, which involves only the variable ϕ, we have

$$\frac{1}{F}\frac{d^2F}{d\phi^2} = -\frac{\sin^2\theta}{R}\frac{d}{dr}\left(r^2\frac{dR}{dr}\right) - \frac{\sin\theta}{T}\frac{d}{d\theta}\left(\sin\theta\frac{dT}{d\theta}\right)$$
$$- \frac{8\pi^2\mu}{h^2}\left(E_n + K'\frac{e^2Z}{r}\right)r^2\sin^2\theta \quad (260)$$

Equation (260) can be satisfied for all values of the coordinates only if each side is separately equal to a constant, which we shall call $-m^2$. We then have the two separate equations

$$\frac{1}{F}\frac{d^2F}{d\phi^2} = -m^2 \quad (261)$$

$$-\frac{\sin^2\theta}{R}\frac{d}{dr}\left(r^2\frac{dR}{dr}\right) - \frac{\sin\theta}{T}\frac{d}{d\theta}\left(\sin\theta\frac{dT}{d\theta}\right)$$
$$- \frac{8\pi^2\mu}{h^2}\left(E_n + K'\frac{e^2Z}{r}\right)r^2\sin^2\theta = -m^2 \quad (262)$$

If each term in Eq. (262) is divided by $\sin^2 \theta$, all the terms involving r can be collected on one side of the equation, and all the terms involving only θ on the other side of the equation. This relationship can be true in general only if each side is separately equal to a constant, which we shall call L. We then have the following equation:

$$\frac{1}{R}\frac{d}{dr}\left(r^2\frac{dR}{dr}\right) + \frac{8\pi^2\mu}{h^2}\left(E_n + K'\frac{e^2Z}{r}\right)r^2 = \frac{m^2}{\sin^2\theta}$$

$$-\frac{1}{T\sin\theta}\frac{d}{d\theta}\left(\sin\theta\frac{dT}{d\theta}\right) = L \quad (263)$$

Writing Eq. (263) in the form of two separate equations, we have

$$\frac{1}{\sin\theta}\frac{d}{d\theta}\left(\sin\theta\frac{dT}{d\theta}\right) + \left(L - \frac{m^2}{\sin^2\theta}\right)T = 0 \qquad (264)$$

$$\frac{1}{r^2}\frac{d}{dr}\left(r^2\frac{dR}{dr}\right) + \frac{8\pi^2\mu}{h^2}\left(E_n + K'\frac{e^2Z}{r}\right)R - \left(\frac{L}{r^2}\right)R = 0 \qquad (265)$$

We have now separated the variables in the partial differential equation (256), and we have three ordinary differential equations to solve — (261), (264), and (265).

We now wish to solve Eqs. (261), (264), and (265) for the allowed values of the energy, E_n, and the corresponding eigenfunctions, ψ_n. The procedure is as follows: We first solve Eq. (261) for $F(\phi)$ and find that only certain values of m yield well-behaved solutions. These values of m are then used in Eq. (264) and the values of L which yield well-behaved solutions, $T(\phi)$, are found. Finally, the acceptable values of L are used in Eq. (265), and we find that only certain values of E_n produce well-behaved solutions, $R(r)$. These values of E_n are then the energy values of the one-electron system we are studying.

Putting Eq. (261) in the usual form of a differential equation, we have

$$\frac{d^2F}{d\phi^2} + m^2F = 0 \qquad (266)$$

The solution of this equation is easily seen to be

$$F(\phi) = A\sin m\phi + B\cos m\phi \qquad (267)$$

In order to make Eq. (267) single-valued, so that

$$F(\phi) = F(\phi + 2\pi)$$

m must be an integer or zero. . The quantum condition on m is then

$$m = 0, \pm1, \pm2, \ldots \qquad (268)$$

The values of m which make the ϕ-function well-behaved are now substituted into Eq. (264), and the allowed values of L are investigated. This problem is beyond the scope of this book, so only the results will be stated. It is found that in order that $T(\theta)$ may be well-behaved, L must be of the form

$$L = l(l+1) \tag{269}$$

where
$$l = |m|, \quad |m|+1, \quad |m|+2, \ldots \tag{270}$$

Thus, the quantum number, l, must be at least as great as the absolute value of the quantum number, m.

The value of L from Eq. (269) is now substituted into Eq. (265), and the values of E_n which yield well-behaved solutions, $R(r)$, are investigated. This requires too much mathematical skill to be worked out here, but the results will be given. It is found that all positive values of E_n yield well-behaved functions, $R(r)$. This is not surprising, since positive values of the energy correspond to ionization, so that the electron is not affected by the nucleus. Only certain negative values of E_n, however, give well-behaved eigenfunctions. These allowed values are as follows:

$$E_n = \frac{-2\pi^2\mu Z^2 e^4 K'}{n^2 h^2} \tag{271}$$

where
$$n = l+1, \quad l+2, \quad l+3, \ldots \tag{272}$$

Again we find quantization introduced as a result of demanding only well-behaved solutions. We see that the energy values found according to quantum mechanics are identical with those given by Eq. (180) as found by the Bohr theory.

To sum up the results of the quantum mechanical solution of the system with one electron, we found that the eigenfunction for the energy could be written as the product of functions, each of which depended on only one of the variables, r, θ, ϕ. Indicating by subscripts the quantum numbers upon which each function depends, we can now write Eq. (257) in the form

$$\psi_{nlm}(r,\theta,\phi) = R_{nl}(r)T_{lm}(\theta)F_m(\phi) \tag{273}$$

The three quantum numbers, each mainly associated with a particular coordinate, are as follows:

$n = $ *total quantum number* (associated with r)

$l = $ *azimuthal quantum number* (associated with θ)

$m = $ *magnetic quantum number* (associated with ϕ)

All the quantum numbers are required to be integers, but their relative values are restricted by the following inequality:

$$n > l \geq |m| \tag{274}$$

Any given value of n and the corresponding value of E_n given by Eq. (271) represent a quantum state characterized by a triplet of numbers which satisfies (274). Since more than one set of quantum numbers corresponds to a given energy, the energy states of the one-electron system are said to be *degenerate*. This degeneracy is removed and the energy is found to depend also on l and m if the atom is subjected to an external electromagnetic field. Examples are the Stark effect (external electric field) and Zeeman effect (external magnetic field), where the energy levels are found to have a fine structure depending on l and m as well as n.

The fine structure of the spectra of alkali metals could not be explained in detail by the old quantum theory. In 1925 Uhlenbeck and Goudsmit showed that empirical agreement between theory and experiment could be produced if it were assumed that the electron had angular momentum of spin about its axis. They found that associated with the electron spin, the component of angular momentum along any axis should have one of the values $+\frac{1}{2}(h/2\pi)$ or $-\frac{1}{2}(h/2\pi)$. We therefore assign a *spin quantum number*, m_s, which takes on only the values $+\frac{1}{2}$ or $-\frac{1}{2}$. As a consequence of this spin, the electron has a magnetic moment along any axis given by either of the values $+eh/4\pi mc$ or $-eh/4\pi mc$, where e and m are the charge and mass of the electron. With these assumptions, details of certain spectra could be explained.

In 1928 Dirac devised a relativistic form of the quantum mechanical equation for the energy of an electron. The solution of this problem not only led to the relativistic fine structure of the energy levels, which had been found by Sommerfeld as an extension of the Bohr theory, but in addition the electron was automatically endowed with the proper value of magnetic moment. When an electron is in a magnetic field, Dirac's equation predicts that the electron should behave exactly as if it had the spin angular momentum and accompanying spin magnetic moment postulated earlier by Uhlenbeck and Goudsmit. We can thus avoid unnecessary pictures of the structure of the electron. In addition, Dirac's theory forecast the existence of positrons, which were actually discovered four years later. We will return to this in Section 6.11.

Because of the phenomenon of the spin magnetic moment and its associated quantum number, m_s, four quantum numbers are needed to specify the complete state of an electron. A given electronic energy state will be specified by the quartet of quantum numbers, (n,l,m,m_s). In the presence of an electromagnetic field, the energy of the electron depends on all four quantum numbers, although the value of n is always the most important determining factor.

5.8. MULTI-ELECTRON SYSTEMS AND THE PAULI PRINCIPLE

The simplest two-electron system is the normal helium atom, which consists of two electrons associated with a nucleus of two positive units of charge. The Schrodinger equation can be stated fairly easily for this case, but the solution will not only contain the coordinates of each electron with respect to the nucleus, but also the coordinates of one electron with respect to the other. This is too difficult a problem to be solved directly, since it is comparable to the three-body problem in celestial mechanics, so various approximation methods must be used. By carrying out the approximation to many terms, Hylleraas has found the energy of neutral helium with great precision. Calculations for certain other simple systems, such as the hydrogen molecule ion and the hydrogen molecule, have also been carried through with high accuracy. Thus, problems of this sort, in which the Bohr theory could be worked out but gave incorrect results, are solved correctly by the methods of quantum mechanics.

When more than three or four particles are involved, however, additional simplifying assumptions must be made. The most successful method is to assume that the actual state function of the system may be represented as the product of functions, each function containing only the coordinates of a single electron. This separates the coordinates of each electron from those of all the others, and ignores electron-to-electron coordinates. With each electron is associated a one-electron state function similar to that found for hydrogen and a quartet of quantum numbers (n, l, m, m_s). The energy of the atom is then taken to be equal to the sum of the individual energies of the electrons. Various methods have been used for arriving at the closest approximation, and considerable success has been achieved. It would probably be generally accepted that the difficulties of treating complex atoms are mainly mathematical and that the quantum mechanical solution will yield correct values, if a way can be found to perform the difficult mathematical operations.

An atom is considered to be a system in which a number of electrons equal to the atomic number of the element revolve in orbits about the positively charged nucleus. Of course, the quantum mechanics does not imply any such model of the atom, but merely yields measures of energy values and other observable quantities. However, it is convenient to have a mechanical picture of the atom. In the approximation described above, each electron will have associated with it a set of one-electron quantum numbers, and the total energy of the atom will be the sum of the energies of the electrons.

The question now arises as to whether there are any restrictions on the values of the quantum numbers associated with each electron. The answer was given in 1925 by Pauli, who postulated that no two electrons associated in the same system can be in exactly the same quantum state. Thus, each electron must differ from all the other electrons in that atom in at least one of the four quantum numbers (n,l,m,m_s). This postulate, which is fundamental to all of quantum mechanics, is known as the *Pauli Exclusion Principle*. It is interesting to note that while Pauli first stated this principle on purely empirical grounds, in 1940 he succeeded in deriving it from more general considerations of quantum field theory. Its application and value will be illustrated in the explanation of the building up of the periodic table of elements in the following section.

5.9. THE PERIODIC TABLE OF ELEMENTS

We will build up the periodic table element by element, constructing each successive element from the one preceding it by adding one electron and simultaneously increasing the nuclear charge by one unit. Since the stable state of any system is its state of lowest energy, each added electron must have a quartet of quantum numbers such that the minimum amount of energy is added to the atom by the addition of this electron. The quartet of quantum numbers of each electron must satisfy the inequality of Eq. (274), since each electrón will possess a one-electron state function and corresponding quantum state. In addition, the quantum numbers of each added electron must be such that the Pauli principle is not violated. That is, the quantum numbers of each added electron must differ in at least one particular from the quantum numbers of each other electron already associated with the atom.

Electrons which have the same value of the principal quantum number, n, are said to belong to the same *shell*. This is useful, since the value of n plays the greatest part in determining the energy of each electron. In accordance with spectroscopic notation, shells with values of $n = 1,2,3, \ldots$, are labelled with the letters $K,L,M, \ldots$, respectively. Similarly, since l plays the next most important part in determining the energy of a given electronic state, electrons in a given shell which have the same value of l are said to be in a *sub-shell*. The sub-shells with values of $l = 0,1,2,3,4,5, \ldots$ are labelled with the letters $s,p,d,f,g,h, \ldots$, respectively. (The first four letters stand for *sharp, principal, diffuse, and fundamental* series respectively.)

In general, increasing either n or l increases the energy of a given electronic state. However, since the quantum mechanical calculations for all atoms have not been carried through, it often becomes necessary to decide experimentally whether an increase of one unit in n or l will result in

a smaller increase in energy.   For this reason, as electrons are successively
added to form more complex atoms, it is not always possible to predict with
certainty whether n or l should be increased.   However, the following rules
are almost always effective:

1. keep the sum, $(n + l)$, as small as possible;

2. if two states are available which have the same value of $(n + l)$,
    choose the state with the smaller value of n.

In accordance with the first rule, a state with $n = 2$ and $l = 0$ will be used
in preference to a state with $n = 2$ and $l = 1$.   In accordance with the
second rule, a state with $n = 3$ and $l = 2$ will be used in preference to a
state with $n = 4$ and $l = 1$, since the first state has a smaller value of n,
even though both states have the value 5 for the quantity $(n + l)$.   These
rules will be illustrated in the building up of the periodic table in the following pages.

The simplest atom is hydrogen, which has only a single electron.   From
Eq. (271), we see that the lowest algebraic value of the energy is obtained
when $n = 1$, so this is the normal state of hydrogen.   In order to satisfy
the inequality of Eq. (274), l must be zero, which requires m also to be zero.
The spin quantum number, m_s, can take on either of the values $+\frac{1}{2}$ or $-\frac{1}{2}$.
Writing the quantum numbers of the normal state of hydrogen in the order
(n,l,m,m_s), the single electron of hydrogen is specified by $(1,0,0,\pm\frac{1}{2})$.

If we add one electron to hydrogen, in order to construct helium, we
find that each electron must have $n = 1$ to have lowest energy.   Since this
value of n requires both l and m to be zero, the two electrons must have
different values of m_s, in order to satisfy the Pauli principle.   The electron
states of helium are therefore $(1,0,0,\pm\frac{1}{2})$ and $(1,0,0,-\frac{1}{2})$.   If we try to
add a third electron with $n = 1$, we see that l and m must still both be zero,
in order to satisfy the basic inequality; however, whatever value of m_s
we gave to this third electron, its quantum numbers would duplicate one
of the electronic states already used in forming helium.   Thus, only two
electrons can be used with $n = 1$, and we say that the K-shell is completed
with helium.   The quantum mechanical solution of normal helium shows
that the charge distribution around the helium nucleus is spherically sym-
metrical, so that this atom should interact weakly with other atoms.   This
is confirmed by the fact that helium is an inert gas.

Since n and l are of major importance in the energy states of normal
atoms, we will not continue to specify all four quantum numbers of each
electron associated with an atom.   Writing the value of n for a given
electron as a number and using the sub-shell labels $(s,p,d,f,g, \ldots)$ given
above to specify the value of l, hydrogen has the electronic structure 1s.
This means that the hydrogen electron has $n = 1$, and $l = 0$.   Similarly,
the electronic structure of helium will be abbreviated $1s^2$, the superscript

indicating that there are two $1s$-electrons, each with $n = 1$ and $l = 0$. In this case, it is implied that the two $1s$-electrons differ in some other quantum number, here m_s, in order to satisfy the Pauli principle.

The third element in the periodic table is lithium, with $Z = 3$. We add an electron to helium to form lithium. Since the two electrons of helium have completed the K-shell, we must add electrons in the L-shell with $n = 2$. The next lowest energy is obtained by adding a $2s$-electron, with $n = 2$ and $l = 0$. This added electron has the quantum state $(2,0,0,\pm\frac{1}{2})$ and the structure of lithium is abbreviated $1s^2 2s$. In order to obtain beryllium, which has $Z = 4$, the added electron is also a $2s$-electron. Thus, the electrons in the $2s$ sub-shell of beryllium must have the quantum numbers $(2,0,0,+\frac{1}{2})$ and $(2,0,0,-\frac{1}{2})$, and the electronic structure of beryllium is abbreviated $1s^2 2s^2$. Since no more electrons can be added in the $2s$ sub-shell without violating the Pauli principle, the $2s$ sub-shell is filled.

When we construct boron, $Z = 5$, by adding an electron to beryllium, the next lowest energy state is obtained by adding a $2p$-electron, with $n = 2$ and $l = 1$. Here, m may take on any of the values $(-1, 0, +1)$ while m_s may be $+\frac{1}{2}$ or $-\frac{1}{2}$. The structure of boron is therefore represented as $1s^2 2s^2 2p$. Continuing to add electrons in the $2p$ sub-shell, it is clear that only six $2p$-electrons can be added without violating the Pauli principle—for each of three values of m there are two possibilities for m_s. Adding these electrons successively gives us carbon $(Z = 6)$, nitrogen $(Z = 7)$, oxygen $(Z = 8)$, fluorine $(Z = 9)$, and neon $(Z = 10)$. With the element neon, we find that we have completed both the $2p$ sub-shell and the L-shell, since no more electrons can be added with $n = 2$. The structure of neon is written as $1s^2 2s^2 2p^6$. Theoretically, the completed $2p$ sub-shell represents a spherical distribution of charge, similar to that of helium, so that neon should be an inert gas, which it is. In fact, all completed p sub-shells are spherical distributions of charge, so that an inert gas is produced each time a p sub-shell is completed. The *second period* of the table of elements ends with neon.

When we construct sodium, $Z = 11$, the K and L shells are already filled. The added electron which introduces the smallest energy increase is found to be a $3s$-electron, with $n = 3$ and $l = 0$. The structure of sodium is thus $1s^2 2s^2 2p^6 3s$, which may be contracted to the shorter form $K...L...3s$. The $3s$ sub-shell is completed with the addition of one more $3s$-electron, which gives us magnesium, $Z = 12$. These two elements should be similar to lithium and beryllium, since they have one or two s-electrons outside of completed shells, and in fact this similarity is quite marked.

The electrons which add the next lowest amounts of energy to the atoms are the $3p$-electrons. After magnesium completes the $3s$ sub-shell, six $3p$-

electrons are added, completing the $3p$ sub-shell at argon, $Z = 18$, which has the structure $K...L...3s^23p^6$. As might be expected, the addition of successive p-electrons outside of the completed s sub-shell yields elements which are very similar to the corresponding elements in the second period of the table. The *third period* ends with completion of the $3p$ sub-shell at argon, which is found to be an inert gas, similar to helium and neon.

After argon, we have a choice between adding $3d$-electrons or $4s$-electrons. Since $4s$-electrons have the smaller value of the sum $(n + l)$, the first rule given earlier in this section favors them. For that reason, the next two elements are formed by the addition of the two $4s$-electrons, producing potassium, $Z = 19$, and calcium, $Z = 20$. These two elements are very similar to the first two elements in the second and third periods. The fourth period is then continued by adding the ten possible $3d$-electrons, given by $m = -2,-1,0,+1,+2$, and $m_s = +\frac{1}{2},-\frac{1}{2}$. This completes the M-shell at zinc, $Z = 30$, which has the electronic structure $K...L...M...4s^2$. (We are ignoring some irregularities: in the cases of chromium and copper one of the $4s$-electrons drops back into the $3d$ sub-shell.) Because of the order in which the $4s$ and $3d$ electrons are added, the first members of the fourth period are not closely related to the corresponding members of the second and third periods. The fourth period is completed by successively adding six $4p$-electrons, ending with krypton, $Z = 36$. The last six members of the fourth period, which are formed by the addition of $4p$-electrons over completed K,L, and M shells, are very similar to the last six members of the third period. As before, the completed $4p$ sub-shell leads to the inert gas, krypton, which ends the fourth period.

The *fifth period* is formed by the successive addition of two $5s$-electrons, ten $4d$-electrons, and six $5p$-electrons. Although there are occasional irregularities during this process, the elements formed are very similar to the corresponding elements in the fourth period. This period ends with the inert gas xenon, $Z = 54$, which has the electronic structure $K...L...M...4s^24p^64d^{10}5s^25p^6$.

The *sixth period* begins with the addition of two $6s$-electrons, forming caesium and barium. However, a single $5d$-electron is added to form lanthanum, $Z = 57$, before the N-shell $(n = 4)$ is completed by the successive addition of fourteen $4f$-electrons. The fourteen elements formed in this way $(Z = 58$ to $Z = 71)$ are known as the *rare earths*. The rare earths are all very similar, since the two $6s$-electrons and the one $5d$-electron all lie outside the $4f$ sub-shell, shielding the effect of adding several $4f$-electrons. After this, the sixth period is completed with the addition of nine more $5d$-electrons and six $6p$-electrons with occasional irregularities. As before, the sixth period is concluded with an inert gas, radon, $Z = 86$, which has the structure electronically given by $K...L...M...N...5s^25p^6$-$5d^{10}6s^26p^6$.

The *seventh period* is begun by adding two 7s-electrons, thus producing francium and radium, which are similar to first two elements in each preceding period. After adding one or two 6d-electrons, 5f-electrons are added in succession. Since these elements are similar to the rare earths, they are often called the *radioactive rare earths*.

The prediction of the general features of the periodic table of elements by quantum mechanics is a striking success for the theory. Detailed calculations which have been performed on some elements give additional information regarding the nature of ionic and homopolar molecules, valence and ferromagnetism. Thus, quantum mechanics, with the aid of the Pauli principle, illuminates the whole field of atomic and molecular structure and properties in a very satisfactory way.

5.10. THE NATURE OF CHEMICAL BONDS

A great triumph of quantum mechanics was the explanation of the two types of chemical forces which lead to the formation of molecules. It is necessary to account for the heteropolar or ionic type of bond, exemplified by NaCl, and the homopolar or covalent type of bond, exemplified by H_2. The quantum mechanical treatment of this problem is described below.

In 1916, well before the development of quantum mechanics, Lewis had suggested that the bond between atoms forming a molecule was due to the sharing of a pair of electrons by the two atoms. According to quantum mechanics, the square of the state-function of a particle at a given point gives the probability of finding the particle in the neighborhood of the point. Thus, chemical forces should begin to occur when two atoms are close enough for the state-functions of their electrons to overlap. The problem is to compute the force between atoms as a function of their distance apart.

The theory of the hydrogen molecule was worked out by Heitler and London in 1927, and improved by James and Coolidge in 1933. The results of the theory for the dissociation energy of the hydrogen molecule are in complete agreement with experiment. Since the two electrons involved are indistinguishable physically, the state function used as a solution for the Schrodinger equation must not change essentially if the labels of the two electrons are exchanged, and must satisfy the Pauli principle. When two hydrogen atoms are brought near one another, the effect of this requirement is an attraction or repulsion, according as the spins of the electrons are anti-parallel or parallel. We therefore speak of an *exchange force* as acting. This exchange force has no classical analogue and is fundamental to the quantum mechanical description of nature.

In the case of more complicated molecules, a molecule will be formed only if pairs of electrons with anti-parallel spins can be formed. If an atom has *free spins*, not restricted by the Pauli principle, it can form molecules, since its electrons with free spins can have their spins in required directions. In the case of the noble gases, the electrons are arranged in pairs of equal and opposite spins, as described in the previous section in connection with the period table of elements. Thus, the inert gases have no free spins and cannot form molecules.

We can now understand the stability of an ionic compound, such as NaCl. The ions Na^+ and Cl^- attract each other at long range according to Coulomb's law of electrostatics. Since each ion has the electronic structure of a rare gas, the exchange forces will be repulsive. As the two ions approach, the electrostatic force of attraction increases slowly and the repulsive exchange force increases rapidly. The molecular size is then determined by the distance at which these two forces become equal.

In general, the valence of an atom is the number of its free spins multiplied by 2. Thus, hydrogen has a spin of $\frac{1}{2}$ and a valence of 1, while helium has a spin of 0 and is chemically inert. Similarly, the spins of nitrogen, oxygen, and fluorine are $\frac{3}{2}$, 1, and $\frac{1}{2}$ respectively, while their valences are 3, 2, and 1. An exception is the case of carbon, which has a spin of 1, but may have a valence of either 2 or 4. The explanation for this is that carbon does not always combine in its lowest energy state, but often may combine in an excited state with a spin of 2. Other elements also combine in excited states and may have more than one valence. We may sum up the valence properties of atoms by saying that the valence of an atom is determined by the spins of a few of its lowest energy states. Quantum mechanics thus clarifies the concept of valence and allows quantitative calculations for the simpler molecules.

5.11. THE STERN-GERLACH EXPERIMENT

In this experiment, which was performed in 1921, the first measurements of the magnetic moments of neutral atoms were made. The measurements provide direct evidence for the quantization of the spin angular momentum and the associated magnetic moment of the electron. Since completed electron shells have no net magnetic moment, the magnet moment of an atom is due to the spins of unpaired electrons in the outer shells.

Consider a magnetic moment, p, which is either parallel or anti-parallel to a magnetic field B. The energy of the magnet is then given by

$$E = \pm pB \tag{275}$$

The magnet will experience a net force only if the magnetic field is non-uniform. The force on the magnetic in the x-direction is then given by

$$F_x = \frac{\partial E}{\partial x} = \pm p \frac{\partial B}{\partial x} \tag{276}$$

Thus, a group of atoms with a net magnetic moment will be separated into two groups when the atoms pass through a non-uniform field, if the magnetic moments are quantized either parallel or anti-parallel to the field. On the other hand, if the magnetic moments are in random directions, as should be the classical case, portions of the atom beam would be deflected in all directions.

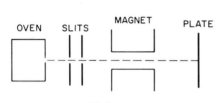

OVEN   SLITS   MAGNET   PLATE

FIG. 42

Schematic diagram of Stern-Gerlach experiment to show that atomic magnetic moments are quantized.

The apparatus is shown diagrammatically in Fig. 42. Atoms emerge from the oven and are collimated into a narrow ribbon by slits. The beam then passes through the non-uniform field of the magnet and is then registered on the plate. The magnet cross-section, as well as the splitting of the ribbonlike beam into two parts, is shown in Fig. 43. From the splitting we see that the magnetic moment of the atom is quantized either parallel or anti-parallel to the field.

The first experiments were performed on silver, which has the electron structure $K...L...M...4s^2 4p^6 4d^{10} 5s$. The single $5s$ electron has a spin of $\pm\frac{1}{2}$ and an associated magnetic moment $\pm eh/4\pi m$, which is called the *Bohr magneton*. From measurements on the deflection of a beam of silver atoms, Stern and Gerlach found the magnetic moment of a silver atom to be quite close to one Bohr magneton.

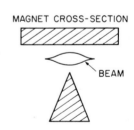

MAGNET CROSS-SECTION

BEAM

FIG. 43

Diagram of magnet to produce inhomogeneous field, which spreads the beam of atoms as shown.

Cadmium follows silver in the periodic table and has the same structure, except that cadmium has two $5s$ electrons. Since the spins of these electrons are oppositely directed, in order to satisfy the Pauli principle, the magnetic field should have no effect on a beam of cadmium atoms. This was verified experimentally. Similarly, zinc has two $4s$ electrons and is unaffected by a non-uniform magnetic field. On the other hand, the effect has been observed in various atoms with a single outer electron, such as H, Li, Na, K, Cu, and Au. Thus, the space quantization of electron spins is well verified.

5.12. ATOMIC SPECTRA

As a final example of the application of quantum mechanics, we will discuss briefly some features of atomic spectra. We will make the same approximation that we made in connection with the periodic table of elements, so that the actual state-function of the atom can be considered as the product of many one-electron functions. In this approximation, the quantum state of the atom is determined by the individual quantum states of the electrons, and the total energy of the atom is the sum of the energies of its electrons.

Next to that of hydrogen the simplest atomic spectra are those of the alkali metals lithium, sodium, potassium, rubidium, and caesium. This is not surprising, since our analysis of the periodic table shows that each of these atoms has a single electron outside of completed shells and sub-shells. This single valence electron is responsible for the optical spectra of these elements. An approximate picture of such an atom is a nucleus of charge Ze closely surrounded by a cloud of $(Z - 1)$ electrons, while at some distance from the nucleus the single valence electron moves in a hydrogen-like orbit.

When an atom acquires energy through a collision or any other process, we may consider this single electron to be raised to an excited energy state. For the case of lithium, the electronic structure is given by $1s^2 2s$. The $2s$-electron can then be raised to any higher state, such as $2p,3s,3p,3d,4s,4p$, etc. The corresponding energy level is then designated $2P,3S,3P,3D,-4S,4P$, etc. The capital letter is used to indicate that the energy level refers to the atom as a whole. If, for instance, the valence electron is in the $4s$-state, the electron configuration of the atom is $1s^2 4s$ and the corresponding atomic energy level is $4S$.

The energy levels of lithium are shown in Fig. 44. One main difference between these energy levels and those of hydrogen is that in this case the energy level depends on the azimuthal quantum number, l, as well as the total quantum number, n. This is not surprising, since the nucleus and closed electronic shell do not produce exactly the same electrostatic field as the nucleus of a hydrogen atom. Energy level diagrams for the other alkali metals are similar.

Selection rules for allowed transitions are predicted by quantum mechanics. The total quantum number, n, is not restricted and may change by any amount or remain constant. The azimuthal quantum number, l, however, must increase or decrease by one unit. These rules may be summed up as follows:

$$\Delta n = 0,1,2,3, \ldots$$
$$\Delta l = \pm 1$$

(277)

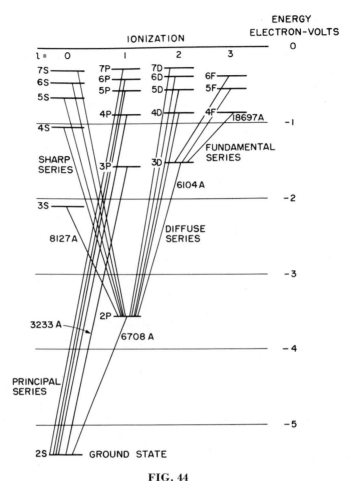

FIG. 44

Energy level diagram of lithium, showing various allowed transitions.

Exceptions are found occasionally, but the spectral lines are faint, showing that the *forbidden transitions* are unlikely. If an electron is raised to an excited state, it can only return to the normal, 2S, state by certain transitions which obey the selection rules. For instance, an electron which has been raised to the 3D state cannot return directly to the 2S normal state, since this would involve a change in *l* of two units. As shown on the diagram, the electron first jumps down to the 2P state and then jumps to the 2S state. Applying these rules, the various allowed transitions for lithium are shown in Fig. 44, and the corresponding spectral series are indicated.

The extension of these ideas to more complicated atoms becomes quite complex. Relativistic effects and electromagnetic interactions between the electrons introduce considerable multiplicity into the energy level diagrams. Since the mathematical calculations cannot be carried through precisely, values of energy levels are obtained experimentally. Similar selection rules apply, which are based on qualitative quantum mechanical analysis. The reader is referred to treatises on the subject of atomic spectra for the details of more complicated spectra.

5.13. HEISENBERG'S MATRIX MECHANICS

Although the axiomatic foundations of quantum mechanics are strikingly different from the usual theories of classical physics, the formulation is simple. Briefly, the experimental values of a physical observable are the eigenvalues of the operator corresponding to that observable. Requirements of good behavior, imposed on the functions appearing as solutions, have the effect of introducing quantization in an entirely natural way, without the need for any special postulates. The theory may seem mathematically difficult and complicated, but this is only a matter of unfamiliarity with the mathematical apparatus used. In addition it may be said that quantum mechanics has been successfully applied to problems which were insoluble by the most powerful techniques of classical physics. The wide success of this theory in the field of atomic structure fully justifies the apparent arbitrariness and novelty of the basic postulates. While refinements in detail may be expected, it seems likely that quantum mechanics will occupy a permanent place among the great achievements of the twentieth century.

The emphasis in this chapter has been on the Schrodinger scheme for constructing suitable operators, since that is the one which is most commonly used. It should be noted that this method is not unique. For instance, the momenta can be used as the fundamental variables, so that all operators are functions of p and d/dp, although this is seldom useful. However, one important alternative is the *matrix mechanics* of Heisenberg, which was actually announced in 1925, a year before Schrodinger's publications.

In the Heisenberg matrix mechanics, the operator representing an observable is an infinite square matrix. (A matrix is an array of numbers, similar in appearance to a determinant, and its properties are determined by the collection of numbers taken as a whole. A vector is represented as a matrix with only a single row or column.) When a matrix operates on a vector, in general a new vector is produced, in a way similar to a differential operator producing a new function by operating on a given function. If, however, the new vector is the original vector merely multiplied by a constant, we call this constant an *eigenvalue* of the matrix corresponding to that particular *eigenvector*. The experimental values of a given observable are then the eigenvalues of its corresponding matrix, which agrees with postulates II and III in our scheme of quantum mechanics. There are rules by which the correct matrix can be found, but unfortunately there is no general mathematical technique for finding the eigenvalues of an infinite matrix, so that special methods must be devised for each new problem. However, some problems which had defied the Bohr theory were solved by Heisenberg, Born, and Jordan, using matrix mechanics.

In 1927 Schrodinger and Eckart proved that the Heisenberg and Schrodinger schemes are mathematically equivalent. The correct matrix and its eigenvalues can be found by first solving the Schrodinger equation for the observable in question. Since there are standard mathematical procedures for finding the eigenvalues of differential operators, problems are nearly always solved today by using the Schrodinger method, but the terminology of matrix mechanics is still used often.

ADDITIONAL READING

Pauling, Linus and Wilson, E. Bright, *Introduction to Quantum Mechanics*. New York: McGraw-Hill Book Co., Inc., 1935. An excellent presentation of the ideas and results of quantum mechanics intended mainly for the physicist and chemist without extensive mathematical training.

Rojansky, Vladimir, *Introductory Quantum Mechanics*. Englewood Cliffs, N. J.: Prentice-Hall, Inc., 1938. A thorough exposition of the Schrodinger, Heisenberg, and Dirac quantum mechanics from a viewpoint similar to that of the present book.

Margenau, Henry and Murphy, George Mosely, *The Mathematics of Physics and Chemistry*. Princeton, N. J.: D. Van Nostrand Co., 1943. A concise presentation of many of the mathematical features of quantum mechanics is given here.

White, Harvey Elliott, *Introduction to Atomic Spectra*. New York: McGraw-Hill Book Co., Inc., 1934. A thorough treatment of the subject.

Herzberg, Gerhard, *Atomic Spectra and Atomic Structure*. New York: Dover Publications, 1944 (2nd Ed.). A clear exposition of the application of quantum rules to atomic problems.

PROBLEMS

1. Find the eigenvalues of the operator $i(d/dx)$ and compare these eigenvalues with those found for the operator (d^2/dx^2).

(*Ans.* Any real number.)

2. Consider the operators x and d/dx. Determine the difference between $x(d/dx) = XD$ and $(d/dx)x = DX$ operating on an arbitrary function of x. This difference is called the *commutator* of x and d/dx.

3. Find the energy eigenfunctions and eigenvalues for a free particle ($V = 0$) which is confined to a finite range along the x-axis. Interpret your result as a standing wave and show that if the momentum of the particle is p, then its associated wavelength is given by

$$\lambda = \frac{h}{p}$$

This wavelength was postulated in 1924 by DeBroglie.

(*Ans.* $\psi = A \sin (Kx)$, where $K^2 = 8\pi^2 mE/h^2$)

4. Write out in full the quantum numbers of each electron of neon.

5. An electron is confined to a range of 10 angstroms. Compute the uncertainty in its momentum and velocity.

(*Ans.* 5.27×10^{-21} gm-cm/sec; 5.80×10^6 cm/sec)

6. Repeat Problem 5 for a proton confined to the same range.

7. Refer to Problems 5 and 6. Assume that an electron and a proton have a momentum equal to the uncertainty calculated above; compute the energy of each.

8. Generalize Problem 1 by proving that if u is an eigenfunction of the operator O belonging to the eigenvalue N, then u is also an eigenfunction of the operator O^2 belonging to the eigenvalue N^2. Thus, all of the eigenfunctions of O are also eigenfunctions of O^2. Is the converse true?

9. The valence electron of potassium is raised to a $5P$ state. In an energy level diagram, show all of the possible routes by which the electron can return to its normal state.

10. Consider a system in a pure energy-state, so that its energy is certainly a particular eigenvalue, say E_n. Use the mean-value theorem to prove that in this case the state-function of the system must be the eigenfunction belonging to E_n.

11. Derive Eq. (250) from Eq. (248) and (249).

12. Derive Eq. (252) from Eq. (250) and (251).

chapter six

X-rays

One great discovery which has had an important effect on twentieth century physics is the discovery of X-rays by Roentgen in 1895. This is a good example of the combination of ingredients often necessary for a major experimental discovery. These ingredients might be characterized as luck (having the phenomenon occur at all), alertness (noticing that something novel has happened), and skill (investigating the new effect well). Systematic investigations often turn up new aspects of nature, but not always in the expected direction, so that the investigator must be continually on the watch for unusual effects.

In this chapter the production of X-rays and their main properties will be described. We will then see how X-rays provide us with a great deal of information regarding the structure of atoms themselves as well as the structure of molecules and crystals. Just as optical spectra provided us with information about the energy levels of the valence electrons of atoms, X-ray spectra provide us with information regarding the energies of the more tightly bound electrons in the inner shells. Finally we shall discuss a few of the many applications of X-rays to technology, medicine, and applied science.

6.1 ROENTGEN'S DISCOVERY

In 1895, while investigating electrical discharges through gases and the effects of cathode rays, Roentgen found that a fluorescent screen *outside* the tube would light up, even when it was shielded from the direct light of the gaseous discharge. Apparently, some penetrating radiation was being emitted by the gaseous discharge tube. For lack of a better name for these

strange and new radiations, they were named *X-rays*. After investigating
the properties of these radiations for several months, Roentgen reported
many basic facts about X-rays in several papers appearing in 1896.   These
basic properties are listed below.

1. Fluorescence is excited in many materials, such as calcium tungstate,
    barium-platino-cyanide, and others.

2. Photographic emulsions are affected by X-rays, thus providing an
    excellent method for the study of the radiations.

3. Electrified objects lose their charge when irradiated with X-rays.

4. Various materials are more or less transparent to X-rays, the differ-
    ences in transparency providing the basis for the study of the internal
    structure of objects which are opaque to visible light.

5. X-rays can be collimated with slits or pin-holes, showing that the
    radiations travel in straight lines, like light.

6. Magnetic fields do not deflect an X-ray beam, showing that X-rays
    are not a stream of charged particles.

7. Reflection and refraction of X-rays do not occur.   (Later it was
    found that these effects could be observed to a very small degree.)

8. X-rays are generated whenever a beam of electrons strikes an
    obstacle.   Furthermore, elements of high atomic weight are the
    most efficient sources of X-rays.

These observations by Roentgen summarize the important qualitative
facts concerning X-rays and demonstrate the thoroughness of his investigations.

Immediately after Roentgen's announcement of his discovery, many
investigations of this novel radiation were begun all over the world.   Within
three months X-rays were being used in medical diagnosis, and today the
important applications of X-rays in all branches of science would make a
most impressive list.

The basic requirements for the generation of X-rays are a stream of
rapidly moving electrons and a target for the electrons to strike.   Thus,
we need a source of electrons, a way to accelerate them to high energies,
and provision for the beam of electrons to strike a target.   The X-rays
produced must also have some way of being brought out where the experimenter can use them.

The earliest X-ray tubes used the electron avalanche produced in a
gaseous discharge tube, as described in Chapter 1.   A typical gas-filled
tube of this sort is shown in Fig. 45.   The tube is filled with gas at a pres-

sure of 0.01 to 0.001 millimeter of mercury and a high voltage is maintained between the two electrodes. A few stray electrons are accelerated by the electric field, and if the relation between the gas pressure and the applied voltage is correct, an electron avalanche will occur. The X-rays are then generated when this electron avalanche strikes the target.

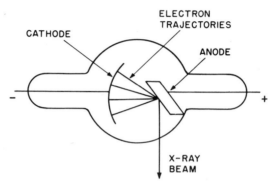

FIG. 45

X-ray tube using electrical discharge through a gas at low pressure.

The cathode of the X-ray tube may be curved, as shown in Fig. 45. Since the electric field is perpendicular to the cathode at all points, this has the effect of bending the electric field. In this way the electrons are focused on the *focal spot* of the anode. For efficient generation of X-rays, the anode is usually made of a heavy metal, such as wolfram or molybdenum. Since a large amount of heat is generated in the anode by the intense electron bombardment, refractory materials like wolfram or molybdenum are particularly satisfactory, although metals like copper can be used if cooling is provided.

One difficulty with a gas-filled X-ray tube of this sort is controlling the tube current. If the current is increased by increasing the anode voltage, the electrons have higher energies when they strike the anode, thus producing more penetrating X-rays. X-rays which are highly penetrating are said to be *hard* X-rays, so that hard X-rays are obtained from a high-voltage X-ray tube. After a gas-filled tube has been in use for some time, the pressure of gas in the tube becomes somewhat lower, since some of the gas is adsorbed by the walls of the tube. In order to maintain a given electron current through the tube, a higher anode voltage must be used, which produces harder X-rays. For this reason, a tube operating at low pressure is called a *hard tube*, and in general a low vacuum is called hard. This variation of tube current with the age of the tube is a major drawback of the gas-filled tube.

In 1913 Coolidge devised a tube which avoids the current difficulties
of the gas-filled tube by using a heated filament as a source of electrons.
The tube current can then be easily varied by varying the heating power
supplied to the filament. The tube is evacuated to the best possible
vacuum, so that any loss of gas remaining by adsorption at the walls is an
advantage. With this type of tube, the electron current and the anode
voltage can be varied independently, so that all of the major troubles of the
gas-filled tube are eliminated. Otherwise, the two types of tubes are
similar.

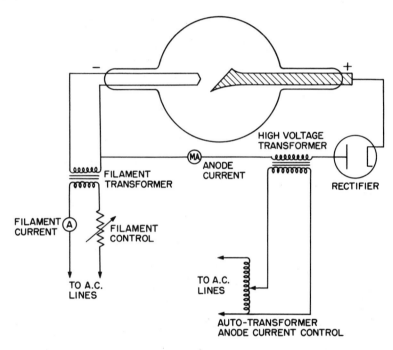

FIG. 46

Hot-cathode, high-vacuum X-ray tube (Coolidge tube)
with associated rectifier and control circuits.

One method for obtaining anode voltages up to about 200 kilovolts is
to use an oil-filled transformer. The alternating voltage may be rectified
by a high-voltage rectifier, so that a direct high voltage is applied across the
X-ray tube, or the alternating voltage may be applied directly across the
tube. If an alternating voltage is applied across the X-ray tube, X-rays
of varying hardness are produced, but in many applications this may not
be a disadvantage, while the cost of a rectifier tube is saved. A typical
arrangement, using a Coolidge-type tube and a rectifier, is shown in

Fig. 46.   Using voltages up to several hundred kilovolts, this sort of arrangement produces sufficiently penetrating X-rays for most purposes.

Even higher anode voltages can be attained by various methods. Transformers in cascade have been used to reach voltages in the neighborhood of a million volts, while various ingenious schemes involving charging condensers in parallel and discharging them in series have been used to reach voltages of the order of several million volts.   Two electron accelerators which attain even higher energies are described in Section 9.5 in connection with nuclear bombardment.   These are the Van de Graaff generator, which reaches about ten million volts, and the betatron, which has exceeded two hundred million volts.   Thus, today it is possible to generate X-rays with electrons ranging in energy from a few kilovolts to many megavolts.

6.2. DETECTION OF X-RAYS

Fluorescent screens coated with materials such as calcium tungstate are useful for observing the qualitative features of X-ray phenomena, but the intensity of the radiation can be estimated only roughly from the brightness of the screen.   Photographic emulsions are affected by X-rays in a way similar to the action of light, so that upon development silver grains are left in the emulsions wherever X-rays have struck it.   While photographic films are extremely useful for observing the effects of X-rays, quantitative work involving X-ray intensities is slow.   In quantitative work with intensities of X-rays, the *reciprocity rule* of photography is assumed to hold. This rule states that the time of exposure to produce a given darkening of

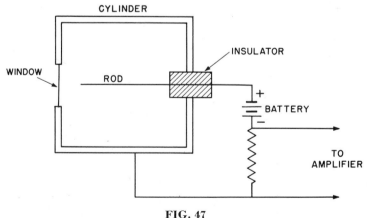

FIG. 47

Ionization chamber for measuring X-ray intensities.

the emulsion is inversely proportional to the intensity of the radiation striking the emulsion. Using this rule, the intensities of two beams of X-rays are compared by varying their times of exposure until they produce the same blackening of the film. The intensities of the X-ray beams are then in inverse ratio to their times of exposure.

For most determinations of X-ray intensities the *ionization chamber* is the most useful and rapid device. Fig. 47 shows a typical ionization chamber, which consists essentially of a conducting rod inside a cylinder. When X-rays pass through the window of the ionization chamber, ions are produced in the gas which fills the chamber. If now the central rod is maintained at a positive potential with respect to the outer cylinder, positive ions will be collected by the outer cylinder and negative ions or electrons will be collected by the central rod. The current flowing through the ionization chamber is amplified and measured finally with a galvanometer. If a large enough voltage is applied across the two elements of the ionization chamber, all the ions formed by the X-rays will be collected. We then speak of the *saturation voltage* and *saturation current* in the same sense as we previously used these terms in connection with thermionic emission in Section 2.1.

Since the number of ions produced per second by X-rays of a given hardness is proportional to the intensity of the beam, two beams of X-rays are compared by comparing the saturation currents produced by each in a given ionization chamber. This can be done rapidly and accurately, and this method for comparing X-ray intensities has been accepted as the standard method. The fundamental unit of quantity of radiation is the *Roentgen unit* (abbreviated R), which is defined as the quantity of X-radiation which will produce one electrostatic unit of ions of a given sign per cubic centimeter of air at 0°C and a pressure of 76 centimeters of mercury. Intensities of X-rays are then expressed in units such as Roentgens per second.

If we treat an ionization chamber as a condenser of capacity C, then the relation between the charge collected by an electrode, Q, and the measured fall in potential between the electrodes, V, is given by

$$Q = CV \qquad (278)$$

If the total charge collected by the ionization chamber is divided by the effective volume of the chamber, the result is the quantity of X-radiation in Roentgen units which has entered the chamber during the time of the measurement. Corrections for the actual pressure and temperature of the air in the chamber have to be made, of course, in accurate work. Instruments of this kind can be made as small as a fountain pen, so that personnel can carry them as a check on the total quantity of X-radiation received.

It will be shown in the next section that X-rays are electromagnetic waves and therefore are absorbed as photons. Individual X-ray photons can be detected by the detectors of nuclear radiations described in Sec. 8.2, such as the Geiger counter and the photomultiplier.

6.3. THE NATURE OF X-RAYS

Various experiments suggested the nature of X-rays, before the crystal diffraction experiments by Friedrich, Knipping and Laue in 1912 practically settled the issue. We will consider here some of the evidence available about 1912 regarding these radiations, and then will discuss the crucial work with crystals.

The process of generation of X-rays seems to involve stopping electrons suddenly with an obstacle, the target inside the tube. According to classical electromagnetic theory, the deceleration of these electrons will produce electromagnetic radiation, in the same way that accelerated electrons in a radio antenna radiate radio waves. The failure of magnetic fields to deflect an X-ray beam seems to confirm this classical idea that X-rays are electromagnetic waves emitted during the stopping of the electrons in the target. We will see later that classical theory provides only a partial explanation of the origin of the entire X-ray spectrum, but at present we will tentatively assume that X-rays are waves.

Polarization effects are characteristic of transverse waves, since a longitudinal wave cannot exhibit directional selectivity. In the case of light these effects are well known, and in fact, polarization effects provide the best proof that light is a transverse wave. In 1906 Barkla demonstrated the polarization of X-rays. He found that X-rays scattered in certain directions by a block of paraffin were polarized, since a second block of paraffin could scatter these X-rays only in certain specific directions. This is very similar to the polarization of light by the scattering produced by small particles in a suspension. Thus, it apears likely that X-rays are transverse electromagnetic waves, perhaps of the same nature as light, except for characteristics such as wavelength and frequency.

An estimate of the wavelength of X-rays was obtained by Walter and Pohl in 1909. They passed X-rays through a wedge-shaped slit which was only a few hundredths of a millimeter wide at the widest part. Their experiments were interpreted by Sommerfeld, who showed that if this was a case of diffraction of electromagnetic waves, then the wavelengths involved must be of the order of one angstrom.

When X-rays strike various materials, *secondary electrons* are emitted with energies ranging from zero up to the energy of the electrons in the X-ray generating tube. If we assume that these electrons are produced by X-ray photons in a way similar to the photoelectric effect, then the Duane-Hunt relation of Eq. (69) should hold, giving us a relation between the wavelength of the incident radiation and the energy of the most ener- getic electrons emitted.   Since secondary electrons with maximum energies of 50 kev are found to be produced by X-rays generated by a tube operated at 50 kilovolts, we would expect to be dealing with wavelengths of the order of one angstrom or less.   Thus, the assumption that secondary electrons are produced by a sort of X-ray photoelectric effect yields an order of magnitude of X-ray wavelengths which agrees with that obtained by diffracting X-rays with a wedge-shaped slit as described above.

Summing up the evidence regarding the nature of X-rays, X-rays were early found to be unaffected by magnetic fields, showing that they are not a stream of charged particles.   The classical theory of the generation of X-rays during the deceleration of electrons striking the target, and polariza- tion experiments seem to indicate that X-rays are transverse electromag- netic waves.   Additional confirmation of the wave theory of X-rays is provided by diffraction experiments and the X-ray photoelectric effect, both of which yield wavelengths of the order of one angstrom.   In the next section we will see how diffraction of X-rays by crystals not only confirmed the wave theory of X-rays but provided the most useful way of measuring X-ray wavelengths.

6.4. CRYSTAL DIFFRACTION OF X-RAYS

Diffraction is a phenomenon which is almost inexplicable without using some sort of wave theory.   The great utility of diffraction gratings in the measurement of optical wavelengths suggests the determination of X-ray wavelengths by some sort of a diffraction device, which, if it worked, would provide striking proof that X-rays are indeed waves.   This would then be a crucial test of the wave theory of X-rays.   However, in order to observe the diffraction of a wave, the diffracting obstacle must be of approximately the same size as the wavelength used.   Since the best ruled gratings have spacings between the rulings of about 10,000 angstroms, ruled gratings used in the usual way could not be expected to be very effective in diffracting X-rays, provided that our estimate of the X-ray wavelengths of about one angstrom is correct.   Actually, ruled gratings can be used to diffract X-rays, as shown by Compton in 1922, provided very small glancing angles are used.   We shall discuss this later, but at present the diffraction of X-rays by crystals will be discussed.

In 1912 von Laue presented the clever speculation that crystals might serve as three-dimensional gratings for the diffraction of X-rays.   This is suggested by the idea that the external symmetry of crystals might also extend to the internal arrangement of the atoms making up the crystal. Provided the spacings between atoms in a crystal were of the right order of magnitude, such a regular, three-dimensional arrangement of scattering centers might lead to interference effects.   In this way X-rays might be proved to be waves, and this method might also yield a value of the X-ray wavelength.

Accepting this hypothesis tentatively, let us investigate the order of magnitude of the spacings between atoms in a crystal.   Since NaCl has the external appearance of a cube, let us assume that Na⁺ and Cl⁻ ions are

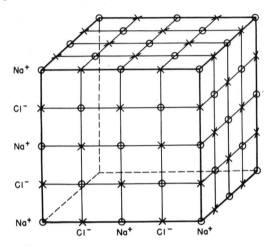

FIG. 48
Arrangement of ions in NaCl.

arranged in a simple cubic structure, as shown in Fig. 48, and compute the average spacing between the ions on this basis.   Since NaCl has a molecular weight of 58.46 and a density of 2.163 grams per cubic centimeter, the number of molecules in a cube one centimeter on a side is given by

$$\text{No./cm}^3 = \frac{2.163}{58.46} (6.023 \times 10^{23}) = 22.3 \times 10^{21}$$

However, there are two ions in each molecule, so that the number of ions in a one centimeter cube is 44.6×10^{21}.   If the arrangement of these ions is similar to the simple cube of Fig. 48, then the number of ions along an edge of the one centimeter cube would be

$$\text{ions/cm} = (44.6 \times 10^{21})^{1/3} = 3.55 \times 10^7$$

The distance between ions is just the reciprocal of the number of ions along a one centimeter edge of the cube.   The distance between ions is called the

principal grating space and is denoted by the symbol, d_0.   Thus, for NaCl
we find for the value of d_0

$$d_0 = \frac{1}{3.55 \times 10^7} = 2.820 \times 10^{-8} \text{ cm} = 2.820 \text{ angstroms}$$

We see then that for this crystal the average separation between ions is just
about the right size to diffract X-rays.

The first demonstration of the diffraction of X-rays by a crystal was
reported by Friedrich, Knipping and Laue in 1912.   A collimated beam of
X-rays passed through a crystal of ZnS and then struck a photographic

FIG. 49

A typical Laue photograph taken by X-rays.   (From
Nuclear Radiation Physics, by R. E. Lapp and H. L.
Andrews, Prentice-Hall, 2nd ed., 1954.)

plate.   The pattern on the photographic plate showed not only a central
spot corresponding to the undiffracted and undeflected beam, but also
various faint spots, showing that parts of the beam had been diffracted in
certain definite directions.   The calculations based on the positions of
these spots indicated wavelengths of a few tenths of an angstrom, confirming the earlier guesses of X-ray wavelengths.   Thus began the important
researches in X-ray spectroscopy and X-ray analysis of crystals.   Fig. 49
shows a typical pattern obtained in this way.

In the same year W. L. Bragg showed that the planes of atoms in a crystal acted like mirrors in reflecting an X-ray beam. This idea greatly simplified the analysis of diffraction patterns. For a simple cubic crystal, such as NaCl, many different sets of parallel and equidistant planes can be drawn. The important characteristics of the various planes of atoms are their separations, orientations, and the relative density of ions in the planes. Because we have in effect a three-dimensional grating, reflections from the various parallel planes of a given type may not add up constructively unless certain conditions are satisfied. For a given plane of ions, there is only one direction in which radiation scattered by the various ions will be reinforced. Just as in the case of a plane mirror, the direction of reinforcement is such that the angle of incidence equals the angle of reflection. This applies to any particular plane of ions. Now consider reflections from two planes

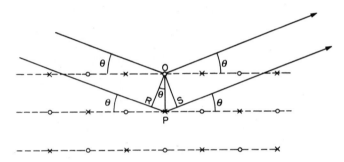

FIG. 50

Reflection of X-rays from two successive planes of atoms in a crystal.

separated a distance, d, as shown in Fig. 50. The difference in path between waves reflected at the first plane and waves reflected at the second plane must equal an integral number of wavelengths, if we are to have reinforcement. From the diagram it is seen that this path difference is RPS, since the angles ORP and OSP are right angles. If θ is the angle between the incident or reflected beam and the plane (*not* the angle between the incident beam and the normal to the plane, as is usual in optics), then we find the following relation:

$$RP = PS = d \sin \theta \qquad (279)$$

We can now state the following conditions for reflection with reinforcement at some angle θ:

1. Angle of incidence equal to angle of reflection, so that we have specular reflection from each individual plane.
2. The angle of incidence or reflection, θ, must satisfy the equation

$$n\lambda = 2d \sin \theta \qquad (280)$$

where $n = 1,2,3, \ldots$ in order that reflections from various parallel planes may reinforce one another.

Equation (280), which is known as the *Bragg law*, was verified by the Braggs and others during 1912 and 1913. A typical arrangement is shown in Fig. 51. A collimated beam of X-rays is reflected from the crystal at an angle θ, and the positions of reinforcement are located with a suitable detector, such as a photographic plate or an ionization chamber. As is shown on the diagram, the incident beam is diverged through an angle 2θ.

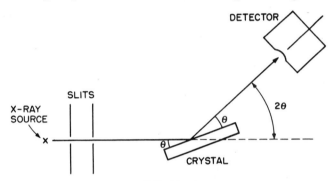

FIG. 51

Apparatus for measuring X-ray wavelengths, using Bragg diffraction.

As the crystal is rotated, various angles of incidence yield maximum reinforcement at angles, 2θ, corresponding to various sets of parallel planes with separations, d, and in various orders, n. Using a photographic film as a detector, the crystal can be rocked back and forth, with reinforcement occurring only at those angles of incidence which satisfy Eq. (280). In this way, reflections from all sets of planes in all orders are obtained automatically during a complete run, since all angles are obtained during a run.

A single large crystal does not have to be used. If a crystal is ground into a fine powder, each particle of the powder will be a miniature crystal with various sets of reflecting planes. If collimated X-rays are now allowed to fall on this powder, we obtain *Laue powder patterns*. A typical arrangement is shown in Fig. 52. For X-rays of a given wavelength, some particles will be correctly oriented to give reinforcement in each order. Similarly, all the various separations characteristic of various sets of parallel planes will be represented by some powder particles. Since the powder particles may have any azimuthal orientation about the pencil of X-rays, we find a circle on the photographic plate for each angle, $\phi = 2\theta$, which satisfies Eq. (280) for some particular set of parallel planes of ions and corresponding grating spacing, d. In this way, reflections from all sets of parallel planes in all orders are obtained on a single photograph.

We see that the existence of crystal diffraction of X-rays is a crucial proof that X-rays are waves. In addition, if crystals of known grating spacing and structure are used, X-ray wavelengths can be computed from the diffraction pattern. As we have shown in the case of NaCl, the grating spacing of a simple cubic crystal can easily be computed, so the experimental groundwork for X-ray spectroscopy is laid.

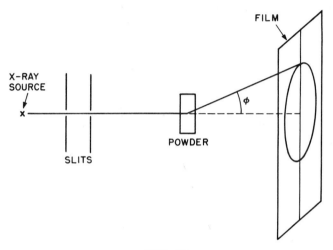

FIG. 52
Arrangement for obtaining Laue powder patterns of X-rays.

Only brief mention can be made here of X-ray crystallography, which is the investigation of the structure of crystals using X-rays, because of the complexity of this subject. Basically, the problem is to unravel the structure of a given crystal from a study of the diffraction pattern produced by the crystal when known X-ray wavelengths are used. However, there are seven fundamental crystal systems, which are subdivided into thirty-two classes, so this is quite a complicated problem to analyze. Not all of the classes of crystals have yet been observed in nature, but comparison of diffraction patterns with those of known crystals is often helpful. In general, however, we make use of the fact that only certain sets of parallel planes can be drawn for a given crystal in such a way as to include enough ions to produce observable diffraction. Thus, the distances between sets of parallel planes, d of Eq. (280), are limited to certain characteristic values for each class of crystal. The relation between the various values of d determines the characteristic pattern produced by each class of crystal, so that the class of crystal is found directly from the type of pattern observed. Knowing the wavelength used, the principal grating constants of the crystal are then found, which completes the analysis.

6.5. WAVELENGTH MEASUREMENTS WITH RULED GRATINGS

Although Roentgen had been unable to detect reflection of X-rays, in 1922 Compton found that reflection could take place if sufficiently small glancing angles were used. This might allow the diffraction of X-rays without requiring a ruled grating with an impossibly large number of lines per centimeter. If this were possible, direct measurements of X-ray wavelengths could be made, which would not depend on any assumptions regarding the structure of crystals or of the value of Avogadro's number.

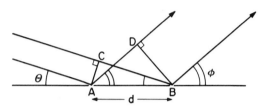

FIG. 53

Glancing-angle diffraction of X-rays from two successive rulings of a grating.

Consider diffraction at small angles from two successive rulings of a grating, as shown in Fig. 53. If we draw lines CA and DB so that angles ACB and ADB are right angles, the path difference between rays 1 and 2 is seen to be $CB - AD$. We can write

$$\Delta P = CB - AD = d \cos \theta - d \cos \phi \qquad (281)$$

The condition for reinforcement thus becomes

$$n\lambda = d(\cos \theta - \cos \phi) \qquad (282)$$

Since both the angles involved in Eq. (282) are small, we can use the following approximation for the cosine:

$$\cos x = 1 - \frac{x^2}{2} \dots \qquad (283)$$

With this good approximation, Eq. (282) takes the form

$$n\lambda = \frac{d}{2} (\phi^2 - \theta^2) \qquad (284)$$

Let us now compute the grating spacing required for typical values of the quantities in Eq. (284). Assume a wavelength of one angstrom, an angle of incidence of 0.001 radian (3.5′ of arc), angle of diffraction of

0.002 radian (7′ of arc), and diffraction in the first order. Substituting these values into Eq. (232), we have

$$1 \times 10^{-8} = \frac{d}{2} (4 \times 10^{-6} - 1 \times 10^{-6})$$

Therefore

$$d = \frac{1}{150} \text{ cm}$$

Thus, with the conditions specified, we need a grating with only 150 lines per centimeter, which is quite a coarse grating, easily ruled.

The first wavelength measurements using a ruled grating were made by Compton and Doan in 1925. Since wavelengths measured in this way are absolute, in the sense that they are derived directly from measured lengths, they are considered to be the fundamental standards of X-ray wavelengths. Using these absolute wavelengths, the spacings of crystals can be measured, without making any assumptions regarding crystal structures or the values of physical constants. When this was done, it was found that the calculated values of crystal constants were slightly incorrect.

The trouble lay in the value of the electronic charge which was used to compute Avogadro's number, using Eq. (1). Millikan's value of the electronic charge was too small, because of an error in the value of the viscosity of air, as described in Section 1.5. More recent values of the electronic charge and Avogadro's number are more accurate. For instance, an earlier calculated value of the grating space of NaCl was 2.814 angstroms, while with Bearden's observations using wavelengths measured with a ruled grating the value was 2.81971 angstroms. This should be compared with the value of 2.820 angstroms computed earlier in this chapter using the most recent value of Avogadro's number. This agrees excellently with previous computations.

Before X-ray wavelengths could be measured accurately with ruled gratings, the early value of the grating space of NaCl was taken to be correct. The X-unit (abbreviated X.U.) is defined so that the grating space of NaCl is exactly 2814.00 X.U. Thus, the X-unit is almost but not exactly equal to 0.001 angstrom or 10^{-11} centimeter. At present, X-ray wavelengths can be compared more precisely and easily with crystals than with ruled gratings, so the practice is to express all measurements made with crystals in terms of X-units. If necessary, such wavelengths can be converted to metric units by increasing them by about 0.20%. For most purposes the distinction is immaterial.

6.6. X-RAY SPECTROSCOPY

Monochromatic X-rays were discovered by W. H. Bragg in 1913.   Using
the arrangement shown in Fig. 51, the ionization current is measured at
various glancing angles of incidence, θ.   If the ionization current is plotted
against the glancing angle, the curve of Fig. 54 is found. Fairly sharp
maxima are found for the sharp spectral lines, the wavelengths of which
can be calculated using Bragg's law given by Eq. (280).   A second triplet

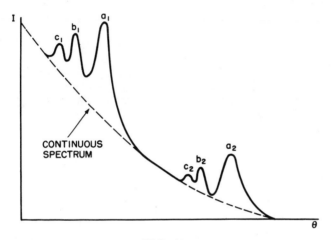

FIG. 54

Plot of ionization current as a function of glancing angle
for Bragg diffraction of X-rays from a crystal.

of lines of lower intensity is found to be the second order spectrum, and
higher orders can be observed.   When different crystals are used to measure the wavelengths emitted by a given target operated in a tube at a
given voltage, the same wavelengths are found, showing that the wavelengths measured are characteristic of the target of the X-ray tube.   The
monochromatic wavelengths are superimposed on the *continuous spectrum*,
which is indicated by a dotted line.   Thus, a typical X-ray spectrum consists of certain discrete spectral lines plus a continuous spectrum.

Great regularity is found among the characteristic wavelengths of the
various elements.   For all elements the characteristic triplet, *abc*, shown in
Fig. 54 is found, with the *a*-line being well separated from the *b* and *c* lines.
Furthermore, the intensities are always in the order $a > b > c$.   The main
difference between the triplets of various elements is in the wavelengths.

A typical triplet is that of wolfram, where $a = 0.211A$, $b = 0.184A$, and $c = 0.179A$. The range of values of the a-line is shown in the following table:

Element:	Na	Fe	Ag	Pb	U
a-line:	11.89	1.934	0.560	0.168	0.108

The b and c lines vary in the same way from element to element.

In addition to the characteristic triplet just described, which is known as the K-series triplet, a quadruplet of longer wavelength is also found. This quadruplet is known as the L-series, and the wavelengths of this series exhibit the same sort of regularity from element to element as do the wavelengths of the K-series. For the heavy elements, M and N series of even longer wavelength are found. The characteristic radiations are almost completely independent of the state of chemical combination of the element. Each element emits its own characteristic radiations, regardless of its association with other types of atoms.

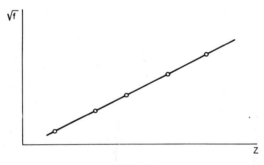

FIG. 55
Illustration of Moseley's law of linearity between the square root of the frequency of a characteristic X-ray line of each element and its atomic number.

Moseley discovered an important regularity in X-ray spectra in 1913–1914. If the atomic number of each element is plotted against the square root of the frequency of a particular line in the spectrum of each element, such as the K_a-line, a straight line is obtained. A typical curve of this sort is shown in Fig. 55. Until Moseley's discovery of this systematic relationship, the atomic numbers of the elements in the periodic table had been assigned on the basis of their chemical properties and atomic weights. On the basis of the characteristic X-ray wavelengths emitted, atomic numbers of the elements could now be established with certainty. As an example, the atomic weights of cobalt and nickel are 58.94 and 58.69, which made their positions in the periodic table uncertain. From their X-ray spectra, it was clearly established that the atomic number of cobalt is 27, while the atomic number of nickel is 28. In addition to removing uncertainties in the atomic numbers of certain elements, Moseley's law established the atomic numbers of unknown elements needed to fill gaps in the periodic table.   In this way elements such as hafnium were discovered.

Returning to Eq. (182) in the treatment of the Bohr theory of one-electron atoms, it is seen that the frequency should be proportional to the square of the atomic number, as Moseley found.   However, the Moseley law is expressed more accurately in the form

$$\sqrt{f} = A\,(Z - B) \qquad\qquad (285)$$

In Eq. (285) the terms A and B are constants which are different for each particular characteristic line.   It will be seen below that the prediction of Moseley's law by the Bohr theory is no coincidence.

6.7. THE CONTINUOUS X-RAY SPECTRUM

While the wavelengths of the characteristic lines are determined by the material of the target, the continuous spectrum (sometimes called "white" X-rays by analogy with white light) depends mainly on the voltage applied

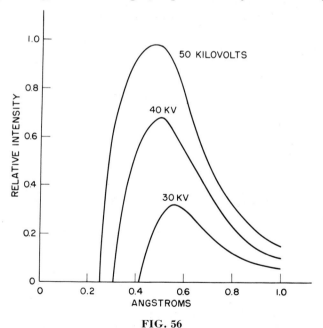

FIG. 56

Typical curves of the intensity of X-rays produced by a thick target as a function of wavelength at various applied voltages.

to the X-ray tube. Some typical curves of intensity of the continuous spectrum as a function of wavelength are shown in Fig. 56. It is seen that for any particular applied voltage there is a definite lower limit to the wavelengths appearing in the continuous spectrum. The actual shape of the curves depends not only on the voltage applied to the X-ray tube, but also to a certain extent on the material of the target, the thickness of the target, and the current in the X-ray tube.

The qualitative explanation of the continuous spectrum is simple. When an electron is slowed down by passing near an atom, the electron may lose an amount of energy, ΔW. This energy is then emitted as a quantum of radiation. This is known as a *radiative collision*, and the associated radiation is known as *Bremsstrahlung* or "braking radiation." This is an important process in the absorption of cosmic rays and will be considered again in Section 11.5. When a radiative collision occurs, the frequency of the radiation emitted is related to the loss of energy of the electron by the Einstein frequency condition of Eq. (171). We then have

$$hf = \Delta W \tag{286}$$

Since electrons will undergo collisions ranging from direct hits on atoms to glancing collisions, different electrons will lose different amounts of energy. This explains the presence of a continuous range of emitted wavelengths. A typical electron will give up its energy in several collisions, each collision producing a quantum of radiation.

If an electron is stopped in a single collision, thus converting all its kinetic energy into a single quantum of radiation, we will obtain the largest frequency or shortest wavelength possible for a particular applied voltage. If the electron is accelerated through a voltage, V, its kinetic energy when it strikes the target is eV. We then have

$$hf_{\max} = \frac{hc}{\lambda_{\min}} = eV \tag{287}$$

Putting in the values of the constants and solving Eq. (287) for the minimum wavelength in angstroms emitted by a tube operating at a particular voltage, we find

$$\lambda_{\min} = \frac{12,396.44}{V} \tag{288}$$

This is the familiar Duane-Hunt relation derived in Eq. (69) in connection with the photoelectric effect. From Eq. (288), the minimum wavelength generated by an X-ray tube operating at a voltage, V, can be computed.

The shape of the continuous spectrum can be explained by assuming that there is a most probable type of collision, with a corresponding loss of energy. The wavelength corresponding to this loss in energy then occurs at the peak of the intensity curve. For thin targets, electrons will pass through the target after suffering one collision or no collision at all, so that electrons have no opportunity to give up their energy in a number of low-energy collisions. Thus, for thin targets the intensity at long wavelengths (low-energy collisions) is low, and the peak of the intensity distribution curve moves over almost to the *cut-off wavelength*, λ_{min}. For thick targets, the peak of the continuous spectrum occurs at a wavelength which is about 1.3–1.5 times the cut-off wavelength, showing that the most probable energy loss is $\frac{2}{3}$ to $\frac{3}{4}$.

Before we conclude the study of the continuous spectrum, it should be noted that the efficiency of energy conversion in an X-ray tube is low. If this efficiency is defined as the ratio of radiant energy output of the tube to the energy carried by the electrons bombarding the target, we find experimentally efficiencies of the order of 0.01% to 0.1%. An empirical expression for the intensity emitted by an X-ray tube is given below.

$$I = (1.1 \times 10^{-8})Zi\left(\frac{V}{d}\right)^2 \tag{289}$$

In Eq. (289), the intensity in Roentgens per minute at a distance d (inches) is given for a tube operated at a voltage V (kilovolts), and with a tube current i (milliamperes), and using a target with atomic number Z. This expression is useful in estimating safety and dosage factors.

6.8. DISCRETE X-RAY SPECTRA

The process by which the discrete spectral lines are emitted involves the theory of the structure of atoms. As described in Section 5.9, atoms are built up by successively adding electrons with quantum states similar to those of the hydrogen atom. Since these added electrons must possess quantum numbers which obey the Pauli principle, we find that the K-shell could include only two electrons. The electrons in the K-shell have the lowest algebraic value of energy of any shell, so they are very tightly bound to the nucleus. The next shell consists of eight L-shell electrons, and in heavier atoms we have M, N, and O shells.

The electrons added to form each successive element are added subject to the requirement that each added electron must add the minimum amount of energy to the atom, in order to have a stable atom. In general, the value of n plays the biggest part in determining the energy of a given quantum state, so that the K-shell electrons have the lowest energies, the L-shell electrons have the next lowest energies, and so forth. The energies of electrons within a given shell depend somewhat on the values of the other quantum numbers, which introduces a fine structure into X-ray spectra.

Suppose now that a fast-moving electron strikes an atom in such a way as to remove one of its K-shell electrons completely. This might be the case for an atom of the target of an X-ray tube, or electrons might bombard a gas or liquid. Since the exterior electrons of this ionized atom are no longer shielded from the electrostatic attraction of the nucleus by the usual two K-electrons, there is a tendency for one of these exterior electrons to drop into the vacancy left in the K-shell. If, for instance, an L-electron drops into this vacancy in the K-shell, the difference in energy between the original L-state of this electron and its final K-state is emitted as a quantum of radiation. In this particular case, the K_a line is emitted. According to the Einstein equation, the frequency of this line is given by

$$(hf)_{K_a} = E_L - E_K \qquad (290)$$

Similarly, the K_b line is emitted when an M-electron drops into the vacancy in the K-shell, and the K_c line is emitted when an N-electron drops into the K-shell.

It might be expected that transitions from the L-shell would be more probable than transitions from the M-shell, which in turn would be more probable than transitions from the N-shell, since a mechanical model of the atom would have the K-shell closest to the nucleus and the other shells increasingly farther away in the order L, M, N, etc. This expectation is confirmed by the fact that the intensities of the K-lines are in the order $a > b > c$. Since no K_d line is observed, the probability of a transition from the O-shell to the K-shell must be vanishingly small.

A bombarding electron might knock an L-electron from a target atom, instead of a K-electron. In this case, electrons from the M, N, and O shells might drop into the L-shell to fill the vacancy. Each of these transitions leads to a member of the L-series, in the same manner as described in connection with the origin of the K-series. Just as in the case of optical spectral series, the letter designating a given X-ray series indicates the final state of all transitions yielding members of that series. According to our picture, a vacancy in a given shell may be filled by electrons from shells farther out from the nucleus, each shell-to-shell transition leading to a line in the X-ray series. In heavier atoms X-ray series are produced by transitions ending on the M and N shells, after an M or N electron has been knocked out of the atom. These corresponding series are known as the M-series or the N-series.

An energy level diagram can be drawn illustrating the relation between the energy levels of electrons and the corresponding transition energies, just as was done in the case of optical spectra. Since the values of the azimuthal quantum number, l, and the spin quantum number, m_s affect the energy levels slightly, within a given shell there are various energy states. However, these differences are small and lead to the fine structure of X-ray spectra.

It is convenient in labelling energy levels to use a new quantum number in place of m_s. The *total angular quantum number*, j, is found by taking the vector sum of l and m_s. Since m_s can take on only the values $+\frac{1}{2}$ and $-\frac{1}{2}$, the values of j for a one-electron state are $(l + \frac{1}{2})$ and $(l - \frac{1}{2})$. The *selection rules* for allowed transitions are as follows:

$$\Delta n = 1,2,3, \ldots$$
$$\Delta l = \pm 1$$
$$\Delta j = 0, \pm 1$$

In order to satisfy these selection rules, not all possible transitions occur between energy levels on a diagram. However, some faint *forbidden lines* have been found, which correspond to transitions which are not allowed.

A typical energy level diagram and the accompanying allowed transitions are shown in Fig. 57. Presumably, an accurate computation of the energy levels of atoms according to quantum mechanics would allow X-ray spectra to be predicted, but this has not been done for the heavy elements because of their electronic complexity. In practice, energy levels and their associated quantum numbers are derived from experimental values of X-ray wavelengths. In the diagram the fine structure of the energy levels within each shell is exaggerated for clarity, as compared to the differences between shells, which are quite large. The fine structure of the N and O shells was omitted entirely, so that only a few typical transitions are shown for the L and M series. We see that the interpretation of X-ray spectra in terms of quantum mechanics can give a great deal of information regarding exact values of electronic energy states within atoms. Used in this way, X-ray spectroscopy acts like a super-microscope, allowing us to look inside the structure of even the atom.

Additional confirmation of the ideas of energy levels and transitions leading to the emission of radiation is furnished by the existence of *X-ray excitation potentials*, which are similar to the excitation potentials described in connection with optical spectra in Section 4.4. Experimentally, it is found that, for a given target, none of the K-series lines appears until a certain critical voltage is applied across the X-ray tube. When this *K-excitation voltage* is reached, all of the K-series lines appear simultaneously. Referring to Fig. 57, it is seen that the K-series cannot be excited until a K-electron is raised from its normal state to the state of ionization. (The L and M shells are assumed to be filled, so that a K-electron cannot stop there, but must leave the atom entirely.) After a K-electron has been knocked out of the atom, then an L, M, or N electron can fall into the

vacancy left in the K-shell, with the consequent emission of a line in the
K-series.   Because of this process, none of the lines in the K-series can be
excited until the bombarding electrons have sufficient energy to knock a
K-electron completely out of the atom, and once the K-electron has been
removed, any of the K-series lines can appear as an outer electron falls into
the vacancy created in the K-shell.   Thus, the existence of critical X-ray
potentials confirms our ideas of atomic energy transitions leading to the
emission of X-radiation.

Although the excitation energy for the K-series is actually equal to the
difference between the energy of the K-shell and ionization (ionization is

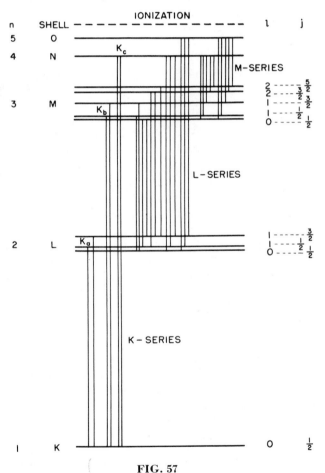

FIG. 57

Transitions between various energy levels and resulting
X-ray series produced.   (Fine structure of L and M shells
exaggerated for clarity; fine structure of O and N shells
omitted.)

usually taken to be the zero level of energy), this difference is almost exactly equal to the difference between the energies of the K-shell and the N-shell. This is true because the electrons in the N-shell have energies differing very little from zero as compared to the large binding energies of the K-shell electrons. Thus, the K-excitation voltage can be computed quite accurately from the wavelength of the K_c line, since this corresponds to a transition from the N-shell to the K-shell, using the Duane-Hunt relation in Eq. (288). In short, the K-series does not appear until the voltage applied to the X-ray tube is high enough for the continuous spectrum to include the wavelength of the K_c line.

Since there are three different energies which electrons in the L-shell may have, there are three corresponding *L-excitation voltages*, depending on the energy of the particular L-electron which is knocked out of the atom. Only when the third and highest excitation potential is applied do all of the L-series lines appear. Similarly, there are five M-series excitation voltages, seven N-series excitation voltages, and so forth, provided that the atomic number of the target is high enough for each shell to be completely filled. Excitation voltages provide a direct check on the existence of energy levels and the correctness of the energy level diagrams, even though energy levels derived from X-ray wavelengths are used most often in precise work.

6.9. THE ABSORPTION OF X-RAYS

Consider a collimated beam of monochromatic X-rays, as shown in Fig. 58. It is found experimentally that if the thickness of the absorber is small the decrease in intensity of the X-ray beam is proportional to the thickness of the absorber. If we let dI be the change in intensity of the beam in passing

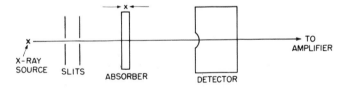

FIG. 58

Arrangement for measuring the absorption of X-rays by a solid absorber.

through an infinitesimal thickness, dx, of the absorber, and I be the intensity of the beam before striking the absorber, then we can write

$$dI = -\mu I \, dx \tag{291}$$

The constant of proportionality, μ, is called the *linear absorption coefficient*. Provided that μ is independent of x, which seems to be the case experimentally, we can integrate Eq. (291). We find

$$\ln I = C - \mu x \tag{292}$$

If we let I_0 be the intensity when $x = 0$, then the constant is seen to have the value $C = \ln I_0$. We can write Eq. (292) in the form

$$\ln \frac{I}{I_0} = -\mu x \tag{293}$$

A useful form of Eq. (293) is obtained by taking the antilogarithm of both sides, obtaining

$$I = I_0 \exp (-\mu x) \tag{294}$$

Equations (293) and (294) describe the absorption of monochromatic X-rays quite well.

Suppose we define the *half-value thickness, T*, as the thickness of absorber which is sufficient to reduce the intensity of a given beam of X-rays to one-half its initial value. From Eq. (293) we have

$$\ln \frac{I}{I_0} = \ln (0.5) = -0.693 = -\mu T \tag{295}$$

Thus, the relation between the half-value thickness and the linear absorption coefficient is seen to be

$$\mu = \frac{0.693}{T} \tag{296}$$

Frequently the half-value thickness is determined experimentally and Eq. (296) is used to compute the absorption coefficient. Another common method of determining the absorption coefficient is to plot $\ln (I/I_0)$ versus x. Then the slope of the straight line obtained is equal to $-\mu$, according to Eq. (293). This is most conveniently done by using semi-logarithmic graph paper, since no logarithms have to be looked up in tables. From the form of the absorption equations, it is clear that a large value of μ means rapid absorption and thus soft X-rays, while hard X-rays have a small value of μ and are more penetrating.

It is often useful to use the *mass absorption coefficient* in place of the linear absorption coefficient. If d is the density of the absorber, the mass absorption coefficient is defined as μ/d. Eq. (294) then takes the form

$$I = I_0 \exp \left(-\frac{\mu}{d} xd \right) \tag{297}$$

One advantage of the mass absorption coefficient is that it is independent of whether the absorber is in the gaseous, liquid, or solid state. If we consider a unit area of the absorber, then x is numerically equal to the volume and thus xd is equal to the weight per unit area of the absorber. Experimentally, the weight of an absorber of known area is measured and the linear thickness is computed from this value and the density of the absorber. If Eq. (297) is used, the thickness can be expressed directly in grams per square centimeter, without making any assumptions regarding the density of the absorber. This is another advantage of using the mass absorption coefficient, since the density of a metal foil may not be the same as the density of a solid sample of the same metal. For these reasons, absorption coefficients are often given in grams per square centimeter and the results of absorption experiments are given in the same unit.

The total apparent absorption in the experiment shown in Fig. 58 is due to two factors, since the detector responds only to the radiation which actually reaches it. Some energy is lost from the original beam by scattering of the beam away from its initial direction, so that the scattered portion of the beam doesn't reach the detector. There is also a true absorption of X-ray energy inside the absorbing material. We can therefore write the mass absorption coefficient, μ/d, in terms of the *scattering coefficient*, σ, and the *true absorption coefficient*, τ, in the form

$$\frac{\mu}{d} = \frac{\sigma}{d} + \frac{\tau}{d} \qquad (298)$$

Experimentally, the true absorption coefficient is determined from measurements of μ and σ. The mass scattering coefficient, σ/d, is computed classically to have the value 0.2 per gm/cm^2, but this value is found to be correct only for light elements at wavelengths of a few tenths of an angstrom. The quantum mechanical theory of Compton scattering, which is described in Section 6.10, gives much better results. However, for X-rays produced by voltages below about 100 kilovolts the loss of intensity by scattering is not too important.

The main absorption process for X-rays of moderate energy (less than 100 kilovolts) is the photoelectric effect. In this process the energy of an X-ray quantum is completely given up to an electron from one of the inner shells of an atom in the absorber. (The electrons from the outer shells cannot remove enough energy from the X-ray beam to have a significant effect on absorption.) In the case of a photoelectron coming from the K-shell, the energy of the X-ray photon is used up in two ways: a certain amount of energy must be used to remove the electron from the shell, and the remainder is given to the electron in the form of kinetic energy. Since the photoelectric work-function at the surface of all substances is of the order of a few volts, this can be completely ignored, but the kinetic energy used up by the electron in reaching the surface of the absorber may not be at all negligible.   Then there is a distribution in the energies of the photo-electrons observed outside the absorber.

For the photoelectrons which are either emitted at the surface of the absorber or lose no energy in reaching the surface of the absorber we can write

$$(\tfrac{1}{2}mv^2)_{\max} = hf - E_k \qquad\qquad (299)$$

If the energy of the X-ray photon is less than the K-series excitation energy E_k, no photoelectrons will be knocked out of the K-shell.   Since the energy transition which produces the K_c line is almost exactly equal numerically to the energy of the K-shell, an alternative statement is that photoelectrons from the K-shell will not be produced unless the continuous spectrum of the X-ray tube includes the K_c line which would be emitted by the material of the absorber.

Similar remarks apply to the production of photoelectrons from the L and M shells.   Since electrons in the L-shell may have three slightly differ-

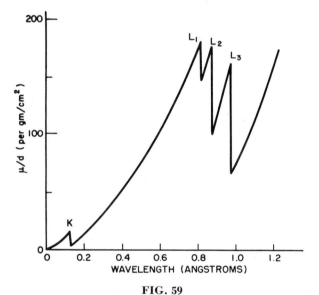

FIG. 59

Variation of mass-absorption coefficient of lead with X-ray wavelength.

ent energies, three groups of photoelectrons are found from the L-shell, the three groups differing slightly in energy.   As in the case of absorption of X-rays by the production of photoelectrons from the K-shell, the L-shell is not effective in absorbing X-ray energy unless the energy of the X-rays at least equals one of the three L-excitation voltages.

The typical variation of μ/d with wavelength is shown in Fig. 59 (for lead). At very short wavelengths, photoelectric removal of K-electrons is mainly responsible for the absorption of X-ray energy. At the K-*absorption limit* at about 0.14 angstroms, the incident X-rays no longer have enough energy to remove a K-electron from lead, so this process ceases and the absorption drops radically. As the wavelength is increased, the removal of L-electrons photoelectrically becomes more and more likely, so the absorption coefficient increases. When the energy of X-ray photons becomes insufficient to remove the most tightly bound L-electrons, they no longer take part in absorption, so the absorption drops at the L_1-absorption limit. There are similar drops at the other two L-absorption limits, which are at energies corresponding to the L-excitation voltages of lead. At even higher wavelengths we would expect to find five M-absorption limits corresponding to the five M-excitation voltages, as the energy of incident X-ray photons became insufficient to remove an electron of the corresponding energy. Other elements have absorption curves which are the same as that given for lead, except that the characteristic absorption limits vary from element to element, being in each case almost exactly the same as the corresponding excitation energies for the emission of X-ray series.

Empirically, it is found that the absorption coefficient varies approximately as the cube of the wavelength and as the cube of the atomic number of the absorber. (This may be made plausible by assuming that the effectiveness of a photon is proportional to its wavelength, so that the volume of a photon's effectiveness would be proportional to the cube of its wavelength.) For the mass absorption the empirical equation is

$$\frac{\mu}{d} = k\lambda^3 Z^3 \tag{300}$$

In using Eq. (300) to compute absorption coefficients by extrapolation from known data, an absorption limit must not be crossed. The empirical expression given by Eq. (300) holds for any one of the increasing sections of the curve of Fig. 59, but each section has a different value of the constant, k, since different shells of electrons are responsible for the absorption in each section of the curve.

At wavelengths shorter than the K_c line of the absorber, no absorption limits are encountered, so that at high enough energies the photoelectric absorption of X-rays is proportional to the cube of the wavelength absorbed or inversely proportional to the cube of the frequency or photon energy. At energies of the order of hundreds of kilovolts the photoelectric effect rapidly becomes unimportant as an absorption process. In the following sections we will discuss the absorption of X-rays at these higher energies by Compton scattering and pair-formation. Finally, we will combine all three absorption processes and plot the absorption curve over a wide range of X-ray energies.

6.10. COMPTON SCATTERING OF X-RAYS

At energies in the hundreds of kilovolts, the loss of intensity of an X-ray passing through an absorber is no longer explained entirely by the photo-electric effect. In 1923 Compton discovered and explained a scattering process, known as the *Compton effect*, which becomes increasingly important in absorption at higher energies. In lead, for instance, the photoelectric effect and the Compton effect contribute equally to the absorption coefficient at an X-ray energy of approximately 500 kilovolts; at higher energies the Compton effect rapidly becomes more important.

From the photoelectric effect we know that a photon is absorbed just as if it were a particle of energy hf, which gives all its energy to the photo-electron. Compton extended this corpuscular idea of the interaction between photons and electrons by assuming that a photon would possess momentum as well as energy. Referring to Eq. (143) in Section 3.11, the relation between the energy of a particle and its momentum is given by

$$E^2 = (pc)^2 + (m_0 c^2)^2 \qquad (301)$$

If this relation is assumed to hold for photons, which have zero rest-mass, we should have

$$E = pc \qquad (302)$$

Since the energy of a photon is given by $E = hf$, its associated momentum should be

$$p = \frac{E}{c} = \frac{hf}{c} = \frac{h}{\lambda} \qquad (303)$$

Compton assumed that a collision between a photon and an electron would obey the usual laws of mechanics, so that the laws of conservation of energy and momentum would hold. In applying these laws, the photon would be treated just like an ordinary material particle of energy hf and momentum hf/c.

Let us consider a photon striking an electron which is initially at rest, as shown in Fig. 60. (A correction can be made for the initial motion of the electron, but this correction is not very large.) The photon will be assigned an energy $E = hf = hc/\lambda$ and a momentum $p = h/\lambda$. After the collision, the photon will rebound in some direction making an angle θ with its initial direction, and we will assume that the momentum and energy of this modified photon are changed by the collision. The electron will recoil in a direction making an angle ϕ with the initial direction of the incident photon, and it will acquire a velocity, v, during the collision. Relativistic expressions are used for the momentum and energy of the electron, since this provides generality for the results. (Oddly enough, no approximations are needed in this case, but if the corresponding classical expressions for the momentum and energy are used, approximations must be made to obtain the final result of the theory.)   We will now apply the conservation principles of classical mechanics to this collision, just as if it were a collision between a moving ball and a ball at rest.

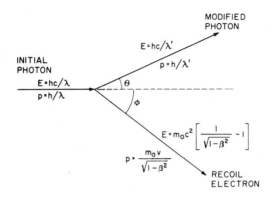

FIG. 60

Impact of a photon on an electron initially at rest.

Since the electron is assumed to be at rest before being struck by the photon, the conservation of energy equation becomes

$$\frac{hc}{\lambda} = \frac{hc}{\lambda'} + m_0 c^2 \left[\frac{1}{\sqrt{1 - \beta^2}} - 1 \right] \tag{304}$$

Equating the horizontal components of momentum before and after collision, we have

$$\frac{h}{\lambda} = \frac{h}{\lambda'} \cos \theta + \frac{m_0 v \cos \phi}{\sqrt{1 - \beta^2}} \tag{305}$$

Balancing the vertical components of momentum after collision, since there was no vertical component of momentum before collision, we have

$$0 = \frac{h}{\lambda'} \sin \theta - \frac{m_0 v \sin \phi}{\sqrt{1 - \beta^2}} \tag{306}$$

We now have three equations in the five variables λ, λ', θ, ϕ, and v (or β), so that any two of the unknown quantities can be eliminated.   Usually the two variables referring to the electron, v and ϕ, are eliminated, leaving a relation for the wavelength of the photon scattered in a given direction θ, in terms of the wavelength of the original photon.

Let us solve Eqs. (305) and (306) for the terms involving the angle, ϕ. Squaring and adding these equations,

$$\left(\frac{h}{\lambda'}\right)^2 \sin^2 \theta + \left(\frac{h}{\lambda} - \frac{h \cos \theta}{\lambda'}\right)^2 = \frac{m_0^2 v^2}{1 - \beta^2} \qquad (307)$$

The angle, ϕ, has been eliminated from Eq. (307) since $\sin^2 \phi + \cos^2 \phi = 1$. The right-hand side of (307) can be rewritten in the form

$$\frac{m_0^2 v^2}{1 - \beta^2} = \frac{m_0^2 c^2 \beta^2}{1 - \beta^2} = \frac{m_0^2 c^2}{1 - \beta^2} - m_0^2 c^2 \qquad (308)$$

Collecting terms in (307) and using the identity in (308) we have

$$\left(\frac{h}{\lambda}\right)^2 + \left(\frac{h}{\lambda'}\right)^2 - \frac{2h^2 \cos \theta}{\lambda \lambda'} = \frac{m_0^2 c^2}{1 - \beta^2} - m_0^2 c^2 \qquad (309)$$

If Eq. (304) is divided by c, it can be written in the form

$$\frac{h}{\lambda} - \frac{h}{\lambda'} + m_0 c = \frac{m_0 c}{\sqrt{1 - \beta^2}} \qquad (310)$$

If we square (310) and substitute the right-hand side into (309), we eliminate β. We then have

$$\left(\frac{h}{\lambda}\right)^2 + \left(\frac{h}{\lambda'}\right)^2 - \frac{2h^2 \cos \theta}{\lambda \lambda'} = \left(\frac{h}{\lambda} - \frac{h}{\lambda'} + m_0 c\right)^2 - m_0^2 c^2 \qquad (311)$$

Collecting terms in (311) we have

$$\frac{-2h^2 \cos \theta}{\lambda \lambda'} = \frac{-2h^2}{\lambda \lambda'} + \frac{2m_0 c h}{\lambda} - \frac{2m_0 c h}{\lambda'} \qquad (312)$$

After multiplying (312) through by $\lambda \lambda'$, we have

$$-2h^2 \cos \theta = -2h^2 + 2m_0 c h (\lambda' - \lambda) \qquad (313)$$

Finally, solving Eq. (313) for the change in wavelength between the original photon and a photon scattered at an angle θ, we find

$$\lambda' - \lambda = \frac{h}{m_0 c} (1 - \cos \theta) \qquad (314)$$

Thus the scattered wavelength is always greater than the incident wavelength.

If numerical values of the constants are put into Eq. (314), we find that the constant $(h/m_0 c)$ has the value 2.426×10^{-10} centimeter. Measuring the change in wavelength in angstroms, we have

$$\lambda' - \lambda = 0.02426(1 - \cos \theta) \qquad (315)$$

It should be noted that the change of wavelength of the scattered photon is independent of the value of the incident wavelength and of the nature of the scattering material. This change in wavelength is zero in the *forward direction* (initial direction of incident photon) and increases up to a maximum value of 0.0485 angstroms at $\theta = 180°$, which corresponds to reflection of the photon.

Experimentally, two wavelengths are found at any given angle of scattering, θ. The wavelength, λ', predicted by the Compton theory is found as well as the wavelength of the incident photon, λ. The presence of this *unmodified line* can be explained on the basis that here we have scattering by an atom as a whole, instead of scattering by a free electron. Because of the presence of the mass of the scattering particle in the denominator of Eq. (314), the change in wavelength produced by scattering from an atom will be extremely small. The change in wavelength predicted by the Compton theory is verified quite accurately, although the random initial motions of the scattering electrons give the Compton wavelength a finite breadth.

Instead of eliminating ϕ and v from Eqs. (304)–(306), we could have eliminated any other pair of variables, obtaining in each case a useful relation for the remaining three variables. If we eliminate θ and λ', which pertain to the modified photon, we find the following expression for the kinetic energy, T, of an electron recoiling in the direction ϕ, in terms of the energy of the incident photon, E:

$$T = \frac{2m_0 c^2 \cos^2 \phi}{(1 + m_0 c^2/E)^2 - \cos^2 \phi} \qquad (316)$$

Similarly, if the modified photon goes off in the direction, θ, then the energy of the recoil electron is

$$T = \frac{E(1 - \cos \theta)}{1 - \cos \theta + m_0 c^2/E} \qquad (317)$$

An important case occurs when the electron recoils in the forward direction, so that $\phi = 0°$ and $\theta = 180°$. In this case the energy of the initial photon, E, can be found from the measured kinetic energy of the electron, T, from the relation

$$E = \frac{m_0 c^2}{\sqrt{1 + 2m_0 c^2/T} - 1} \qquad (318)$$

In the case of high-energy (short wavelength) X-rays, crystal spacings are too large for convenient measurement of wavelength by crystal diffraction. If the recoil energy of electrons in the forward direction is measured, Eq. (318) allows the energy of the photon to be calculated. Since $E = hf$, the wavelength is then found very simply. This method is often used at high energies.

Before continuing with the processes of X-ray absorption, an effect which is the inverse of the Compton effect will be discussed. In the theory of the scattering of X-rays by particles, Compton assumed that photons interacted with matter as if they possessed a momentum given by Eq. (303) as $p = h/\lambda$. At about the same time, in 1924, de Broglie postulated that the same relationship should also hold for moving particles. That is, a wavelength, λ, is to be associated with a particle of momentum, p, according to the same equation. This wavelength is known as the *de Broglie wavelength*. In connection with this, the reader should refer to Problem 3 of Chapter 5, where the eigenfunctions of a free particle were obtained. It was shown that these eigenfunctions could be interpreted as a standing wave of exactly the wavelength postulated by de Broglie, so that this wave aspect of a particle has a firm quantum mechanical basis.

If particles actually have wave properties, we should be able to observe such typical wave phenomena as interference and diffraction for the case of a stream of particles. Consider an electron accelerated through 100 volts, so that its velocity is 5.94×10^8 cm/sec. The associated wavelength of such an electron would then be

$$\lambda = \frac{6.62 \times 10^{-27}}{9.1 \times 10^{-28} \times 5.94 \times 10^8} = 1.23 \times 10^{-8} \text{ cm} = 1.23 \text{ angstroms}$$

Thus, the wavelength to be associated with an electron of reasonable energy is in the X-ray range, so that diffraction of a beam of electrons by a crystal is suggested.

In 1927 Davisson and Germer reported the diffraction of a beam of electrons by a nickel crystal. The angles of maximum electron intensity yielded wavelengths in good agreement with de Broglie's relation. In 1928 G. P. Thomson reported diffraction of electron beams by metal foils and Kikuchi reported the diffraction of an electron beam by a thin sheet of mica. Rupp observed the diffraction of an electron beam by a ruled grating used at very small glancing angles, which is similar to the analogous experiment described in connection with X-rays. The diffraction of a beam of helium atoms by a lithium fluoride crystal was observed by Estermann and Stern in 1930, and more recently, beams of neutrons from a nuclear pile reactor have been shown to have a wavelength given by Eq. (303). Under conditions involving interference or diffraction there seems to be no doubt

of the correctness of the de Broglie equation, and the wavelength associated with a particle has as strong an experimental basis as the charge or
mass of the particle.

6.11. PAIR FORMATION

At energies above a million volts (wavelengths less than 0.012 angstroms),
the process of *pair formation* plays a part in the absorption of X-rays. As
mentioned briefly in Section 3.11, under suitable conditions a photon can
convert itself into a pair of particles—a positive electron and a negative
electron. This discovery was made by C. D. Anderson in 1932 and the
positive electron has been named the *positron,* the word electron being used
only for negative electrons. These new particles have been shown to have
the same charge-to-mass ratio as electrons and to interact with matter in
exactly the same way as electrons, except for having a positive charge.

Since mass is being created from energy in this process, the X-ray
photon must have at least enough energy to produce two electronic masses.
According to Einstein's mass-energy relation, Eq. (140), the energy
required to create an electron is 0.511 mev.   (See the result of Problem 5,
Chapter 3.)   Thus, pair formation cannot take place until the energy of the
X-ray photon is at least twice this value or 1.022 mev, which is confirmed
experimentally.   If the energy of the photon is greater than this threshold
energy, the excess energy is shared equally between the positron and the
electron in the form of kinetic energy.   If the kinetic energy of one of these
particles is measured, the initial energy of the photon can be computed.   At
high energies, this method is often used to measure the energy (and thus the
wavelength) of X-ray photons, since at high energies crystal diffraction is
not satisfactory.

It is interesting to note that the existence of the positron was predicted
in 1928 by Dirac's relativistic quantum theory of the electron, to which we
referred in connection with the hydrogen atom in Section 5.7.   According
to this theory, the total energy of an electron is given by

$$W = \pm \sqrt{(p^2 c^2 + m_0^2 c^4)} \tag{319}$$

Furthermore, both the positive and negative sign must be retained in
Eq. (319), so that we must admit negative energies.   Classically, we could
retain only the positive sign, and if there were initially no electrons with
negative energy, none would ever appear.   According to quantum mechanics, however, even if all the electrons were initially in states of positive
energy, there would be a finite chance of transitions to negative energy
states, so that we cannot ignore the negative sign.   (There are mathe-

matical difficulties if both signs are not retained, in addition to the reason given above.)

According to the theory, electrons with negative energy would uniformly fill all space with infinite density, and for this reason, electrons with negative energy would not be detectable. The possible energies of an electron are shown in Fig. 61. As shown in the diagram, if an electron with

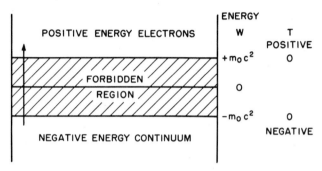

FIG. 61

Possible energies of an electron, showing a transition from
a negative to a positive energy state.

negative energy acquires at least $2m_0c^2$ (1.022 mev) of energy, it may be raised to a positive energy state, where it is now observable. When this happens, perhaps as a result of a high-energy photon striking the negative-energy electron, a vacancy or "hole" is left in the continuum of electrons with negative energy. This "hole" now appears as a positive particle. The net result is that when a photon of sufficient energy raises an electron from a state of negative energy up to a state of positive energy, two particles "appear"; the electron itself becomes observable as a negative electron, and the "hole" left by the electron appears as a positron. The success of Dirac's theory in predicting the existence of the positron is striking, even though the theory may not be entirely satisfactory in explaining the details of pair-formation quantitatively.

The lifetime of the positron is very short, being of the order of 10^{-9} second, depending on the density of matter in its vicinity. When the positron disappears, it combines with an electron. The mass of the two particles is converted into radiant energy called *annihilation radiation*, which is an effect just the reverse of the process of pair-formation. The positron is moving very slowly when this occurs, so that a total of 1.022 mev of energy is produced in this annihilation process, which is emitted either as a single photon of this energy or as two photons of energy 0.511 mev emitted in opposite directions, in order to conserve momentum. This is explained by Dirac's theory. When an electron drops into the "hole" which acts like a positron, both the electron and the apparent positron disappear simultaneously.   Since the electron suffers an energy transition of at least $2m_0c^2$ in dropping from a positive energy state to a negative energy state, this difference in energy is emitted as radiation, just as if this were an energy transition of an electron associated with an atom.

6.12. SUMMARY OF X-RAY ABSORPTION PROCESSES

Three processes of X-ray absorption have been described.   In the case of the photoelectric effect, which is predominant at low energies, the energy of the photon is given up entirely in removing an electron from an atom of the absorber. At moderate energies the Compton effect begins to be important; here, the photon is merely weakened in colliding with an electron, without being completely absorbed.   At energies above one mev, pair-production begins to take place, in which an electron and a positron are created and the photon disappears.

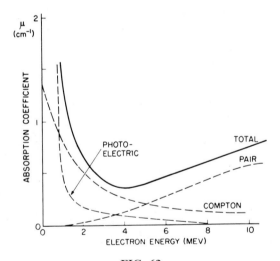

FIG. 62

Variation of X-ray absorption in lead with energy of incident photons.

The relative probability and importance of these three absorption processes depends on the energy of the photon and the atomic number of the absorbing material.   The lower the atomic number of the absorber, the lower the energy at which the Compton effect becomes important.   On the other hand, pair production is most prolific in elements of high atomic number, since this occurs most easily in the neighborhood of a strong nuclear electric field.   The contributions of these three processes to the absorption coefficient of lead are shown in Fig. 62, as calculated by Heitler.   In the case of lead, the photoelectric and Compton effects contribute equally to the absorption coefficient at about 0.5 mev, while pair-production and the Compton effect become equal at about 5 mev.   As shown in the diagram, the absorption coefficient passes through a minimum at approximately 3.5 mev.   For lighter elements this minimum occurs at higher energies. Because of the presence of the minimum in the absorption curve, the energy (and wavelength) of a photon cannot be determined from a measurement of the absorption coefficient of the photon in lead, unless it is certain that the measurement is either well below or well above the minimum of the curve.

6.13. APPLICATIONS OF X-RAYS

The uses of X-rays are well-known in medical diagnosis, and this was one of the earliest applications of X-rays.   Since bones are of greater atomic weight than tissue, the absorption of bones is greater than that of tissue, so that bones show up as light regions on a photographic negative when

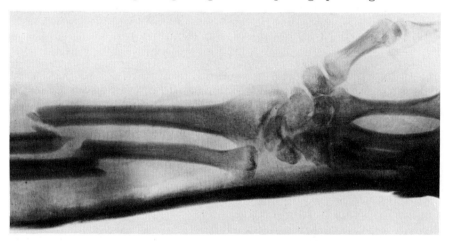

FIG. 63
Radiograph of the lower arm and wrist, showing both bones
broken in the lower arm. (Courtesy of Dr. A. E. Kabakjian.)

X-rays are passed through the body.   In order to make intestinal pictures, the patient drinks a harmless compound of bismuth or barium, either of which is a good absorber which shows up dark in a positive X-ray photograph.   To obtain contrast in other parts of the body, methyl iodide may be injected into the part under study, since it is a better absorber than tissue. A typical positive medical diagnostic radiograph is shown in Fig. 63, in which a fracture of both bones of the wrist is seen.

Irradiation of living cells may be lethal to the cells. The process seems to be that the X-rays knock high-energy photoelectrons from atoms in the cells, and these photoelectrons may eject additional electrons from atoms in nearby cells. The changes in molecular structure produced in this way may cause biological changes in the cells or may even kill them. Rapidly growing cells, such as cancerous growths appear to be, are more susceptible to destruction in this way than normal cells, so that a selective effect occurs which is the basis for radiological treatment of cancers. Thus, cancers may be destroyed without harming too many nearby healthy cells. This selective effect may be improved in various ways. For instance, a *cross-fire* of several X-ray beams may all be concentrated on the cancer, which then absorbs several times as much radiation as any of the tissue through which any individual beam has to pass.

Mueller found in 1927 that X-rays can alter or destroy the genes of fruit-flies, thus producing mutations. This has been found to be true of many organisms, and using X-radiation provides a way of producing a large number of mutations in a short time, instead of waiting for occasional spontaneous mutations to occur, perhaps as a result of cosmic radiations. This method has been widely used in experimental agriculture and horticulture. However, the majority of such mutations is undesirable; that is, the mutation may be crippling, or the organisms or its descendants may not survive. By selecting the occasional favorable mutants, plants with new and desirable characteristics may be produced. Mutations may be produced by cosmic rays in a similar manner, and this undoubtedly plays an important part in evolution.

Technological applications of X-rays are almost too numerous to consider. For instance, flaws in large castings which are inaccessible to direct observation may be discovered when the casting is X-rayed. Thickness of materials can be measured without cutting or disturbing the sample, by comparing the absorption of the X-rays in the sample with the absorption in a standard sample of known thickness. This measurement can be made continuously and automatically in a mill rolling steel plate, and the errors in thickness may be used to adjust the rollers so that the correct thickness is produced. A large number of additional applications will be found in the book by Clark listed at the end of this chapter.

Before leaving the study of applications of X-rays, some mention should be made of the health and safety aspects of using X-rays. While X-rays can be an immensely powerful tool in many fields of research, injury and even death can result from their careless use. One must be extremely careful in the neighborhood of the high voltage supply which operates the X-ray tube itself. Whereas the effects of electrical shock are almost immediately apparent, this is not usually the case with X-radiation. These physiological effects are described below.

Since the physiological damage caused by X-rays is due to the ionization produced in cells, radiation dosage expressed in terms of Roentgen units is very useful. The Roentgen unit is significant because the energy absorbed by tissue is proportional to the ionization produced in air over the range of X-ray energies from about 50 kev up to several mev. It should be remembered that the Roentgen unit measures the energy absorbed per unit mass, so that a dose of 1000 Roentgen units applied to a cancer might effect a cure, while 1000 Roentgen units applied to the whole body would almost certainly be lethal.

The effects of X-radiations on living cells depend not only on the total dose received, but also on the rate of absorption. The *reciprocity rule* applies over a limited range, that is, a dose of 0.1 Roentgen unit received during an 8-hour day has the same effect physiologically, no matter what the rate at which the dose is received. However, an extremely intense burst of X-radiation may overwhelm the tissue repair mechanism, leaving no time for tissue repair. For example, a dose of 600 Roentgen units spread out over thirty years would probably have no observable effect, while the same dose absorbed during a single day would almost certainly be fatal. After years of experience with X-rays, no case of injury has been authenticated for any technician who has been exposed to 0.1 Roentgen unit per day or less. This is taken as the safe tolerance dose for continual exposure, although occasional larger doses can probably be taken without harm.

Various non-fatal physiological effects usually warn an X-ray operator before serious damage is done. Since the number of white blood-cells decreases after a moderate overdose of X-rays, white cell counts are made as a matter of routine on technicians who are regularly exposed to X-rays, and a count should be made whenever an overdose is suspected. In addition to this effect, X-rays may cause loss of hair, temporary or permanent sterility, mutations in the offspring, almost unhealable burns, cancer, and death. Since the effects are often cumulative and do not appear immediately, all unnecessary exposure to X-rays should be avoided, and adequate shielding should be provided for all technicians regularly working with X-rays. The practice of "harmless" fluoroscoping, often used in fitting shoes, should be avoided, as the cumulative effect may eventually be harmful. X-rays are very useful and beneficial, and with adequate safety devices and proper shielding, can be used with complete safety by a competent operator.

ADDITIONAL READING

Robertson, John Kellock, *Radiology Physics*. Princeton: D. Van Nostrand Co., 1948 (2nd Ed.). An excellent elementary presentation aimed at medical students and radiological technicians.

Clark, George L., *Applied X-rays*. New York: McGraw-Hill Book Co., Inc., 1940 (3rd Ed.). A wealth of information is given about applications of X-rays, particularly to problems of the determination of structures of crystals and other materials.

Lonsdale, K., *Crystals and X-rays*. Princeton: D. Van Nostrand Co., 1949. Good treatment of crystallography, with many plates and figures.

Atomic Energy Commission, *The Effects of Atomic Weapons*. Washington: Combat Forces Press, 1950. Most modern treatment of physiological effects of radiation.

Heitler, W., *The Quantum Theory of Radiation*. London: Oxford University Press, 1944 (2nd Ed.). The standard work on emission and absorption of radiation.

Compton, Arthur Holly and Allison, Samuel King, *X-rays in Theory and Experiment*. Princeton: D. Van Nostrand Co., 1935. A standard work on the subject.

PROBLEMS

1. When the three K-lines of cobalt are reflected from the principal planes of KCl, strong reflections are found in the first order at $14°47'$, $14°53'$, and $16°30'$. Find the wavelengths of these lines, given that the grating space of KCl is 3.14 angstroms. (*Ans.* 1.605, 1.616, 1.785 angstroms)

2. The four wavelengths of the L-series of wolfram are 1.48, 1.28, 1.24, and 1.095 angstroms. Strong reflections from the principal planes of calcite in the second order are found at the angles $29°12'$, $25°0'$, $24°10'$, and $21°14'$ respectively. Find the average value of the principal grating space of calcite.

3. The wavelengths of the K-series of copper are 1.539, 1.389, and 1.378 angstroms. Explain how copper might be used to filter the L-series of wolfram (given in Problem 2) in such a way that all of the wolfram wavelengths are attentuated except the line at 1.48 angstroms.

4. 50 kilovolts is applied to an X-ray tube with a wolfram target. Compute the maximum energy and the stopping potential of the photoelectrons ejected from silver by these X-rays. The K-series of silver has the wavelengths 0.560, 0.496, and 0.486 angstroms.

5. Compute the K-excitation potential of silver.   (*Ans.* 25,500 volts)

6. The mass absorption coefficient of iron ($Z = 26$) for X-rays for wavelength 0.25 angstroms is 1.93 per gm/cm². Find the mass per square centimeter of iron which will reduce the intensity of such a beam of X-rays to 1%.

7. Referring to Problem 6, find the actual thickness of iron needed to reduce the intensity to 1% and also the half-value thickness for this wavelength.
          (*Ans.* 0.304 cm, 0.0457 cm)

8. Estimate the half-value thickness of iron for X-rays of wavelength 0.1 angstrom.

9. Estimate the mass absorption coefficient of copper ($Z = 29$) at a wavelength of 0.50 angstroms from the data given in problem 6 for iron.
          (*Ans.* 21.3 per gm/cm²)

10. If the energy, E, of the incident photon in the Compton effect is very much greater than m_0c^2, show that the maximum recoil energy of the electron is $(E - \tfrac{1}{2} m_0c^2)$.

11. Use the notation of Fig. 60 and derive the following:

$$\cot \phi = (1 + hf/m_0c^2) \tan (\theta/2)$$

Thus, simultaneous measurements of the directions of the scattered photon and the recoil electron yield a value for the energy and frequency of the incident photon.

12. Find the modified and unmodified wavelengths at angles of 30° and 60° when X-rays of wavelength 0.1 angstrom are scattered by the Compton process.

13. Compton-electrons ejected in the forward direction by X-rays are found to have a stopping potential of 50 kilovolts. Find the initial energy and wavelength of the X-ray photons.   (*Ans.* 141 kev; 0.0878 angstroms)

14. In the situation of Problem 13, what is the wavelength of the scattered photon? Verify that energy is conserved in this scattering process.

15. If an electron is accelerated through V volts, show that its associated wavelength in angstroms is given by

$$\lambda = \frac{12.2}{\sqrt{V}}$$

16. Refer to Problem 15 and consider the case in which the kinetic energy of the electron, T, is large enough so that the effects of relativity must be

considered.   Show that the wavelength of such an electron in angstroms is

$$\lambda = \frac{0.0242}{[(T/m_0c^2)^2 + 2T/m_0c^2]^{1/2}}$$

17. Prove that a third body (a nucleus) must be involved in the process of pair-formation, in order for momentum and energy to be conserved.

18. When a K-shell electron has been knocked out of an atom of atomic number Z, an L-electron will be affected by a net nuclear charge of $(Z - 1)e$, since the remaining K-electron will partially shield the nucleus.   When an L-electron jumps to the K-shell, n changes from 2 to 1.   Use the Bohr theory to compute the K_a line of each element listed in Sec. 6.6 and compare the values obtained.

19. When a thin foil is irradiated with X-rays, groups of electrons with stopping potentials of 24, 100, 110, and 115 kilovolts are observed.   Compute the wavelengths of the K-series of this element when used as the target in an X-ray tube.

chapter seven

molecular structure
and molecular spectra

In the three preceding chapters we have studied the structure and spectra of individual atoms. Optical spectra were found to provide information about the outer electrons of atoms, while X-ray spectra gave information about the inner electrons. Quantum mechanics was then shown to provide a theoretical scheme for correlating these data into a theory of atomic structure involving atomic energy levels. In this chapter we will see that similar information can be derived for combinations of several atoms into molecules.

Since the earliest information regarding the nature and structure of molecules was provided by the kinetic theory of gases, this will be considered first. The ideas of molecular structure and internal energy derived from this theory will then be found to explain molecular spectra. The quantum mechanical explanation of molecular spectra will then be discussed, and the data of molecular spectra will be correlated by means of molecular energy level diagrams.

7.1. KINETIC THEORY OF GAS PRESSURE

Since liquids and solids are almost completely incompressible, it must be difficult to make molecules approach one another closer than a certain distance. For the purposes of kinetic theory, we will consider molecules as hard, elastic spheres, which exert no forces on one another or on the walls of any container except during the instant of a collision. Actually, the forces involved during the collision of two gas molecules are probably short-range repulsive forces. Kinetic theory ascribes kinetic energy to molecules because of the temperature of the gas, so we shall assume that various gas molecules are moving with various speeds in all directions. We shall assume further that the molecules occupy no appreciable volume and that all collisions are elastic, in the sense that no kinetic energy is lost. For many gases, the effects of the volume occupied by the molecules and the long-range forces between molecules are very small.

We shall consider a sample of gas to be confined to a cube of side L. Each molecule may have a different velocity, so the velocity components parallel to axes XYZ will be assumed to be different for all molecules. We will let u,v,w be the components of velocity parallel to the axes X,Y,Z respectively, and V will be the total velocity of a given molecule. For molecule No. 1, for instance, the velocity will be given by the expression

$$V_1^2 = u_1^2 + v_1^2 + w_1^2 \tag{320}$$

For the second molecule, the velocity is given by

$$V_2^2 = u_2^2 + v_2^2 + w_2^2 \tag{321}$$

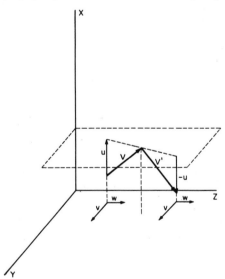

Similar expressions hold for the velocity of every other molecule in the cubical container.

We will now consider a molecule which hits a wall of the container which is perpendicular to the X-axis, as shown in Fig. 64. Assuming that the impact at the wall is elastic, the components of velocity parallel to this wall, v and w, will be unchanged by the impact, while the component perpendicular to the wall, u, will be unchanged in magnitude but reversed in direction. For molecule No. 1, the average force exerted on the wall is given by the change in momentum of the molecule divided by the time during which this change in momentum is

FIG. 64

Impact of a particle on a surface perpendicular to the X-axis.

spread. We can write then for the x-component of force on the wall produced by the impact of molecule No. 1 the value

$$F_{1x} = \frac{\Delta(mu_1)}{\Delta t_1} \tag{322}$$

Now the change in momentum is given by

$$\Delta(mu_1) = mu_1 - (-mu_1) = 2mu_1 \tag{323}$$

The average time over which this change in momentum is spread is the time necessary for the molecule to strike this face, rebound from the parallel face a distance L away, and return. This time is given by

$$\Delta t_1 = \frac{2L}{u_1}$$

Thus the average force exerted on this face by molecule No. 1 is

$$F_{1x} = \frac{2mu_1}{2L/u_1} = \frac{mu_1^2}{L} \tag{324}$$

Similarly, the force exerted on this face by molecule No. 2 is

$$F_{2x} = \frac{mu_2^2}{L} \tag{325}$$

Adding up the forces due to impacts of all the N molecules contained in the cube, we have for the total force on this face the value

$$F_x = \frac{m}{L}(u_1^2 + u_2^2 + u_3^2 \ldots + u_N^2) \tag{326}$$

The pressure acting on this face is the force per unit area, so we have

$$p_x = \frac{F_x}{A} = \frac{F_x}{L^2} = \frac{m}{L^3}(u_1^2 + u_2^2 + u_3^2 + \ldots + u_N^2) \tag{327}$$

In an exactly similar way, we find for the pressures on faces which are perpendicular to the Y and Z axes respectively the values

$$p_y = \frac{m}{L^3}(v_1^2 + v_2^2 + \ldots + v_N^2) \tag{328}$$

$$p_z = \frac{m}{L^3}(w_1^2 + w_2^2 + \ldots + w_N^2) \tag{329}$$

Since experimentally the pressure exerted by a gas on the walls of its container is the same in all directions, we can take the pressure in each direction to be the same value, p. Adding Eqs. (327)–(329), we find

$$3p = \frac{m}{L^3}(u_1^2 + v_1^2 + w_1^2 + u_2^2 + v_2^2 + w_2^2 + \ldots + u_N^2 + v_N^2 + w_N^2) \tag{330}$$

However, the quantities grouped in triplets are the expressions for the squares of the total velocities of the molecules, as given in Eqs. (320) and (321). Therefore, we can write Eq. (330) in the form

$$3p = \frac{m}{L^3}(V_1^2 + V_2^2 + \ldots + V_N^2) \tag{331}$$

Let us now define the *mean square velocity*, C^2, by the equation

$$C^2 = \frac{1}{N}(V_1^2 + V_2^2 + \ldots + V_N^2) \tag{332}$$

The quantity C defined by Eq. (332) is known as the *root-mean-square velocity*, abbreviated rms velocity. In terms of C, Eq. (331) takes the simple form

$$3p = \frac{m}{L^3} NC^2 \tag{333}$$

Finally, we notice that the volume of the gas is just L^3. If we let $V = L^3$ and solve Eq. (333) for the product pV, we find

$$pV = \tfrac{1}{3}mNC^2 \tag{334}$$

However, since m is the mass of each gas molecule and N is the total number of molecules, the product mN is just equal to the total mass of gas in the cubical container, M. We then have

$$pV = \tfrac{1}{3}MC^2 \tag{335}$$

An alternative form of Eq. (335) is obtained by replacing the ratio M/V by the density of the gas, d. We then have

$$p = \tfrac{1}{3}dC^2 \tag{336}$$

If the rms velocity, C, depends only on the temperature, then Eq. (335) is a derivation of Boyle's law, $pV =$ constant.

Let us calculate the rms velocity of air molecules at 0°C and a pressure of 76 centimeters of mercury. Solving Eq. (336) for C, we have

$$C = \sqrt{\frac{3p}{d}} \tag{337}$$

The density of air under these conditions is 0.001293 grams per cubic centimeter and the pressure corresponding to 76 centimeters of mercury is 1.013×10^6 dynes per square centimeter. Substituting these values into Eq. (337), we find for the rms velocity of air molecules the value

$$C = 4.84 \times 10^4 \text{ cm/sec} = 1586 \text{ ft/sec} = 1080 \text{ mph}$$

If we take the atomic weight of air to be 14 and the mass of an atom of unit atomic weight to be 1.66×10^{-24} gram, the kinetic energy of a diatomic air molecule under these conditions is

$$\text{K.E.} = \tfrac{1}{2}mv^2 = \tfrac{1}{2}(28 \times 1.66 \times 10^{-24})(4.84 \times 10^4)^2$$
$$= 5.45 \times 10^{-14} \text{ ergs} = 0.034 \text{ electron-volts}$$

For one mole of air weighing 28 grams, the total kinetic energy is

$$(\text{K.E.})_{\text{total}} = 5.45 \times 10^{-14} \times 6.023 \times 10^{23} = 3.28 \times 10^{10} \text{ ergs}$$
$$= 803 \text{ calories}$$

We see that considerable energy is stored in a gas by virtue of the random motions of its molecules.

Experimentally, gases which are well above their critical temperatures (and thus at temperatures even farther removed from their liquefaction points) obey the *perfect gas law* given for one mole by

$$pV = RT \tag{338}$$

An *ideal gas* is defined as a gas which obeys Eq. (338) exactly; many real gases, such as He and H_2 at room temperature, are very close to being ideal gases. Comparing Eq. (338) with Eq. (335), we have

$$pV = RT = \tfrac{1}{3}MC^2 \tag{339}$$

If one mole of the gas is considered, R is found to have the same value for all gases which are sufficiently ideal. The value of R for one mole is

$$R \text{ (per mole)} = 8.31 \text{ joule/}°\text{K} = 1.99 \text{ calories/}°\text{K}$$

Since R is almost the same for all gases, Eq. (339) shows that the average kinetic energy of random motion of various gases at a given temperature is the same for all gases.

Comparing Eq. (339) and (334) for one mole, so that N is Avogadro's number, we have

$$pV = RT = \tfrac{1}{3}mNC^2 \tag{340}$$

Solving Eq. (340) for the average energy of a gas molecule, $\tfrac{1}{2}mC^2$, we find

$$(K.E.)_{\text{av}} = \tfrac{1}{2}mC^2 = \tfrac{3}{2}\frac{R}{N}T \tag{341}$$

The constant R/N is given the letter, k, and is known as *Boltzmann's constant*, which is the gas constant per molecule, and in terms of k Eq. (341) takes the form

$$(K.E.)_{\text{av}} = \tfrac{3}{2}kT \tag{342}$$

The value of Boltzmann's constant is seen to be:

$$k = 1.38 \times 10^{-23} \text{ joule/}°\text{K} = 8.63 \times 10^{-5} \text{ ev/}°\text{K}$$

From Eq. (342) we see that the average kinetic energy of each molecule of a gas is the same for all gases at the same temperature. For gases at the same temperature, the velocities of the molecules are inversely proportional to the square roots of the molecular weights. Thus, molecules of hydrogen have four times as large an rms speed as molecules of oxygen, if both gases are at the same temperature.

7.2. THE MAXWELLIAN DISTRIBUTION OF MOLECULAR SPEEDS

So far we have disregarded the individual variations in speed which molecules are sure to have as a result of random collisions. Consider a large number of perfectly elastic spheres which are continually colliding with each other, with the velocities of the spheres changing at each collision. If the number of spheres is large enough, the number of molecules which have speeds within any given range is constant, even though the speeds of individual molecules will be continually varying as collisions occur. The problem is to find the distribution of speeds of the group of molecules when the gas is in equilibrium. This problem was solved in different ways by Maxwell and by Boltzmann, and both names are often attached to the resulting distribution law.

Two types of distributions are of interest. In the first case, we may be interested in the fraction of the molecules which have their x-components of velocity within a specified range. If there are N molecules in all, the fraction $\Delta N/N$ with x-components of velocity between u and $u + \Delta u$ is given by the expression

$$\frac{\Delta N}{N} = \sqrt{\frac{m}{2\pi kT}} \exp\left(-\frac{1}{2}\frac{mu^2}{kT}\right) \Delta u \qquad (343)$$

In Eq. (343), T is the absolute temperature of the gas and m is the mass of each molecule. Similar expressions hold for the fraction of the molecules with specified components of velocity parallel to the y and z axes.

A more useful distribution law gives the number of molecules which have speeds between V and $V + \Delta V$, without regard for direction. The result in this case is as follows:

$$\frac{\Delta N}{N} = 4\pi V^2 \left(\frac{m}{2\pi kT}\right)^{3/2} \exp\left(-\frac{1}{2}\frac{mV^2}{kT}\right) \Delta V \qquad (344)$$

The distribution curve of speeds without regard for direction is shown in Fig. 65. It should be noted that the *most probable speed*, V_{max}, which corresponds to the maximum of the distribution curve, is not the same as the root-mean-square speed, C, used in connection with the theory of

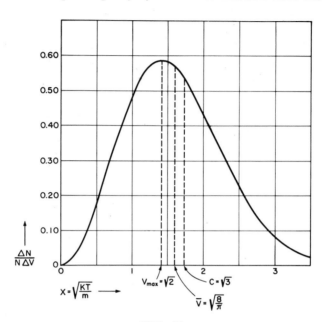

FIG. 65

Maxwellian distribution of molecular speeds, disregarding direction.

gas pressure. In addition, the *arithmetic mean speed*, $\bar{V}$, is different from both of these values. The three speeds are found to have the values

$$V_{max} = \sqrt{\frac{2kT}{m}} \tag{345}$$

$$C = \sqrt{\frac{3kT}{m}} \tag{346}$$

$$\bar{V} = \sqrt{\frac{8kT}{\pi m}} \tag{347}$$

Since our theory of gas pressure allowed each molecule to have a distinctive velocity, we know that ignoring the variation of molecular velocities will have no effect on our result. However, it should be realized that individual molecules may have energies and velocities differing widely from the rms value, which will affect other kinetic theory deductions.

7.3. DIAMETER OF MOLECULES FROM KINETIC THEORY

Since molecules have a finite size, their collisions with one another will affect the properties of the gas. In the following elementary treatment, the molecules will be considered to be perfectly elastic spheres of diameter, D, all of which are at rest except for one molecule which travels with the rms speed, C. We will now compute the average distance that a molecule travels between collisions, which is known as the *mean free path*. During one second the moving molecule will move a distance equal to its rms speed, C. Since the diameter of each molecule is D, if the centers of two molecules approach within a distance D, a collision will take place. If n is the number of molecules per unit volume, the number of molecules contained in a cylinder of radius, D, swept out by the moving molecule is $\pi D^2 C n$. Thus, the number of collisions per second is $\pi D^2 C n$, since this number of molecules is approached within the collision distance by the moving molecule during one second. The average distance between collisions is

$$L = \frac{C}{\pi D^2 C n} = \frac{1}{\pi D^2 n} \qquad (348)$$

L is the mean free path of molecules between collisions. If allowance is made for the fact that all of the molecules are in motion with various velocities given by the Maxwellian distribution laws, the result is as follows:

$$L = \frac{\sqrt{3/\pi}}{4 D^2 n} \qquad (349)$$

From Eq. (349) it can easily be shown that the effect of the actual motions of the molecules is to reduce the average distance between collisions by about 23% as compared to the simple theory.

Since Eqs. (348) and (349) each contain two unknown quantities, L and D, an additional relation is needed if we wish to determine the diameter of gas molecules from kinetic theory considerations. This is provided by the kinetic theory of gas viscosity. The viscous drag of a moving gas is explained on the basis of an interchange of momentum between slow and fast layers of the gas. This interchange of momentum tends to reduce the relative motion of parts of the gas, and therefore we have the effect of a force. A calculation based on this idea gives for the coefficient of viscosity, η, the value

$$\eta = \tfrac{1}{3} nmCL \qquad (350)$$

If the actual Maxwellian distribution of velocities is used in the calculation, Eq. (350) takes the modified form

$$\eta = 0.310 \, nmCL \qquad (351)$$

In the equations just above, n is the number of molecules per unit volume and m is the mass of each molecule. The problem is actually more complicated than we have indicated, since there will be fluctuations from the Maxwellian distribution. The effect of these fluctuations in a very rare gas is to increase the numerical factor in Eq. (350) to about 0.5.

If we use the value of the mean free path from Eq. (348) to eliminate L from Eq. (350), we find

$$\eta = \frac{mC}{3\pi D^2} \qquad (352)$$

Since the mass and diameter of a molecule are presumably constants, Eq. (352) expresses the remarkable conclusion that the coefficient of viscosity of a gas should vary with the temperature in the same way that C does and should not depend at all on the gas pressure. This prediction was first made by Maxwell in 1860 and verified by him for a wide range of pressures.

If the value of the rms speed, C, from Eq. (346) is substituted into Eq. (352), we find for the coefficient of viscosity the value

$$\eta = \frac{1}{\pi D^2} \sqrt{\frac{kmT}{3}} \qquad (353)$$

From the measurement of the viscosity of a gas at a given temperature, the diameter of the molecule can be calculated. Values of molecular radii ($\frac{1}{2}D$) as calculated in this way are of the order of one to two angstroms, which agrees with the order of magnitude of the Bohr orbits of hydrogen. Thus, kinetic theory not only explains the basis of both gas pressure and gas viscosity, but also provides an estimate of the size of molecules. However, the molecular diameter calculated in this way is really an average value of the distance of closest approach of two similar molecules, so that different values may be obtained in different phenomena.

7.4. THE SPECIFIC HEATS OF GASES

In discussing the specific heats of gases, two definitions of specific heat must be used. If the specific heat is measured while the gas is kept at constant pressure (by allowing it to expand), we obtain of the specific heat at constant pressure, c_p. Similarly, if the specific heat is measured at constant volume, we obtain of the specific heat at constant volume, c_v. Since the expansion of the gas in the case of a measurement of c_p will do some external work, some of the heat energy supplied to the gas will be used up as external work rather than as an increase of the gas temperature. For this reason, c_p is greater than c_v.

If we confine our discussion to the specific heat at constant volume, all of the heat energy supplied to the gas will be used to raise the internal energy of the gas. Now from Eq. (342), the average kinetic energy of a gas molecule is $\frac{3}{2}kT$, so that the total kinetic energy of one mole of a gas is given by

$$(\text{K.E.})_{\text{total}} = N(\tfrac{3}{2}kT) = \tfrac{3}{2}RT \tag{354}$$

If we define the *molar heat* at constant volume, C_v, as the heat required to raise one mole of the gas one degree, then we see that the molar heat of all gases should be

$$C_v = \tfrac{3}{2}R = 2.98 \text{ calories/}^\circ\text{K per mole} \tag{355}$$

As a check on Eq. (355), the specific heat of argon is .0752 calories/°K per gram, and since the molecular weight of argon is 40, we find a molar heat of $40 \times 0.0752 = 3.01$. Similarly, the specific heat of helium is 0.753 and its molecular weight is 4, so that the molar heat of helium is 3.01 also. The agreement with Eq. (355) seems excellent, and similar good agreement is found for other monatomic gases, such as neon and mercury vapor.

In the cases of gases which are not monatomic, however, Eq. (355) fails. For instance, the specific heat of hydrogen is 2.51 and its molecular weight is 2, so that the molar heat of hydrogen is 5.02 calories. Similarly, the specific heat of oxygen is 0.1555 and its molecular weight is 32, which yields a molar heat of 4.98 calories. Finally, the specific heat of carbon dioxide is 0.1525 and its molecular weight is 44, indicating a molar heat of 6.72 calories, which is over twice as great as the value predicted by Eq. (355). Evidently not all of the heat energy supplied to the gas goes to increase the translational kinetic energy of the gas molecules. Since the measurement is made at constant volume, so that none of the energy is used up as external work, we must postulate additional forms of internal energy of the gas molecules, in order to account for the extra energy absorbed by gases which are not monatomic.

So far we have not considered the structure of molecules, but have treated them as elastic spheres. A simple picture of a hydrogen molecule is two atoms of hydrogen rigidly joined together in the shape of a dumb-bell. In addition to the kinetic energy of translation of such a molecule, which we calculated in connection with the theory of gas pressure, it might also possess kinetic energy of spin or rotation. Additional coordinates (angles) would be needed to describe this type of energy.

The number of coordinates needed to describe the various motions of which a body is capable is called the body's number of *degrees of freedom*. The motion of a point can be described by three space coordinates, so that a point has three degrees of freedom. A slender rod needs three coordinates to describe the motion of its center of mass and two angles to describe its orientation, so that a rod has five degrees of freedom. An arbitrary rigid body requires three space coordinates to describe the motion of its center of mass and three angles to describe its orientation, so that six degrees of freedom are possessed in general by a rigid body.

In the theory of gas pressure developed earlier, it was shown that the average kinetic energy of translation of a molecule is $\frac{3}{2}kT$. Since a point is described by three degrees of freedom, symmetry requires each degree of freedom of the molecule to be assigned one-third of this energy or $\frac{1}{2}kT$, since all three directions are equally probable. This can be generalized in the form of the *principle of equipartition of energy*, which states that an energy $\frac{1}{2}kT$ is associated with each degree of freedom of a molecule, regardless of the type of energy. This principle is proved by the methods of statistical mechanics which may be found in more advanced treatises on the subject. Since the energy per molecule per degree of freedom is $\frac{1}{2}kT$, the energy per mole per degree of freedom should be $\frac{1}{2}RT$.

We can now see why Eq. (355) was successful only in the case of monatomic gases. These simple gases can only possess energy of translation and have only three degrees of freedom. Their molar heat should be $3(\frac{1}{2}R) = 2.98$ calories. (As R has a value almost equal to 2 calories per mole, the molar heat per degree of freedom is almost exactly one calorie.) In the case of diatomic gases, such as oxygen and hydrogen, two more degrees of freedom are needed to describe the orientation of the molecule, which is treated as a rod or dumb-bell. Diatomic molecules therefore have five degrees of freedom and should have molar heats of $5(\frac{1}{2}R) = 4.97$ calories, which is very close to the observed values for many of these gases. Similarly, a triatomic gas like carbon dioxide requires three degrees of freedom to describe its orientation, giving a total of six degrees of freedom. The molar heat of such a gas should therefore be about 6 calories, which is in fair agreement with the experimental values.

All the values of specific heats given above were measured at 15°C. If the temperature of hydrogen is raised to 2000°C, its molar heat rises to 6.20 calories, and at the same temperature the molar heat of oxygen is 6.57 calories. Since a diatomic molecule can have a molar heat of only approximately 5 calories through its energies of translation and rotation, we must hypothesize another form of internal energy which becomes important only at higher temperatures. Obviously, another possible form of energy is a vibration of the two atoms along the line joining them. Since on the average the energy of a vibrating system is half kinetic and half potential energy, two degrees of freedom must be assigned to describe the vibrational energy. A diatomic molecule would then have 7 degrees of freedom and its molar heat should be about 7 calories, which explains the specific heats of hydrogen and oxygen at high temperatures.

Quantum mechanics provides an explanation of the variation of molar heats with temperature. For hydrogen the molar heat is about 3 calories at temperatures up to about 60°K, indicating that only the translatory energy is increased by addition of heat to the gas. The problem of a rotating and vibrating molecule can be solved quantum mechanically. Rotational energy states are characterized by a quantum number, J, and the rotational energy is proportional to $J(J+1)$. Furthermore, J can change only by one unit. At very low temperatures collisions between molecules do not involve enough energy to effect transitions between allowed rotational energy states, so that the rotational energy states play no part in the absorption of energy supplied to the gas. Thus, at sufficiently low temperatures only the translational energy will be increased when the gas is heated, so a molar heat of 3 calories is expected, in agreement with observation.

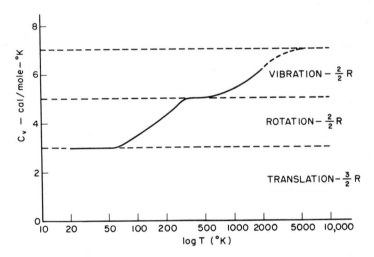

FIG. 66

Variation of the molar heat of hydrogen with temperature.

As the temperature of hydrogen is raised above 60°K, its molar heat increases, reaching a value of 5 calories at about 0°C. Within this temperature range, only a fraction of the collisions between molecules involve enough energy to excite a molecule to a higher rotational energy state, so that not all molecules absorb energy in the form of rotation. From 0°C to about 200°C the molar heat remains constant at 5 calories, but above this temperature it begins to rise again. Clearly, higher vibrational states are being excited. The quantum mechanical solution of the problem of the vibrating diatomic molecule is characterized by a quantum number, v, which may change by only one unit, and the energy is proportional to

$(v + \frac{1}{2})$.   In the range of temperatures above 200°C only a fraction of the molecular collisions involve enough energy to raise a molecule to an excited vibrational energy state, so not all of the molecules are effective in absorbing heat energy in the form of vibrations.   If experiments could be conducted at sufficiently high temperatures, it appears likely that the vibrational energy would make its full contribution to the molar heat, which would then become 7 calories.   The various features of the variation of molar heat of hydrogen are shown in Fig. 66.   In Section 7.6 we will see how the ideas of rotational and vibrational energy states of molecules are confirmed by the spectra emitted and absorbed by molecules.

7.5. SPECIFIC HEATS OF SOLIDS

As was discussed in the preceding section, two degrees of freedom must be assigned to a linear oscillator.   Let us now consider a solid consisting of N atoms each vibrating in three dimensions.   According to the principle of equipartition of energy, the total internal energy of such a solid would be

$$U = 3N(kT)$$

If we consider one mole of the substance, so that N is Avogadro's number, then the internal energy is simply $U = 3RT$.   If heat is added to substance at constant volume, no work is done and all of the heat goes to increase the internal energy of the solid.   If we use the letter Q to represent heat, then the specific heat is

$$C_v = \left(\frac{\partial Q}{\partial T}\right)_v = \left(\frac{\partial U}{\partial T}\right)_v \tag{357}$$

Therefore the molar specific heat of a solid should be $3R$ or very nearly 6 calories per degree per mole.   This value is known as the Dulong and Petit value and is valid for many solids at temperatures in the vicinity of room temperature.   However, at low temperatures the observed values of specific heats are less than the Dulong and Petit value, approaching zero near absolute zero.

  In 1907 Einstein developed a greatly improved theory of the specific heats of solids.   He considered N oscillators in a solid, all vibrating with a characteristic frequency, f.   The energies of the oscillators are then quantized according to the rule introduced by Planck in the theory of black body radiation discussed in Section 2.7.   Therefore, the energy of an oscillator can be only one of the values $0, hf, 2hf, \ldots, nhf, \ldots$, where n is an integer.   In Eq. (42), the average energy of such an oscillator is

$$\bar{E} = \frac{hf}{e^{hf/kT} - 1} \tag{358}$$

Therefore, if the solid consists of N atoms, each vibrating in 3 dimensions, the total vibrational energy of the solid will be

$$U = 3N\bar{E} = \frac{3Nhf}{e^{hf/kT} - 1} \tag{359}$$

When we compute the specific heat at constant volume by differentiating Eq. (359), we find that

$$C_v = \left(\frac{\partial U}{\partial T}\right)_v = \frac{3kN(hf/kT)^2 e^{hf/kT}}{(e^{hf/kT} - 1)^2} \tag{360}$$

Since $kN = R$, at high temperatures the specific heat takes the value

$$C_v = 3R(hf/kT)^2 \left[\frac{1 + hf/kT \ldots}{(1 + hf/kT' \ldots - 1)^2}\right] = 3R \tag{361}$$

Thus we find that in the high-temperature limit the Einstein theory gives the Dulong and Petit value for the specific heat at constant volume of a solid. At low temperatures the exponential factor is much greater than unity and Eq. (360) reduces to

$$C_v = 3R(hf/kT)^2 e^{-hf/kT} \tag{362}$$

The exponential factor is dominant in Eq. (362), so the Einstein theory predicts that C_v should vary as $e^{-hf/kT}$ at low temperatures. However, it is found experimentally that C_v for non-metallic crystals varies as T^3 at low temperatures, while C_v varies as T for metals. Nevertheless the Einstein theory is highly successful in accounting for the variation of C_v with temperature over a wide range of temperatures. In 1912 Debye improved the Einstein theory by letting the N atoms have $3N$ frequencies of vibration. The Debye theory predicts that C_v should vary as T^3 at very low temperatures and fits the data better at low temperatures than the Einstein theory.

7.6. MOLECULAR SPECTRA

Many of the spectral lines observed from a discharge tube filled with a polyatomic gas are emitted by undissociated molecules or by molecular ions. A characteristic feature of molecular spectra, when examined with an instrument of low dispersion, is the presence of broad wavelength regions or *bands*. The band spectrum of a discharge tube filled with air is shown in Fig. 67. As the figure shows, bands usually have a sharp edge, called the *band head*, and gradually shade off into the violet or red. If

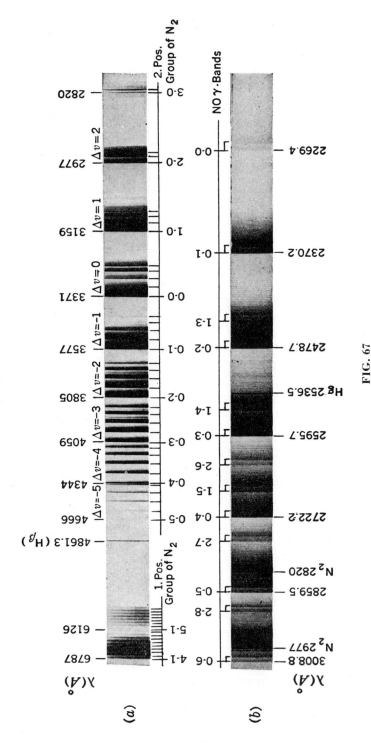

FIG. 67

Band spectra of air. (From *Molecular Spectra and Molecular Structure*, vol. 1, by Herzberg: Prentice-Hall, 1939.)

higher resolution is used, it is found that many bands are composed of many spectral lines crowded closely together. These lines are very regularly arranged, with approximately constant spacing, in contrast to the rapid convergence of a series such as that of atomic hydrogen shown in Fig. 29. We will discuss the spectra of diatomic molecules, such as HCl and CN, but more complicated molecules follow a similar pattern.

As described in connection with the molar heats of diatomic gases, a diatomic molecule can possess energy of rotation and energy of vibration. These two types of energy are in addition to the energy of the electronic configuration of the molecule. We will use the approximation that each of these forms of energy can be considered separately, so that the energy of the molecule is the sum of the three types of energy. A change in one or more of these forms of energy will result in the emission of a quantum of radiation.

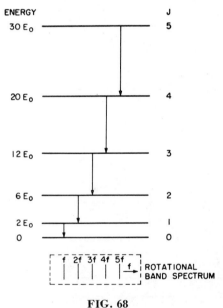

FIG. 68

Energy levels and allowed transitions of a rotating diatomic molecule.

The possible values of the rotational energy of a diatomic molecule with moment of inertia, I, are quantum mechanically found to be

$$E_r = \frac{h^2}{8\pi^2 I} \left[J(J+1) \right] \quad (363)$$

In Eq. (363), J takes the integral values $0,1,2,\ldots$, and allowed transitions take place only when $\Delta J = \pm 1$. Typical energy levels and allowed transitions of a rigid rotator are shown in Fig. 68. It is easily seen that the *rotational spectrum* consists of a series of lines equally spaced in frequency or wave-number, with frequencies which are integral multiples of the lowest frequency in the band. Usually the energy involved in rotational transitions is very small, so that rotational bands are found in the far infra-red or even in the radar region (wavelengths of a few millimeters).

A typical example of a *rotational band* is furnished by HCl, which has a band ranging from 83 to 277 waves per centimeter, with a spacing of 20.68 per centimeter. According to Eq. (363) for allowed transitions which involve a change of one unit in J, the spacing between lines of a rotational band should be $2h/8\pi^2 cI$ waves per centimeter, since $\Delta \bar{f} = \Delta E/hc$. From the observed value of the spacing, the **moment** of inertia of the

HCl molecule can be calculated, and from this the distance between the atoms is found to be about 1.3×10^{-8} centimeter. Since this agrees in order of magnitude with the values of molecular diameters calculated from viscosity measurements, as described above, we can feel quite certain that this band of HCl is produced by changes in the rotational energy of the molecule.

The vibration of two atoms along the line joining them can be considered approximately the same as a linear simple harmonic oscillator obeying Hooke's law, although more complicated force functions agree better with the details of band spectra. The state of a linear oscillator is characterized by a quantum number, v, and the corresponding energy of the state is given by

$$ E_v = \frac{h}{2\pi} \sqrt{\frac{k}{\mu}} \left(v + \frac{1}{2} \right) \tag{364} $$

In Eq. (364), k is the Hookes' law force constant, that is, the ratio of the applied force to the resulting displacement of the particles, and μ is the reduced mass of the two particles forming the molecule. Allowed transitions with the radiation of energy occur for $\Delta v = \pm 1$. The energy levels and allowed transitions of such a simple oscillator are shown in Fig. 69, where it is seen that all transitions give rise to the same frequency, regardless of the quantum numbers of the initial and final states.

An example of such a *vibration band* is the single intense band of HCl with a wave-number of 2886 per centimeter. The energy involved in vibrational transitions of the HCl molecule is much greater than the energy involved in rotational transitions of the same molecule, which are discussed above. From the observed wave-number, the force constant of HCl can be computed, with results which agree in order of magnitude with the known strength of chemical bonding of this molecule. Therefore, this band of HCl is almost certainly a vibrational band, and the quantum mechanical theory is confirmed.

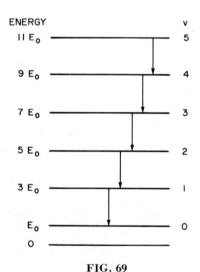

FIG. 69

Energy levels and allowed transitions of a vibrating diatomic molecule.

If vibration and rotation take place simultaneously, the interactions between the motions make the energy levels and corresponding bands more complicated. For each vibrational state the rotational levels will be dif-

ferently spaced, since the moment of inertia of the molecule will be different.
Fig. 70 shows an energy level diagram of such a vibrating rotator, although
the spacing between the two vibrational levels is actually much greater
than the spacing between various rotational levels.   Allowed transitions
are shown for $\Delta v = 1$ for all possible values of $\Delta J = \pm 1$.   The resulting

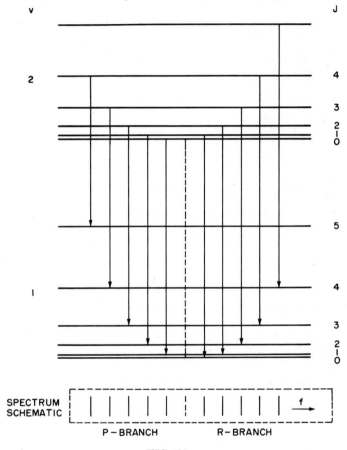

FIG. 70
Energy-level diagram and allowed transitions leading to a
vibration-rotation band spectrum.

vibration-rotation spectrum is shown below the energy level diagram schematically, with the R-branch corresponding to $\Delta J = +1$ and the P-branch
corresponding to $\Delta J = -1$.   Spectra of this sort are commonly found
in the near infra-red.

    The band spectra observed in the visible and the ultra-violet, however,
cannot be explained in terms of vibrational or rotational energy changes,
since the energies involved are too large for these mechanisms.   In addi-

tion, as may be seen in Fig. 67, the spectra are too complicated for such a simple explanation. In order to have large enough energy transitions, the electrons associated with the molecule must also engage in changes of energy states.

For each molecular electronic state, there may also be rotational and vibrational energies. The total energy of the molecule can be approximated by the sum of the three types, rotational, vibrational, and electronic. For each electronic state, of course, the spacings of the vibrational and rotational energy levels may be different, since the molecular configuration will be different. The various energy states of a diatomic molecule are

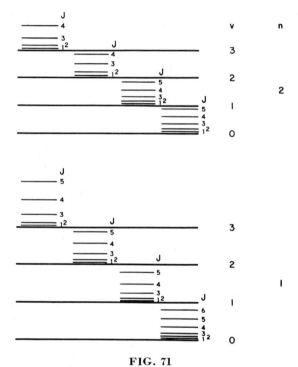

FIG. 71

Typical energy-level diagram for a diatomic molecule. (Vibrational and rotational level spacings greatly enlarged for clarity.)

shown schematically in Fig. 71, although the spacing between the two electronic states is actually much greater than the spacing between vibrational states, and similarly the spacing between rotational levels is much less than shown.

The selection rules for transitions between two electronic states do not limit Δv to the values ± 1, and in principle each vibrational state of the higher electronic state can combine with each vibrational state of the lower electronic state. A *band system* consisting of many bands is produced by all the various transitions which can take place between two different electronic states of a molecule. The energies of transition between two vibrational states give the band heads, while the fine structure of the bands is produced by rotational transitions. For the details of complicated band spectra, the reader is referred to treatises on the subject.

We will conclude this discussion of molecular spectra with a consideration of the inversion spectrum of ammonia, NH_3. The three hydrogen atoms form an equilateral triangle and the nitrogen atom lies on a line perpendicular to the center of this triangle. The ammonia molecule is shown schematically in Fig. 72. We will call the line on which the nitrogen atom is situated the X-axis.

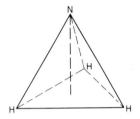

FIG. 72

Arrangement of the atoms forming the ammonia molecule.

The nitrogen atom vibrates along the X-axis, and classically, would always stay on one side or the other of the plane of the hydrogen atoms, since it cannot surmount the potential barrier shown in Fig. 73. If we refer to the tunnel effect treated in Section 5.7, we see that according to quantum mechanics there should be a finite probability that the nitrogen atom will penetrate the barrier and find itself on the other side of the plane of hydrogen atoms. This process is called *inversion*. The effect of inversion on the vibrational energy levels is to split each level into a doublet, as shown in Fig. 73. As an example, let the nitrogen atom vibrate with a frequency, f_1, upon which is superimposed a smaller frequency, f_2,

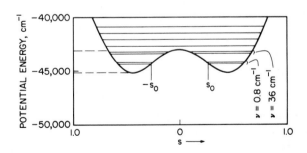

FIG. 73

Diagram of the lowest vibrational energy levels of the ammonia molecule showing the doubling of the levels caused by inversion. (From *Microwave Spectroscopy*, by Townes and Schawlow: McGraw-Hill, 1955.)

of inversion. Classically when frequencies f_1 and f_2 are mixed, the result is frequencies $(f_1 + f_2)$ and $(f_1 - f_2)$. This gives a qualitative explanation of the splitting of each vibrational level into two by inversion, but clearly the correct explanation involves the application of quantum mechanics to the situation.

The ammonia molecule may also rotate, although the rotational energies are much smaller than the vibrational energies. The effect of rotation is to shift the vibrational energies slightly. When the rotational energy states are found by the use of quantum mechanics, it is found that two integers, J and K, are needed to quantize the angular momentum. The total angular momentum of the molecule is given by

$$(h/2\pi) \sqrt{J(J + 1)}$$

and the component of angular momentum parallel to the X-axis is $Kh/2\pi$, where the absolute value of K must be equal to or less than the value of J.

The inversion spectrum is produced by transitions between the two closely spaced levels of the lowest vibrational energy state. For any transition, J and K remain constant, although the particular values of J and K affect the energy changes slightly, so that approximately 100 different frequencies have been observed in the inversion spectrum of ammonia. The customary designation of a particular frequency is to write the J and K values for that frequency in the order J, K. As an example, the $(3, 3)$ line means the frequency produced with $J = 3$ and $K = 3$, which happens to be a frequency of approximately 25 kilomegacycles. Other frequencies have been measured in the range 16–40 kilomegacycles.

In principle, any unsymmetrical molecule with more than three atoms could invert, but ammonia is the only known molecule with a potential barrier sufficiently low for inversion to be at all probable. For instance, it has been predicted that AsH_3 would invert about once in two years, which would obviously be completely unobservable.

7.7. MASERS

Consider a substance which has E_1 and E_2 as its lowest energy states. If we refer to Eq. (33), the probability that a system will be an energy state of value E is proportional to $e^{-E/kT}$. Thus, if we let n_1 and n_2 be the numbers of molecules with energies E_1 and E_2, these numbers will be related in the following way:

$$\frac{n_2}{n_1} = \frac{e^{-E_2/kT}}{e^{-E_1/kT}} = e^{-(E_2-E_1)/kT} \tag{365}$$

According to the Einstein frequency condition of Eq. (171), such a molecule will absorb or emit a frequency, f, given by

$$hf = E_2 - E_1 \tag{366}$$

Thus, we can write Eq. (365) in the form

$$\frac{n_2}{n_1} = e^{-hf/kT} \tag{367}$$

Thus, when the molecules of the substance are in thermal equilibrium,
there will be more molecules in the lower energy state than in the upper
energy state.

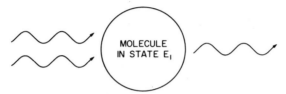

FIG. 74

Absorption of a photon raises molecule's energy from a
lower state to an upper state.

Now let electromagnetic waves of frequency f be passed through this
substance. A molecule in the lower energy state will absorb one of the
incident photons, as is shown in Fig. 74. On the other hand, a molecule in
the upper state will be stimulated to emit a photon, as shown in Fig. 75.
It is important to note that the photon emitted in this way is in phase
with the incident photon. Since at equilibrium there are more molecules

FIG. 75

Emission of a photon by stimulated emission with the
molecule's energy dropping from the upper state to the
lower state.

in the lower state than in the upper state, the net effect on a beam of
electromagnetic waves passing through such a substance is absorption.

In order for stimulated emission to be the dominant process, n_2 must
be made larger than n_1. This was first achieved in 1954 by Townes,

Gordon, and Zeiger, using the apparatus shown schematically in Fig. 76. Ammonia molecules at room temperature emerge from the tank and are collimated into parallel beams by many channels each 0.002×0.006 inches in cross-section. The remainder of the apparatus is kept at a pressure of about 10^{-5} mm. of mercury, so as not to interfere with the beam of

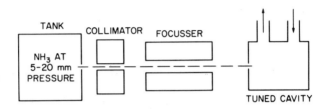

FIG. 76
Diagram of an ammonia maser.

ammonia molecules. The focuser consists of parallel rods as shown looking towards the ammonia tank in Fig. 77. This arrangement produces an electric field which is zero along the axis of the focuser and increases radially from the axis. The effect of the electric field is to change the

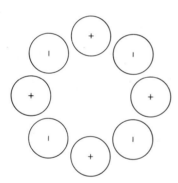

FIG. 77

End-on view of the focuser which brings molecules in the upper state into the tuned cavity and deflects molecules in the lower state away from the tuned cavity.

values of the energy levels somewhat. In the case of ammonia, the energy of the state E_1 is lowered by the electric field, while the energy of the state E_2 is raised. Since the most stable state of any system is its state of lowest energy, the molecules which are in the state E_2 move toward the axis, where the electric field is lowest. Similarly, the molecules which are in the state E_1 move away from the axis, where the electric field is greatest. Thus, most of the ammonia molecules in the state E_1 do not enter the cavity, while the molecules in the state E_2 are brought to a focus along the axis and enter the cavity. In practice, as many as 95% of the molecules which enter the cavity are in the state E_2. Thus, the dominant process inside the cavity will be stimulated emission of radiation, since most of the molecules are ready to emit radiation, rather than to absorb radiation.

Suppose that a small amount of radiation of the proper frequency enters the cavity. These photons stimulate the molecules in the state E_2 to emit photons of the frequency given by Eq. (366). If the cavity is tuned to resonate at this frequency, the photons will stimulate numerous molecules, and it will be possible to take more radiant energy out of the cavity than is put into it. This makes the device an amplifier. Since there are no free charges in the cavity, there is no shot noise, and noise due to the circuit can be reduced by cooling; thus such an amplifier has a very low amount of noise compared to other amplifiers. Since the ammonia molecule operates at microwave frequencies, this device has been named the *maser*, which is an acronym for the term *M*icrowave *A*mplification by the *S*timulated *E*mission of *R*adiation. However, it is customary to use the same term to describe devices using the same principle, even when the frequencies involved are not in the microwave region.

If the number of molecules per unit volume in the cavity is made large enough, the device described above may operate as an oscillator. In this case, a small amount of black-body radiation from the walls will stimulate the emission of some photons, and this oscillation will be sustained if the emission can compensate for losses in the walls of the cavity. Since the energy levels of the ammonia molecule are very sharp, the resonant frequency of an ammonia maser has been maintained to one part in 10^{12}. Such an oscillator can be used to make a very precise clock or to compare times very accurately, as is described in Section 3.4 in connection with attempts to measure the speed of the earth through the ether.

For many purposes, however, the ammonia maser has important drawbacks. It can be tuned over a range of approximately one kilocycle, which is comparatively limited at a frequency of 25 kilomegacycles. Thus it has a very narrow band-width. In addition, the density of ammonia molecules is necessarily low at a pressure of 10^{-5} mm. of mercury; thus the power output of an ammonia maser is very low. In many applications the extreme sharpness of tuning is an advantage, and the low power output can be overcome by amplification at a further stage in the system, but the three-level maser described below is more adaptable, because it eliminates these difficulties.

When atoms with unpaired electron spins (for example, iron, chromium, and gadolinium) are placed in a magnetic field, the magnetic energy of the unpaired electrons depends on their orientation relative to the magnetic field. For a single unpaired electron there are two energy states, corresponding to whether the spin of the electron is parallel or anti-parallel to the magnetic field. (The reader is referred to Sec. 5.11 for the one-electron case.) More generally, if an atom has n unpaired electrons, there will be $(n + 1)$ energy states due to a magnetic field. Furthermore, the difference in energy between the various states depends on the strength of the magnetic field. Thus, in a maser using such a material, the separations between energy levels, and thus the frequencies emitted or absorbed, can be varied smoothly by varying the applied magnetic field. This allows such a maser to be tuned over a considerable range of frequencies, thus eliminating one of the difficulties encountered in the ammonia maser. Furthermore, in a solid, nearby atoms produce magnetic fields which act on the unpaired electrons of a given atom. Since this internal magnetic field varies from point to point within the solid, various unpaired electrons experience varied total magnetic fields. As a result, the energy states of the unpaired electrons in a solid vary somewhat from atom to atom. The effect of this fluctuation of total magnetic fields is to make such a solid resonant to a wider range of frequencies than the ammonia maser, so that the solid-state maser has a wide band-width.

At room temperature of about 300°K, thermal agitation would mask the magnetic effects in typical crystals. For this reason, solid-state masers are cooled to about 4°K by the use of liquid helium. In some applications, the necessity for such extremely low temperatures is a real disadvantage.

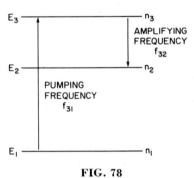

FIG. 78

Lowest three-energy states of a three-level, solid-state maser.

Now consider a magnetic substance; let its three lowest energy levels be E_1, E_2, and E_3 respectively. A schematic energy-level diagram for such a material is shown in Fig. 78, where the energy of each of the three levels is shown as a function of the applied magnetic field. In the case of thermal equilibrium, the number of atoms in the lowest state, n_1, will be greater than the number in the second state, n_2, which in turn will be greater than the number in the third state, n_3. Such a solid will absorb frequencies that correspond to the correct energy differences.

Suppose that a strong electromagnetic wave is now applied to the solid at the frequency f_{31}. Then

$$f_{31} = \frac{E_3 - E_1}{h} \tag{368}$$

The absorption of photons of this frequency reduces n_1, and makes n_3 greater than n_2. If now radiation of frequency f_{32} strikes the crystal, stimulated emission at the frequency f_{32} may occur, where

$$f_{32} = \frac{E_3 - E_2}{h} \tag{369}$$

Such a device was first suggested by Bloembergen in 1956, and was first operated by Scovil, Feher, and Seidel in 1957; gadolinium ethyl sulfate was used. Masers have been operated using ruby (aluminum oxide doped with chromium) and various other crystals. Because the concentration of atoms in a crystal is large, solid-state masers of this type produce more power than gaseous masers of the ammonia type. As an amplifier, the solid-state maser thus possesses none of the difficulties presented by the ammonia maser. However, the use of the solid-state maser necessitates the use of liquid helium, in order to cool the crystal to about 4°K. Certainly, both types of masers will continue to be used.

The extension of the maser principle to the optical region was suggested by Schawlow and Townes in 1958, and first demonstrated by Maiman in 1960. A fluorescent solid, ruby, is used in the form of a cylindrical rod with the ends coated with a highly reflecting surface of silver. Excitation is obtained by illuminating the ruby with a flash lamp, the general pumping action being analogous to that in the three-level maser described above. The output of the ruby maser is a highly collimated beam of light of wavelength 6943 angstroms with a band-width considerably narrower than that of the fluorescent line.

ADDITIONAL READING

Loeb, Leonard B., *Kinetic Theory of Gases.* New York: McGraw-Hill Book Co., Inc., 1927. An excellent text and reference book covering this field.

Lindsay, Robert Bruce, *Introduction to Physical Statistics.* New York: John Wiley and Sons, 1941. An excellent introductory treatment of classical and quantum mechanical statistics, prefaced by reviews of thermodynamics and kinetic theory.

Herzberg, Gerhard, *Molecular Spectra and Molecular Structure.* Englewood Cliffs, N. J.: Prentice-Hall, Inc., 1939. A comprehensive treatise on the structure and spectra of diatomic molecules.

Townes, C. H. and Schawlow, A. L., *Microwave Spectroscopy.* New York: McGraw-Hill Book Co., Inc., 1955. An excellent treatise on the measurement and interpretation of molecular spectra at microwave frequencies.

PROBLEMS

1. The density of hydrogen gas at 0°C and a pressure of 760 millimeters of mercury is 0.08988 grams per liter. Compute the rms speed of hydrogen molecules from Eq. (337) under these conditions.

    (*Ans.* 1.84×10^5 cm/sec)

2. Compute the rms speed of hydrogen molecules from Eq. (346), and compare with your answer to Problem 1. Does hydrogen have the properties of an ideal gas?

3. Compute the velocity of a proton which is in thermal equilibrium at a temperature of 27°C. (*Ans.* 2.71×10^5 cm/sec)

4. Compute the fraction of gas molecules which have velocity components in a particular direction greater than $\sqrt{(2kT/m)}$. (Hint: Integrals of the error-function, exp $(-x^2/2)$ are given in most handbooks of mathematical tables.)

5. Derive Eq. (345) by finding the value of V which maximizes Eq. (344).

6. Use the approximate formula, Eq. (348), to find the mean free path of hydrogen molecules at 0°C and a pressure of 760 millimeters of mercury, assuming the radius of a hydrogen molecule to be one angstrom.

7. Repeat Problem 6 for hydrogen gas at a pressure of one micron of mercury ($\frac{1}{1000}$ of a millimeter of mercury). (*Ans.* 22.5 cm)

8. Given that the viscosity of hydrogen gas is 83.5 micropoises at 0°C, compute the diameter of the hydrogen molecule.

9. Estimate the specific heat at constant volume of neon, which has atomic weight 20.2. (*Ans.* 0.149 cal/gm/°C)

10. Prove that pure rotational spectra should consist of lines equally spaced in frequency, and that all the lines are integral multiples of the lowest frequency, which equals the spacing.

11. Compute the deBroglie wavelength of an electron which is in thermal equilibrium at a temperature of 27°C. (*Ans.* 62.2 angstroms)

12. Repeat Problem 11 for a proton in thermal equilibrium at 27°C.

13. Derive Eq. (346) and (347) from Eq. (344).

14. Consider ammonia gas at room temperature and let the frequency emitted by this molecule between its two lowest energy states be 25 kilo-megacycles. Show that out of every 1000 ammonia molecules there is an excess of about two molecules in the lowest state.

15. Let us *define* the absolute temperature for non-equilibrium distributions by Eq. (367). If 95% of the ammonia molecules are in the upper state, compute the absolute temperature of the gas. (*Ans.* −0.41°K)

part three

nuclei and nuclear particles

chapter eight

natural radioactivity

In this and the following chapters we shall not study the atomic and molecular properties which are produced by the extra-nuclear electrons of atoms, but rather, discuss the nucleus itself and the radiations which are emitted by nuclei. In this chapter we shall be concerned with nuclei which disintegrate spontaneously, and in later chapters we shall study nuclear bombardment by high-speed particles. In the last chapter we shall discuss the effects of radiations which come from beyond our solar system: cosmic rays.

8.1. THE DISCOVERY OF RADIOACTIVITY

The discovery of radioactivity by Becquerel in 1896 provides another example of an important experimental discovery being made in an unexpected direction, similar to the discovery of X-rays by Roentgen while studying the conduction of electricity by gases. In the course of some research into the phosphorescence produced by the action of sunlight on certain salts, Becquerel found that uranium salts would affect photographic plates wrapped in paper. What was even more amazing was the fact that uranium salts would affect photographic plates, even after the uranium had been kept in darkness for several months. Since the strength of this *radioactivity* did not decrease with time, as phosphorescence does, he concluded that radioactivity must be a property of uranium itself. However, in 1898 Marie and Pierre Curie showed that a number of other elements possessed this same property, some being much more active than uranium. An outstanding new property of materials had been discovered, which has had an increasingly important effect on science and technology throughout the twentieth century.

213

A number of simple experiments uncovered many of the properties of radioactivity, although some of the early work was interpreted incorrectly. In addition to affecting photographic emulsions, these radiations were found to ionize gases, cause fluorescence, and make certain crystals electrically more conductive. All these properties of the radiations from radioactive materials are used in various devices for the detection of radioactivity, as will be described in the following section. The intensity of the radioactivity of an element is found to be unaffected by its state of chemical combination, its temperature, or the strength of an applied electromagnetic field. Since all these external influences on atoms affect the external electrons, we suspect that radioactivity must be a property of the nucleus itself or possibly of the inner electrons of the atom, which are well shielded from external influences. In addition, radioactive elements continually liberate energy in the form of energetic particles and electromagnetic waves; if the radiations from radium are absorbed in a calorimeter, it is found that radium emits about 130 calories per hour per gram and this rate of energy emission remains constant. Finally, the radiations from radioactive substances can injure or kill living cells, which is the basis for the therapeutic use of radium and its derivatives. We will discuss these various properties of radioactivity later in this chapter.

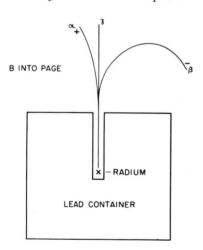

FIG. 79

Resolution of a collimated beam of nuclear radiations into three parts by a strong magnetic field.

A simple experiment shows that the radiations from radioactive elements are fairly complex in character. Let the radiations from a sample of radium be collimated by placing the radium at the bottom of a hole drilled in a block of lead, as shown in Fig. 79. When a magnetic field is applied perpendicular to the beam, it is found that the beam is broken up into three parts, which have been labelled alpha, beta, and gamma respectively. From the directions of the deflections *alpha-rays* are found to be positively charged and *beta-rays* are found to be negatively charged. The *gamma-rays* are not deflected at all even in very large magnetic fields, so they must be either neutral particles or electromagnetic waves. In addition to the deflections produced on each type of radiation by a magnetic field, they are further distinguished from one another by their penetrating powers in various materials. Alpha-rays are completely stopped by 5–10 centimeters of air and gamma-rays will penetrate 1–5 centimeters of lead.   The beta-rays are intermediate, being stopped by a 2–10 meters of air.   Finally the ionization per centimeter in air is greatest for alpha-rays, intermediate for beta-rays, and least for gamma-rays.   The properties of each of these radiations will be discussed more in detail below after a consideration of various devices for detecting radiations and measuring their properties.

8.2. DETECTION OF NUCLEAR RADIATIONS

In this section we shall discuss briefly most of the devices which are used to detect nuclear radiations and to determine their characteristics.   Since some of these devices have been developed fairly recently, the historical order of presentation in this chapter will be interrupted temporarily. However, it is more practical to present material on detection devices all in one place, even though this may be at the expense of continuity in the study of radioactivity.

An early method for detecting the presence and locations of alpha-particles uses the *scintillations* produced when alpha-particles strike a suitable fluorescent material, such as zinc sulphide or calcium wolframate. Each particle produces a flash of light where it hits the fluorescent screen, and the flashes are observed with a low-power microscope in darkness. Since this method is quite slow and laborious, it is seldom used today in its original form.   However, many important experiments, such as the scattering of alpha-particles by nuclei, described in Sec. 4.2, and first nuclear transmutation, described in Sec. 9.1, were conducted using this method. At present the scintillations are detected by a photo-multiplier tube, as described in the following paragraphs, and recorded automatically.

The *electron multiplier* or *photomultiplier tube* is a vacuum tube which uses the phenomenon of *secondary emission* to produce amplification. Whenever a metallic surface is bombarded by electrons, one or more secondary electrons may be knocked out of the surface.   This secondary emission of electrons is undesirable in the tetrode tube and is overcome in the pentode by the addition of a suppressor grid, but in the photomultiplier it is used to advantage.   In the RCA 7746 photomultiplier tube, shown schematically in Fig. 80, photoelectrons are emitted when light strikes the photocathode.   These electrons are attracted to the first *dynode*, and produce a number of secondary electrons when they strike the first dynode. These secondary electrons strike the second dynode, producing more electrons by secondary emission, and so forth.   This process of amplification is repeated nine times, and the final stream of electrons is collected by the anode.

The amplification of a photomultiplier tube is of the order of a million when the tube is operated at a voltage of 100 volts per stage.   The output pulse is very narrow, having a width of about 6×10^{-10} seconds, since all

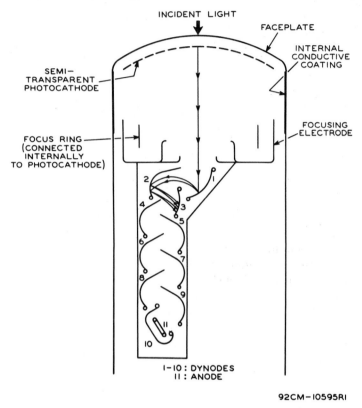

INCIDENT LIGHT

FACEPLATE

INTERNAL
CONDUCTIVE
COATING

SEMI–
TRANSPARENT
PHOTOCATHODE

FOCUSING
ELECTRODE

FOCUS RING
(CONNECTED
INTERNALLY
TO PHOTOCATHODE)

1–10 : DYNODES
11 : ANODE

92CM–10595R1

FIG. 80

Schematic of the multiplier phototube, type 7746.   (Courtesy of RCA.)

of the electrons do not arrive together, but this is several orders of magnitude better than a gas-filled counter, where times of the order of a microsecond are needed for collection of electrons to take place at the central wire.   For work involving high counting rates or measurement of short times between particles, the photomultiplier's short collection time and rapid recovery make it much superior to gas-filled counters.

To use the photomultiplier as a counter of nuclear radiations, the radiations are allowed to strike a suitable phosphor, such as sodium iodide (thallium activated), anthracene or naphthalene (moth balls).   The scintillation produced by a single particle is allowed to strike the photocathode of the photomultiplier tube, and an output voltage pulse is obtained as described above. The resolving time attainable with such a detector is about 0.01 microsecond, being limited only by fluctuations in the transit times of electrons in the photomultiplier and by the decay time of the phosphor.

Visible scintillations can also be produced by particles passing through transparent media, provided that the velocity of the particle is greater than the velocity of light in the medium. This effect was discovered by Cerenkov in 1934 and is known as *Cerenkov radiation.* The theory of this radiation was developed by Tamm and Frank in 1937.

As a charged particle passes through matter, it experiences a succession of small decelerations. As in the case of the emission of the continuous X-ray spectrum, during each deceleration radiation is emitted. However, radiant energy will be observed only in directions in which the wavelets are in phase and reinforce one another. Let the particle move along the path $ABCD$ with velocity v, as shown in Fig. 81. Spherical wavelets originate at times 0, t, $2t$, and $3t$ at the points A, B, C, and D, and

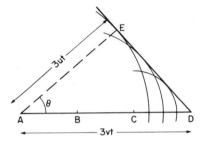

FIG. 81

Reinforcement of successive wavelets in the case of Cerenkov radiation.

travel through the medium with a velocity, u, which is less than v. From the diagram it is seen that the wave-front ED is tangent to all of the wavelets and moves in a direction making an angle θ with the particle's path, where θ is given by

$$\cos \theta = \frac{3ut}{3vt} = \frac{u}{v} = \frac{c}{nv} = \frac{1}{\beta n} \qquad (370)$$

The whole effect is analogous to the shock wave produced by an object moving through air at a speed greater than the speed of sound.

Since the Cerenkov radiation is directional, it may be identified even in the presence of other radiation. By measuring the angle at which the radiation is emitted, the velocity of the particle may be determined. As the radiation travels in a cone of half-angle θ with the particle's path for its axis, by a combination of reflections and refractions it is possible to bring all of the radiation to a focus on the photocathode of a photomultiplier tube. For high energy particles this method is especially valuable, since many other detectors are not very efficient in detecting particles of this energy.

Radioactivity was first discovered through its action on photographic emulsions. The blackening of a photographic plate can be used as a measure of the intensity of radioactivity, and this is still a useful method.

If a photographic emulsion which has been exposed to nuclear radiations is studied under a high-power microscope, it is found that the passage of a single particle leaves a track of silver grains after the plate has been developed.   Evidently silver bromide grains in the emulsion are activated by particles passing nearby.   Tracks of individual particles are analyzed by counting the number of silver grains along each track or by measuring the lengths of tracks.   However, this is a very tedious process and there is a large statistical spread in the data, even for particles of the same energy; this method provides too low a resolution in energy for many purposes. *Photographic registration* of nuclear particles is very important in cosmic ray research at high altitudes or remote locations.   For this type of use the method provides a detector which is continually sensitive and which requires no upkeep or maintenance for long periods of time, so that rare events can be recorded.

The ionization produced by a radioactive particle in passing through a gas is used in *gas-filled counters*.   While these counters have been constructed in many shapes and sizes, a typical gas-filled counter has a wolfram wire a few mils in diameter along the axis of a metal cylinder, as shown in

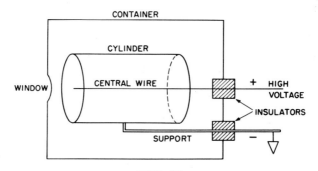

FIG. 82

Cross-section of a typical gas-filled counter for detecting nuclear radiations.

Fig. 82.   The cylinder and coaxial wire are inside a gas-tight container, which may be made of metal or glass.   Depending on the application of the counter, it is filled with a gas or mixture of gases at a pressure ranging from a few centimeters of mercury to several atmospheres.   If the radiations are absorbed easily, a thin-walled window of glass, mica, or aluminum is provided, so the particles can enter the counter.   The output of the counter is usually applied to a vacuum-tube amplifier and finally to a recording instrument, so that the registration of particles can be made automatic.

The output of a gas-filled counter depends on the relation between the voltage applied between the central wire and the cylinder and the gas pressure in the counter.   When a nuclear particle enters the counter, ions are formed in the gas.   The electrons are attracted towards the central wire or anode, and gaseous multiplication by collision takes place if the anode voltage is high enough.   In a time interval which is usually less than a microsecond, the electrons are collected by the central wire.   Treating the counter as a capacitor, the charge collected by the central wire changes its potential according to the relation $\Delta V = \Delta Q/C$, so that a pulse of voltage is produced on the central wire.   In the meantime, the positive ions gradually become neutralized, so that in a time of the order of several hundred microseconds the counter is back to its normal condition.   This *recovery time* can be controlled to a certain extent by the choice of gas mixture and pressure, by the external circuit, and by construction details.

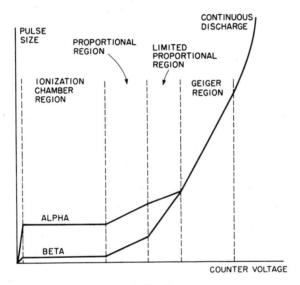

FIG. 83

Variation of output pulse size with applied voltage for a typical gas-filled counter tube.   (Variation of pulse size is actually much larger than shown.)

The way in which the voltage pulse output of a typical gas-filled counter varies with the collecting voltage applied to the central wire is shown in Fig. 83.   It should be noted that the curves are different for alpha and beta particles, since alpha particles produce much more ionization and therefore larger voltage pulses.   At very low voltages, not all of the electrons produced by the ionizing particle are collected, and the voltage pulse is small. At slightly higher voltages, all of the electrons are collected, but gaseous multiplication does not take place; this is called the *ionization chamber region*.   In the *proportional region*, gas amplification factors up to 10^4

occur, but all pulses are multiplied by the same factor, so that the ratio of an alpha to a beta pulse is constant. This allows the experimenter to distinguish the two types of particles by their pulse sizes. As the voltage is increased, we pass through the *region of limited proportionality*, where alpha and beta pulses become more nearly equal, until the *Geiger region* is entered, where all particles produce pulses of the same size. At even higher voltages the tube breaks down into a spark discharge, and may be destroyed.

Throughout the *ionization chamber region*, the current collected by the central wire is equal to the ionization current produced by the nuclear particles entering the counter. The intensities of two sources of radiation are compared by comparing their ionization currents in a given gas-filled counter. Since the ionization current is very small, it is passed through an extremely large resistance (of the order of a billion ohms), and the resulting IR-drop is amplified with a very stable DC amplifier, the output of the amplifier being measured with a galvanometer. Reliable measurements require considerable care in the design and operation of the amplifier, so that ionization chambers are not too commonly used to compare intensities of radioactive sources.

The *proportional region* is used when it is desired to discriminate between alpha- and beta-particles by their pulse sizes. The recording instrument may then be biased so that only the large alpha pulses will be recorded. The pulse produced is quite small, and considerable amplification must be used to actuate a recorder. Counters of this sort register individual particles, and the recording circuits can be designed so that they are rather insensitive to changes in pulse height produced by small changes in the collecting voltage, which removes one disadvantage of ionization chambers.

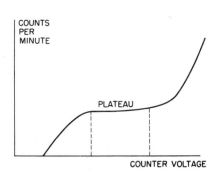

FIG. 84

Variation of counting rate with applied voltage for a typical Geiger counter tube.

In the *Geiger region* (named after the originator of these tubes), an extensive electron avalanche occurs whenever an ionizing particle enters the gas-filled counter. The most valuable feature of the Geiger region is shown in Fig. 84, which shows a plot of the number of counts per minute versus the collecting voltage, all other variables being held constant. A well designed Geiger counter will have a *plateau*, several hundred volts wide, over which the number of counts per minute is independent of the supply voltage. Thus, the counting rate does not vary with small variations in voltage. Because of the large pulse produced by a Geiger counter, little or no amplification is needed to operate a recorder, meter, or headset, and usually the counter is operated on the lower end of the plateau, in order to avoid excessive pulse size and damage to the counter.

Photoconductivity is utilized in *crystal counters*. When a crystal of diamond, AgCl, or LiF is mounted between two metal electrodes as shown in Fig. 85 a pulse of voltage is produced each time as ionizing particle passes

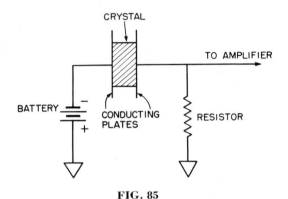

FIG. 85

Detection of nuclear radiations, using a photoconducting crystal.

into the crystal. Some electron multiplication takes place as electrons travel to the positive electrode. The advantages of this type of counter over gas-filled counters are the rapid rise of pulses and the short recovery time they possess. However, satisfactory crystals must be selected by trial and error; while almost all diamonds will count alpha-particles, only about one in fifty will count gamma rays.

A device which in effect photographs the ionization produced by particles moving through a gas as devised by Wilson in 1911. In the *Wilson cloud chamber* use is made of the fact that if ions are formed in a super-saturated vapor, droplets of liquid will condense on the ions. If the vapor is photographed just after the instant at which the ionizing particle enters the vapor, the path of the particle will show up as a track of droplets. The resulting photograph is almost a photograph of the path of the particle itself.

A schematic diagram of a cloud chamber is shown in Fig. 86. Super-saturation of water or alcohol vapors can be achieved by a sudden expansion, since these vapors have negative specific heats under the condition of saturation; an argon-alcohol mixture requires an expansion of only about 10%, while water vapor requires about 35% expansion. An electric field is maintained across the chamber until just before the expansion, in order to sweep away any stray ions which may be formed in the vapor. Immediately after the expansion the light is turned on for a short time and the shutter of the camera is opened. After the proper exposure, the shutter of the camera is closed and the light is turned off. The electric field then is applied until just before the beginning of the next cycle. The whole apparatus can be made to operate automatically, with pictures being made several times a minute. Since automatic operation is bound to yield many

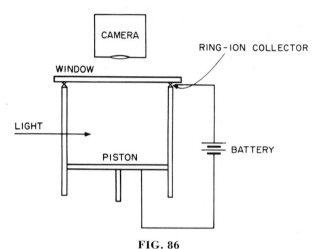

FIG. 86
Schematic diagram of the Wilson cloud chamber.

uninteresting pictures, the cycle of operation can be initiated by the particle itself. This is done by allowing the particle first to pass through a Geiger counter; a voltage pulse from the Geiger counter then initiates a single cycle of the cloud chamber. Since this can be done quite rapidly with electronic circuits, the track of vapor droplets has very little chance to diffuse and good photographs are obtained. An additional improvement is to take two photographs simultaneously from different directions so that tracks can be studied in three dimensions.

The interpretation of cloud-chamber photographs is often difficult. As long as only known particles are being studied, the nature of the particle can be determined from the appearance of its track. For instance, alpha-particles ionize heavily and give very thick tracks, while beta particles ionize only about a hundredth as much and give rather weak, "thready" tracks. If a magnetic field is applied to the cloud chamber, the momentum of the particle can be computed from the curvature of its track by the equation

$$mv = qBr$$

The energy of a particle can often be estimated from the length of the track in the vapor or from the thickness of an absorber inside the chamber which the particle can traverse. Using these criteria, cloud-chamber tracks can give considerable information regarding the nature, mass, charge, and velocity of a particle. Undoubtedly more new phenomena and more new particles have been discovered with cloud chambers than with any other detector of nuclear particles, and even with the difficulties in interpretation of the cloud-chamber photographs, these are still exceedingly useful in nuclear research.

A device similar to the cloud chamber is the *bubble chamber*, which was first described by Glaser in 1952. A liquid is heated under high pressure to a temperature considerably above its normal boiling point. When the pressure is removed, the liquid is left in a super-heated state and is ready to boil strongly. As in the case of the cloud chamber, if ions are produced in the liquid by an ionizing radiation, bubbles of vapor will form on the ions. The track of bubbles is then photographed.

Although diethyl ether was the first liquid used, hydrogen, benzene and many other liquids have since been found to be effective. The chief advantage of the bubble chamber is that the activities of highly energetic particles may be observed in their entirety, whereas in a cloud-chamber the gas molecules are relatively far apart, so that only a portion of the track of an energetic particle actually occurs inside the chamber. Depending on the liquid used, a bubble-chamber may have a stopping power hundreds of times that of a cloud-chamber of the same size. In addition, a bubble-chamber can be returned to the sensitive state more quickly than a cloud-chamber.

8.3. ALPHA, BETA, AND GAMMA RAYS

In this section we shall discuss the evidence for the nature of the three types of radiations emitted by naturally radioactive elements. Although the original Greek letters are still used in connection with these radiations, we shall see that actually they are helium nuclei, electrons, and X-rays respectively, so that the number of fundamental particles is not increased.

As discussed previously, the direction of the deflection of *alpha rays* by a magnetic field shows that they are positively charged particles. Electromagnetic deflection experiments similar to those described in Chapter 1 show that all alpha-particles have the same charge-to-mass ratio, which is one-half the charge-to-mass ratio of the proton. Thus, the charge and mass of the alpha-particle, measured in terms of the proton's charge and mass, must be some pair such as $(q = 1, m = 2)$, $(q = 2, m = 4)$, etc. Several experiments by Rutherford decided this matter.

To measure the charge carried by an alpha-particle, Rutherford, in 1908, counted the number of particles emitted per second by a radioactive source, and then allowed a known number of alpha-particles to be collected by a condenser, charging it up.   After dividing the total charge collected by the condenser by the number of alpha-particles reaching the condenser, he found that the charge of an alpha-particle is just twice the proton charge. Referring to the paragraph above, to give the proper charge-to-mass ratio, the mass of an alpha-particle must be four times the proton's mass.   If a helium atom is stripped of its two electrons, the remaining nucleus will have a charge of two units and a mass of four units.   Thus, the measurement of the charge of the alpha-particle strongly suggests that this particle is actually a helium nucleus.

The clinching experiment, which was also performed by Rutherford, consisted of allowing alpha-particles to pass into a tube through a thin wall.   If alpha-particles are actually helium nuclei, we would expect many of them to acquire electrons by collision with atoms of gas inside the tube and thus become atoms of neutral helium.   Rutherford found that within a few hours enough helium had been formed inside the tube for the characteristic spectrum of helium to be observed when a spark was passed through the tube.   As time passed, the intensity of the helium spectrum grew greater, showing that the amount of helium inside the tube was increasing. From this experiment it is clear that alpha-particles are indeed helium atoms with the electrons stripped off.

An important property of alpha-particles, which is directly related to their energy, is their *range* in various substances, usually air.   Various methods are used to measure the range of alpha-particles in a gas, and slightly different values of the range are obtained for each method.   One method is to measure the ionization current at various distances from the

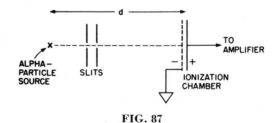

FIG. 87
Arrangement for measuring the ionization produced by
alpha particles in air at various distances from a source.

radioactive source with a shallow ionization chamber, as shown in Fig. 87. If the ionization current is plotted as a function of the distance from the source, the curve of Fig. 88 is found.   The straight portion of the curve is extrapolated to the axis to determine the *extrapolated range, R*.   The extrapolated ranges in air of alpha-particles from naturally radioactive substances are 2–12 centimeters.   The peak at the end of the range-curve

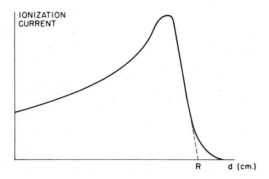

FIG. 88

Typical variation of ionization current with distance for
the arrangement of Fig. 87.

of Fig. 88 is interesting. This peak occurs because, near the end of the
alpha-particle's path, it is moving slowly and remains longer in the vicinity
of air molecules, thus having a greater chance to produce ionization.

If the number of alpha-particles which reach a given distance from the
radioactive source is measured with a Geiger counter, the curve shown in
Fig. 89 is obtained. Statistically some particles will be more or less lucky
than the average in their collisions with air molecules, so that not all mole-

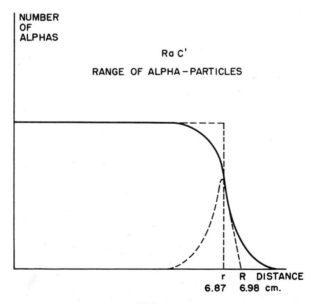

FIG. 89

Determination of the average range of alpha-particles
from RaC' from a measurement of the number of alpha
particles reaching a Geiger counter.

cules will travel exactly the same distance through the air before being stopped. Assuming that the straggling follows a Gaussian error curve, we locate the *average range*, r, at the center of this straggling curve, as shown in Fig. 89. In the case of RaC′, for instance, the difference between the two alpha-particle ranges is about 2%, so that in reading one must determine which range is being used.

The energy of an alpha-particle can be measured by deflecting it in a strong magnetic field; alpha-particles occur naturally with energies of about 4–10 mev. In order to determine the energy of an alpha-particle from its range in some substance, empirical curves must be used relating these two quantities. It is interesting to note that at low energies, the range is proportional to the $\frac{3}{2}$-power of the energy, while at higher energies the range is proportional to the square of the energy.

The *stopping power* of a substance is a measure of its effectiveness in stopping alpha-particles as compared with air at standard pressure and temperature. Since $\frac{1}{1700}$ centimeter of aluminum has the same effect in stopping alpha-particles as one centimeter of standard air, the stopping power of aluminum is said to be 1700. Since thin foils of aluminum are readily obtainable, aluminum is very often used in measuring ranges of alpha-particles and in constructing windows for admitting alpha-particles into Geiger counters and other instruments. As described in connection with the absorption of X-rays, the thickness of a foil is often computed from the weight of a sample of measured area. However, since this thickness is based on the assumption that the foil has a known and constant density, it is customary to express thicknesses of aluminum foil in milligrams per square centimeter. A convenient figure to remember is that 1.62 mg/cm² of aluminum foil is equivalent to one centimeter of air in absorption of alpha-particles over a wide range of alpha-particle energies.

As mentioned previously, *beta rays* must be negatively charged particles to give the observed direction of deflection in a magnetic field. When investigated more closely, beta rays are found to have exactly the same charge-to-mass ratio as electrons, and, in all respects to exhibit the same properties as electrons. Thus, beta rays must actually be electrons. Since the energies of naturally occurring beta rays are of the order of several mev, relativistic expressions must always be used in computing such quantities as energy, momentum, velocity and dynamical mass.

As beta-particles are light and thus easily deflected in collisions with the atoms of an absorber, they do not have a definite range in the same sense as alpha-particles. For natural beta-particle sources, which are not even approximately mono-energetic, it is possible to define a linear absorption coefficient for beta-particles in the same manner as for X-rays, but this is only a happy coincidence. A more useful quantity is the definite thickness which will absorb all beta-particles of a given energy. If this beta-particle range is expressed in milligrams per square centimeter, it is found that the range of beta-particles of a given energy is practically the same in all materials.

The ionization produced per centimeter by beta-particles absorbed in air does not vary with energy in the same way that it does for alpha-particles. Above an energy of about one mev, the range is almost exactly linear with energy, but below one mev empirical curves must be used. At low energies the beta-particles have more time to interact with atoms, so that the ionization is high. At extremely high energies of the order of hundreds of mev, the relativistic contraction of the beta-particle's electromagnetic field into a plane perpendicular to its velocity allows it to sweep out a wider path, producing greater ionization. Fig. 90 shows these various features in a curve calculated by Heitler for the specific ionization of beta-particles in air at various energies.

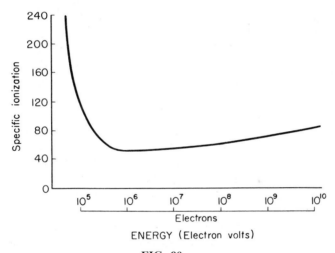

FIG. 90

Ionization per centimeter produced by electrons in air as a function of energy. (Adapted from *Nuclear Radiation Physics*, Second Edition, by Lapp and Andrews: Prentice-Hall, 1954.)

Gamma rays constitute that component of radiation from radioactive substances which is entirely unaffected by a magnetic field. They are found to be electromagnetic waves of exactly the same nature as X-rays, although they are usually of higher frequency and energy. The only distinction between gamma rays and X-rays is their origins. X-rays are produced by electrons striking atoms of a target material, while gamma rays are produced spontaneously by radioactive elements. Gamma rays are detected in exactly the same ways as X-rays, although most gamma rays have wavelengths which are too short to be measured by crystal diffraction, so that Compton recoil electrons or electron-positron pairs must be observed.

Gamma rays are emitted as the result of a nucleus readjusting itself with respect to energy. After a nucleus has emitted some particle, such as an alpha or beta particle, it may be left in an excited state, rather than in its lowest energy state. This excess energy is then emitted in the form of one or more quanta of gamma radiation. Considerable information can often be obtained about nuclear energy levels by studying gamma ray spectra; a typical diagram of this sort is shown in the following chapter in connection with the evidence for the *neutrino* (little neutron) in Fig. 98.

The wavelengths of gamma rays which are longer than about 0.15 angstroms (energies less than about 100 kev) can be measured by the methods of crystal diffraction described in Section 6.4 in connection with X-rays. At shorter wavelengths no crystal exists with a suitable spacing, so that other interactions of gamma rays with matter must be studied. For instance, the energy of a photoelectron knocked out of an atom by a gamma ray equals the incident energy of the gamma ray minus the binding energy of the photoelectron in its atom. If the energy of the photoelectron is measured by magnetic deflection, the energy of the gamma ray can easily be computed. Similarly, if the energy of Compton recoil electrons in a given direction is measured, the energy of the incident gamma ray photon can be computed using Eq. (316). In the process of pair-formation, the kinetic energy of the electron-positron pair equals the energy of incident gamma ray photon minus the energy to create two electron-masses, which is 1.022 mev, so that gamma-ray energies can be deduced from measurements on electron-positron pairs.

There are several other modes of decay of unstable nuclei; we will discuss these briefly. Instead of emitting a gamma-ray, an equal amount of energy may be given directly to an electron of the outer electronic structure in a manner similar to the production of photo-electrons by X-rays. In this process of *internal conversion*, the energy of the electron is the energy the gamma-ray would have had minus the binding energy of the electron, which is usually a K-electron. Therefore the electrons emitted in this process have definite energies, in contrast to those emitted by nuclei, which have a continuous range of energies. When the atom returns to its normal state, X-rays are emitted as described in Sec. 6.8 for the case of discrete X-ray spectra. These characteristic X-rays also help to identify the process as internal conversion.

In some cases the X-rays emitted in the process of internal conversion may knock electrons out of the outer parts of the same atom. This process of self-ionization was discovered in 1925 by Auger and is known as the

Auger effect.   As in the case of internal conversion, Auger electrons have discrete energies characteristic of the atom in question.

Certain unstable nuclei decay by emitting positrons.   In some elements a competing process occurs, known as *K-capture*.   In this case the nucleus captures one of its own *K*-shell electrons.   As will be discussed in the following section, capture of an electron or emission of a positron lowers the atomic number of the atom by one unit.   Therefore, when the atom returns to its normal state, it emits X-rays characteristic of the element one unit lower in atomic number than the original atom emitting the positron.   This enables us to distinguish internal conversion from *K*-capture.

The various properties of gamma rays, such as absorption, interactions with matter, and health aspects, are exactly the same as described previously in connection with X-rays in Chapter 6.   Aside from the fundamental difference in the origins of X-rays and gamma rays, the only other difference is that gamma rays are usually much more energetic.   The reader is urged to review the applicable sections in Chapter 6.

8.4. RADIOACTIVE TRANSFORMATIONS AND THE RUTHERFORD-SODDY RULE

If pure radium is enclosed in a sealed tube, at first only alpha-particles are observed to be emitted from the tube, with no accompanying beta or gamma radiation.   After a lapse of time, however, both beta and gamma rays appear, and the number of alpha-particles emitted per second increases substantially.   If the radium is no longer enclosed and a stream of air blows past it, the activity of the radium is found to remain unchanged with time, while the air now exhibits radioactivity.   Furthermore, the radioactivity in the air can be removed by cooling the air sufficiently.

The inference to be drawn from the simple experiments described above is that radium emits a radioactive gas which is carried off by the stream of air and which liquefies at a higher temperature than air.   This gas is called radon, and its properties can be studied by pumping it out of a sealed tube containing radium.   It is found that radon has its own characteristic optical spectrum, is inert in chemical reactions, has atomic number 86, and has atomic weight 222.   Clearly, we must conclude that radium atoms are not indivisible and immutable, but rather that they disintegrate in some manner, with one of the products of this disintegration being radon, which is detectable through its radioactivity.   The problem is to find the rule which applies to *radioactive transformations* of this kind.

Rutherford and Soddy suggested the solution to this problem in 1912. They hypothesized that when a nucleus emits a particle, such as alpha-particle, the result is a new nucleus with a different mass and charge.   In

this process both mass and charge must be conserved.   If radium, which is
an element of atomic weight 226 and atomic number 88, emits an alpha-
particle of atomic weight 4 and atomic number 2, the resulting new nucleus
must have an atomic weight given by $226 - 4 = 222$ and an atomic
number given by $88 - 2 = 86$.   In this way both nuclear charge and mass
are conserved.   However, such an element would be radon, so that we can
write the equation for this nuclear transformation in the form:

$$_{88}Ra^{226} \rightarrow {}_2He^4 + {}_{86}Rn^{222}$$

Following the usual convention, in the transformation equation given
above the atomic numbers (nuclear charges) are written as subscripts before
the symbol for each element, while the atomic weights (mass numbers) are
written as superscripts after the symbol for each element.   According to
the *Rutherford-Soddy rule,* in any nuclear reaction the superscripts and the
subscripts must balance separately, ensuring conservation of charge and
mass in the transformation.   The product nucleus may itself be radioactive, but this is of no consequence in applying the rule to the equation for
the production of the new nucleus, as is illustrated in the case of the formation of radon by radium.

The Rutherford-Soddy rule also holds in the case of radioactive elements
which emit electrons (beta-particles).   Since the mass of an electron is
negligible compared to the masses of nuclei and nuclear particles, the product nucleus has the same mass number as its parent nucleus.   On the other
hand, since the emission of an electronic charge is equivalent to the absorption of an equal positive charge, the product nucleus is one unit higher in
atomic number than its parent.   A typical example of a transformation
involving emission of an electron is given below.

$$_{82}Pb^{214} \rightarrow {}_{-1}\beta^0 + {}_{83}Bi^{214}$$

To sum up the rule for nuclear distintegrations, the mass numbers and
atomic numbers must balance on the two sides of any nuclear transformation equation.   This rule applies regardless of the type of particle
emitted or how complex the disintegration.   In the following chapters
applications of this rule will be made to cases involving more than one
nuclear particle, including such particles as protons, neutrons, and positrons, and in each case the transformation equations are balanced in the
way described above.

8.5. THE GROWTH AND DECAY OF RADIOACTIVITY

The activity of radioactive elements is found to decrease exponentially
with time.   Because of the similarity of this decay curve to growth problems in general, it is reasonable to assume that we can derive an equation

for this decay from simple assumptions. We will assume that the chance of any particular nucleus disintegrating at a given instant is independent of past or future disintegrations of other nuclei, so that this is, in effect, a random process. In that case, the number of nuclei disintegrating per second at any instant will be proportional to the number of nuclei which are available for disintegration. If there are N nuclei present at a given time, for the disintegration rate, I, we can write the equation

$$I = \frac{dN}{dt} = -\lambda N \tag{370}$$

In Eq. (370), the constant of proportionality, λ, is called the *disintegration constant*, since it gives the fraction of nuclei which will disintegrate per second, or alternatively, the probability that a given atom will disintegrate within a second.

Integrating Eq. (370) and letting N_0 be the number of nuclei present at $t = 0$, for the number of nuclei present at any time, t, we obtain the equation

$$N = N_0 \exp (-\lambda t) \tag{371}$$

If we differentiate Eq. (371) in order to find the activity or intensity, I, in terms of the initial intensity, I_0, I is given by the equation

$$I = \frac{dN}{dt} = -\lambda N_0 \exp (-\lambda t) = I_0 \exp (-\lambda t) \tag{372}$$

From Eq. (372) we see that the hypothesis that radioactive disintegration is a completely random process leads to the exponential decrease in intensity which is found experimentally.

If we take the logarithm of Eq. (372), we find

$$\ln \frac{I}{I_0} = -\lambda t \tag{373}$$

Thus, if we plot the natural logarithm of the relative activity, I/I_0, versus the time elapsed, we should get a straight line of slope $-\lambda$, as shown in Fig. 91. If the intensity of a radioactive element is observed over a period of a time and the data are plotted as shown in Fig. 91, the disintegration constant of the element can be found directly from the slope of the straight line obtained.

A more commonly used measure of the decay of a radioactive element is its *half-value period* or *half-life*, which is defined as the time required for the intensity to decrease by 50%. If we let $I/I_0 = \frac{1}{2}$ in Eq. (373), we find the following relation between the half-life and the disintegration constant:

$$\ln (0.5) = -0.693 = -\lambda T \tag{374}$$

Using Eq. (374), either one of the constants λ or T is sufficient to describe the radioactive decay of an element.   In interpreting experimental data one advantage of the half-life is that a plot of I versus t on semi-logarithmic graph paper allows the half-life to be determined by inspection, as shown in Fig. 91, without making any computations involving natural logarithms or the slope of the line obtained.

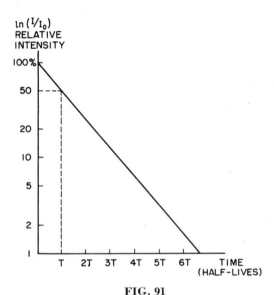

FIG. 91

Semi-logarithmic plot of relative intensity of a radioactive source as a function of time.

If an observed activity is produced by several elements of different half-lives, the plot of the data as shown in Fig. 91 will not yield a straight line.   However, after a sufficiently long time, only the longest-lived element will remain, and the end of the curve will be a straight line.   This straight line can be extrapolated backward to give the number of counts per second produced by the longest-lived element.   These counts are then subtracted from the basic data, and the remainder of the data are analyzed, again by looking for the longest-lived element remaining.   In this way, the half-lives of all the elements present can be determined.   This procedure is illustrated in Fig. 92, where elements of 6-hour and 1-hour half-lives are found to be present.   The straight line due to the 6-hour activity is subtracted from the total activity by extrapolation.   Since the remaining activity is a straight line of half-life 1 hour, this is the only other activity present.   This process is continued in a similar way if more than two activities are present.

An interesting problem is the growth of a daughter substance through the radioactive decay of its parent. In the following equations, subscripts 1 and 2 will refer to the parent and daughter elements respectively. The equation for the decay of the parent is as follows:

$$\frac{dN_1}{dt} = -\lambda_1 N_1 \tag{375}$$

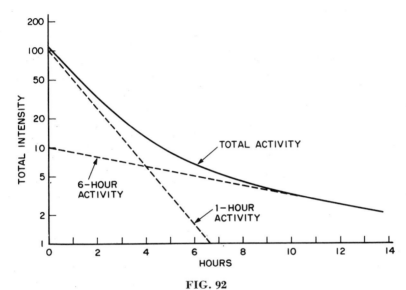

FIG. 92

Method of analyzing an activity produced by two elements of different half-lives.

The daughter element, however, both gains through formation during the disintegration of its parent and loses through its own radioactive decay. For the daughter element we have

$$\frac{dN_2}{dt} = -\frac{dN_1}{dt} - \lambda_2 N_2 = \lambda_1 N_1 - \lambda_2 N_2 \tag{376}$$

If initially there are N_0 atoms of the parent and no atoms of the daughter, it is easily shown that the solutions of Eq. (375) and Eq. (376) are as follows:

$$N_1 = N_0 \exp(-\lambda_1 t) \tag{377}$$

$$N_2 = \frac{\lambda_1 N_0}{\lambda_2 - \lambda_1} [\exp(-\lambda_1 t) - \exp(-\lambda_2 t)] \tag{378}$$

In this case the number of atoms of the daughter element passes through a maximum at a time given by

$$t_{\max} = \frac{\ln (\lambda_2/\lambda_1)}{\lambda_2 - \lambda_1} \qquad (379)$$

For large values of time, only one of the exponentials in Eq. (378) has a value significantly different from zero, and the number of atoms of the daughter element decays with either the daughter's or parent's half-life, whichever is longer.

We speak of a daughter element as being in *radioactive equilibrium* when as many atoms of the daughter are being formed per second by decay of its parent as are being lost per second by the daughter's own decay. In this case the number of atoms of the daughter remains constant, so that

$$\frac{dN_2}{dt} = 0$$

From Eq. (376) we then have the following condition for radioactive equilibrium:

$$\lambda_1 N_1 = \lambda_2 N_2 \qquad (380)$$

Thus, under conditions of radioactive equilibrium the numbers of atoms of parent and daughter are inversely proportional to their disintegration constants, or directly proportional to their respective half-lives. Furthermore, comparison of Eq. (380) with Eq. (370) shows that the disintegration rates of parent and daughter are the same. Thus, the number of characteristic particles emitted by each element per second is the same when elements are in radioactive equilibrium, even though the numbers of the atoms of each type present may be radically different.

The unit of activity or intensity of radioactivity is the *Curie*, which is defined as the activity of the amount of radon in equilibrium with one gram of radium. Experimentally, this represents approximately 3.7×10^{10} disintegrations per second, and in 1950 the Curie was defined by international agreement as being exactly 3.700×10^{10} disintegrations per second. Today the Curie is used for describing the emission of any sort of nuclear radiation, and this unit has lost its connection with radon and radium. Other units in common use are the *millicurie*, which represents 37 million disintegrations per second, and the *microcurie*, which represents 37 thousand disintegrations per second. The *rutherford* is another unit used, and represents 10^6 disintegrations per second. Another term often used is the *specific activity*, which is defined as the number of disintegrations per second per gram of the radioactive element.

8.6. ISOTOPES, ISOBARS, AND ISOMERS

In 1912 J. J. Thomson measured the charge-to-mass ratio of various ions of light elements, using an apparatus very similar to the one described in Chapter 1 in connection with the discovery of the electron. He found that not all ions of a given element were identical, as had been supposed, but rather that a given element might have atoms of slightly different masses. For instance, neon was found to have atoms of atomic weights 20 and 22, while chlorine was found to consist of atoms of weights 35 and 37.

If we assume that we know the charge of the ions, Thomson's electromagnetic deflection experiments provide a means for measuring the mass of atoms. Just as optical spectrometers measure wavelengths of light, devices for measuring masses of ions or atoms are called *mass spectrometers*. Various designs have been worked out to suit various purposes, but basically all mass spectrometers focus a stream of particles with electromagnetic fields, and from the position of the focus one can compute the mass momentum, or energy of the particles.

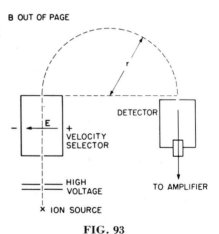

FIG. 93

Schematic diagram of the Bainbridge mass spectrometer.

Spectrometers differ in details, such as precision, resolution, or sharpness of focussing, but they are all fundamentally the same; only one mass spectrometer will be described here.

The Bainbridge mass spectrometer is shown schematically in Fig. 93.   The ions from the ion-source are accelerated by high voltage applied to the collimating slits. They then enter the *velocity selector*, where they are subjected to an electric field, E, and ·a magnetic field, B, at right angles. (See Problem 3, Chapter 1.) The only particles which emerge from the velocity selector are those with velocities such that the electric and magnetic forces on the particle are just equal and opposite. In MKS units, with E in volts/meter and B in webers/sq meter, we have

$$qE = qvB \qquad (381)$$

Particles emerge from the selector with a velocity

$$v = \frac{E}{B} \qquad (382)$$

When the particles are in the magnetic field alone, their paths are circles and come to a focus at the detector, which may be a photographic plate, a Geiger counter, or an ionization chamber. The equation of the trajectory is

$$qvB = \frac{mv^2}{r} \tag{383}$$

When we solve Eqs. (382) and (383) for the mass-to-charge ratio of particles travelling in a circle of radius r, we find

$$\frac{m}{q} = \frac{Br}{v} = \frac{B^2}{E} r \tag{384}$$

Thus, the mass of an ion of a given charge is proportional to the radius of the orbit of the particle, and the mass scale of this spectrometer is linear. Furthermore, this instrument does not need to be calibrated, since only known electromagnetic fields are involved. However, mass spectrometers are usually used to compare atomic masses, and when used for comparison, precision of the order of 0.001% can be attained.

Atoms of the same element are of course identical chemically, since the number of electrons circulating around the nucleus is the same for all atoms of the same element. Two atoms of the same atomic number but with different atomic weights are called *isotopes*. No element is known which does not have at least two isotopes, if we include artificially produced isotopes. Xenon has one of the largest numbers of isotopes, with a total of nine naturally occurring isotopes and at least fifteen artificial isotopes. Altogether approximately a thousand isotopes are known.

As described above, the atomic weights of isotopes can be measured with great precision with various types of mass spectrometers. In every case it is found that the isotopic weights are very close to being whole numbers, with some isotopic weights being slightly greater than whole numbers and some slightly less. For convenience isotopes are distinguished by their *mass numbers*, by which is meant the integer nearest to the actual isotopic weight. Isotopes will be indicated by a symbol such as $_8O^{16}$, where the subscript preceding the chemical symbol for oxygen indicates that the atomic number of oxygen is 8, while the superscript after the chemical symbol indicates that this particular isotope has a mass number 16.

When natural oxygen is investigated with a mass spectrometer it is found to consist of three isotopes, with mass numbers 16, 17, and 18, with the lightest isotope being by far the most abundant. For years before this was known, chemists had defined the atomic weight of naturally occurring oxygen as being exactly 16.00000. According to this *chemical scale* of atomic weights, which is based on a mixture of oxygen isotopes, hydrogen has an atomic weight of 1.00785. In the *physical scale* of atomic weights the atomic weight of the lightest and most abundant isotope of oxygen is defined as being exactly 16.00000. According to this physical scale, natural oxygen has an atomic weight of 16.00435 and hydrogen an atomic weight of 1.00813. The mass of a hypothetical element of unit atomic weight is called an *atomic mass unit* (abbreviated amu); 1 amu has a mass of 1.65978×10^{-24} gram. Atomic weights on the chemical scale can be converted to atomic weights on the physical scale by multiplying chemical atomic weights by the factor 1.000275. Needless to say, before using any table of isotopic weights it should be determined which of the two scales is being used by looking up the isotopic weight of the lightest isotope of oxygen.

The separation of isotopes is an attractive but difficult problem. Since the chemical properties of isotopes of a given element are identical, small differences in the physical properties of isotopes caused by the small differences in atomic weights must be used. In the case of hydrogen, the ratio of the masses of heavy hydrogen to ordinary hydrogen is two, so this is the most favorable element, since differences in physical properties will be greatest in the case of the hydrogen isotopes. In 1931 Urey concentrated the heavy isotope of hydrogen, known as deuterium, by repeated fractional distillations of water. Electrolysis is also successful in separating these two radically different isotopes, but more refined and complicated methods must be used to separate the isotopes of heavier elements. We will return to this problem again in Chapter 10 in connection with the separation of the isotopes of uranium.

Atoms may be alike in some other characteristic aside from atomic number. Two atoms which have the same mass number but different atomic numbers are called *isobars*. A naturally occurring triplet of isobars is the set $_{18}A^{40}$, $_{19}K^{40}$, and $_{20}Ca^{40}$. Since isobars are different chemically, they can easily be separated from one another. Atoms may have both the same atomic number and the same mass number, and yet may differ in some property of their nuclei; atoms of this type are called *isomers*. The nuclear property by which isomers may differ may be the type of particle emitted, the half-life or energy of the particle, or the presence or absence of radioactivity. For example, $_{21}Sc^{44}$ has two isomers, one of which emits an electron with a half-life of 2.44 days and the other emits a positron with a half-life of 3.92 hours. Another example is $_{30}Zn^{69}$, where one isomer emits gamma-radiation and the other emits an electron, both with different half-lives. A final example is provided by $_{22}Ti^{51}$, where both isomers emit electrons, but with half-lives of 2.9 minutes and 72 days respectively.

8.7. THE RADIOACTIVE FAMILIES

During the early years of the twentieth century a large number of radioactive elements were found, practically all lying in the range of the periodic table from lead to uranium. After the discovery of isotopes and the introduction of the Rutherford-Soddy rule in 1912, the pieces of the puzzle

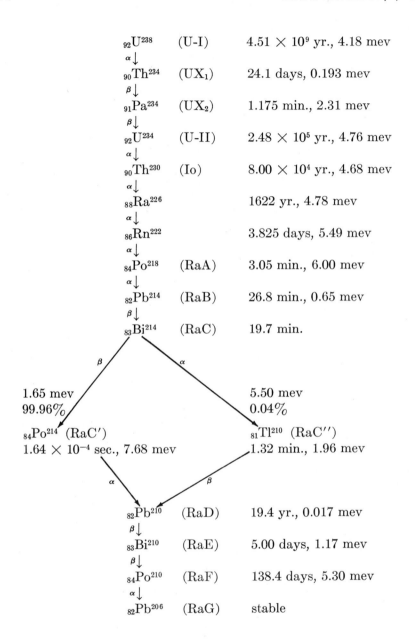

FIG. 94
The uranium family of radioactive elements.

began to fall into a clear picture.   Not all of the radioactive elements were actually separate elements, as most of them could be considered isotopes of the eleven elements from lead to uranium.   Using the Rutherford-Soddy rule to predict the product of a given disintegration, it was seen also that the lighter radioactive elements were descendants of the heavier elements. In fact, it seemed that only a few heavy and long-lived radioactive elements could produce all the known radioactive elements.   At first not all of the intermediate elements in the chain extending from the heaviest to the lightest elements were known, but these intermediate elements were inferred with the aid of the Rutherford-Soddy rule.   At present there is no doubt of the correctness of the decay schemes of the radioactive elements.

A typical *radioactive family* is that of uranium, which has $_{92}U^{238}$ as progenitor of a chain of radioactive elements which ends at $_{82}Pb^{206}$, which is stable.   The uranium family is shown in Fig. 94.   As may be seen from the diagram, during the process of formation of this chain a total of eight alpha-particles and six electrons are emitted in succession.   The early notations for some of the radioactive elements in the uranium family are given in parentheses in the diagram, but actually they are all isotopes of just a few elements.   Since the parent uranium has the longest half-life, all the members of the uranium family found in natural ores are in radioactive equilibrium with uranium.

Three other radioactive families are known, and they all follow a decay scheme very similar to that shown for the uranium family.   The thorium series begins with long-lived $_{90}Th^{232}$ and ends with stable $_{82}Pb^{208}$, while the actinium family begins with $_{92}U^{235}$ and ends with stable $_{82}Pb^{207}$.   A man-made radioactive family begins with $_{93}Np^{237}$ and ends with stable $_{83}Bi^{209}$. Since this isotope of neptunium has a relatively short half-life compared to the progenitors of the other radioactive families, this radioactive family died out on earth long ago, so that it is not properly called a natural radioactive series.   The data on these series are given in the Appendix.

ADDITIONAL READINGS

Lapp, R. E. and H. L. Andrews, *Nuclear Radiation Physics*.   Englewood Cliffs, N. J.: Prentice-Hall, Inc., 1954 (2nd Ed.)   An excellent elementary treatment.

Cork, James M., *Radioactivity and Nuclear Physics*.   Princeton: D. Van Nostrand Co., 1957 (3rd Ed.).   An excellent text, with many references to the literature.

Korff, S. A., *Electron and Nuclear Counters*.   Princeton: D. Van Nostrand Co., 1955 (2nd Ed.).   Principles and applications of counters well explained.

PROBLEMS

1. Data were taken every day at noon on a sample of radon. The number of alpha-particles counted in ten minutes in each day was as follows: Monday, 1560; Tuesday, 1304; Wednesday, 1090; Thursday, 908; Friday, 760; Saturday, 634. From these data determine the half-life and the disintegration constant of radon. (*Ans.* 3.85 days; 2.09×10^{-6} per sec)

2. Radon is pumped off a two-gram sample of radium every 72 hours. How many millicuries of radon are obtained each time?

3. Assuming a hospital had to borrow $50,000 at 4% interest in order to buy the two grams of radium mentioned in Problem 2, what price should the hospital charge for a 10 millicurie seed of radon? Allow a $3.00 service charge, and include a charge for the depletion of the radium and interest on the loan. (*Ans.* $3.20)

4. Compute the mass and volume of the helium produced when one gram of uranium disintegrates for one half-life in such a way that the uranium, its products, and the helium produced are unable to escape.

5. If radium has a half-life of 1600 years and occurs in a proportion of one atom of radium to each three million atoms of uranium, calculate the half-life of uranium. (*Ans.* 4.8×10^9 years)

6. Derive Eq. (378).

7. What are the products when (a) $_{19}K^{40}$ decays by emitting an electron? (b) $_{62}Sm^{152}$ decays by emitting an alpha-particle? (*Ans.* $_{20}Ca^{40}$, $_{60}Nd^{148}$)

8. Compute the weight of one millicurie of (a) U^{238}, (b) Po^{210}, (c) Po^{212}.

9. Prove that the mean or average lifetime of a radioactive nucleus is equal to the reciprocal of the disintegration constant of the nucleus.

10. Find the energy in mev released when one amu is completely converted into energy.

11. Derive Eq. (379).

12. Consider a large, plane slab of radioactive material emitting α-particles. (Neglect edge effects.) For this material, let λ be its disintegration constant, ρ its density, A its atomic weight, and R the range of its α-particles in the material itself. Let N be Avogadro's number. Show that the intensity, I, just outside the surface of the material in α-particles per cm² per second is given by

$$I = \frac{\lambda \rho R N}{4A}$$

13. It is desired to shield a detector from a point γ-ray source. Without any shielding, the intensity falls off as the square of the distance between the source and the detector. Show that for maximum shielding a slab of absorber should be placed with its midpoint equidistant between the source and the detector.

chapter nine

induced nuclear reactions

In the last chapter the transmutations of naturally radioactive elements were studied. This was a spontaneous process, not subject to external control. In this chapter we shall study the effects of bombarding nuclei with various high-speed particles. We shall find that not only can nuclei be transmuted by nuclear bombardment, but also new elements may be produced which are radioactive. This invasion of the nucleus led to the discovery of the neutron and gives information regarding the structure of nuclei. Various machines for accelerating particles to high energies and the effects of these particles on nuclei will then be discussed, and general types of nuclear reactions will be described.

9.1. THE FIRST NUCLEAR TRANSMUTATION

One method of measuring the range of alpha-particles in a gas is shown in Fig. 95. The radioactive source is moved with respect to the screen, and the number of scintillations is observed as a function of the distance from the source to the fluorescent screen. Marsden used this method to determine the range of alpha-particles from RaC' in hydrogen in 1914. He found that the range of these alpha-particles was 28 centimeters, but that the number of scintillations observed did not drop completely to zero at distances above 28 centimeters. In fact, some scintillations were observed even when the source and screen were separated by as much as 100 centimeters, although these long-range scintillations were dimmer than the usual scintillations produced by alpha-particles.

Marsden interpreted this experiment to mean that hydrogen molecules were broken into two parts by the alpha-particles, each part being a proton. The long-range, but dimmer, scintillations were then produced by protons.

If energy and momentum are conserved in the disintegration of a hydrogen molecule by an alpha-particle, each proton should acquire a velocity $\frac{8}{5}$ as great as the velocity of the incident alpha-particle. Since empirically the range of alpha-particles varies as the $\frac{3}{2}$-power of their energy or the cube

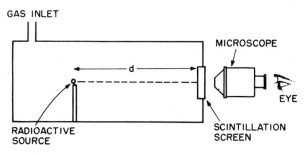

FIG. 95

Apparatus for determining the range of alpha particles in a gas, using the scintillation method.

of their velocity, let us assume that the same empirical law applies to protons also. Since the range of the alpha-particles was 28 centimeters, the range of protons produced by these alpha-particles should be approximately $28(1.6)^3 = 115$ centimeters. The agreement with the observed value of about 100 centimeters is quite striking, considering the approximations involved.

Rutherford repeated Marsden's experiment in 1919, using such gases as air, carbon dioxide, and nitrogen. Long-range scintillations with the appearance of proton scintillations were observed with air and nitrogen, but not with carbon dioxide. Furthermore, even when all traces of hydrogen were removed from the gases used, the scintillations continued to appear, indicating that the long-range scintillations were due to the presence of nitrogen molecules. Finally, Rutherford showed by magnetic deflection that these scintillations were produced by radiations with the same charge-to-mass ratio as protons. (Later these ideas were confirmed by cloud-chamber photographs.) The inescapable conclusion seems that the bombardment of nitrogen by alpha-particles produces protons.

To explain as simply as possible the production of protons by nitrogen, Rutherford suggested that the first nuclear transmutation had been observed, whereby nitrogen was converted into oxygen according to the following reaction:

$$_7N^{14} + {}_2He^4 \rightarrow {}_8O^{17} + {}_1H^1$$

Unfortunately, the isotope of oxygen produced by this transmutation is stable, so that it cannot be observed through its radioactivity, and since direct hits on nuclei are infrequent, not enough oxygen can be produced to be detected chemically. However, the Rutherford-Soddy rule has proved accurate in explaining the production of radioactive families from a long-lived parent, so that one can be quite confident that the reaction by which protons are produced is correct. In modern notation this first of all nuclear transmutations is written in the form $_7N^{14}(\alpha,p)_8O^{17}$. Thus, the twentieth century saw the achievement of the alchemists' dream of changing one element into another.

Rutherford and Chadwick soon found that most of the light elements could be transmuted by alpha-particles, the result being the production of an energetic proton. Furthermore, in the cases of fluorine, aluminum, and phosphorus, the range of the proton was greater than it would have been even if all the alpha-particle's energy had been transferred to the proton. Apparently transmutation of a nucleus may be accompanied by a release of energy, which is carried away by the proton. This release of nuclear energy will be treated later in this chapter.

9.2. THE DISCOVERY OF THE NEUTRON

Only three particles were known in 1932: the electron, the proton, and the alpha-particle. During the next few years the number of particles was more than doubled by the discoveries of the neutron, the positron, the meson, and, possibly, the neutrino. The discovery of the positron was described in Chapter 6 in connection with pair-formation by X-rays. In the next two sections the discoveries of the neutron and neutrino will be described, and in Chapter 11 the discovery of various mesons is discussed.

In 1930 Bothe and Becker noticed that when lithium, beryllium, or boron is bombarded with alpha-particles from polonium, a very penetrating radiation is emitted. Since this radiation can penetrate several centimeters of lead, it is certainly inexplicable in terms of protons, which are stopped by very thin foils of metals. In 1931 Frederic Joliot and his wife Irene Joliot-Curie (the daughter of Pierre and Marie Curie) measured the absorption coefficient of these radiations in lead. Assuming that the radiations were gamma rays, they deduced energies for these radiations of 11–20 mev from an extrapolation of the energy versus absorption coefficient curve then known for lead. At that time only the first part of the curve shown in Fig. 62, giving the variation of absorption coefficient with gamma-ray energy, was known, and they did not realize that the absorption coefficient begins to rise again as higher energies are reached. However, even their basic assumption that these radiations were gamma rays was incorrect, so that the faulty extrapolation is of little importance.

A striking effect was observed by Joliot and Curie when a sheet of paraffin was interposed in the beam of unknown radiation, as shown in Fig. 96. Instead of the paraffin absorbing some of the radiation and cutting down the number of counts registered by the detector, the interposition of the paraffin actually increased the number of counts. This discovery

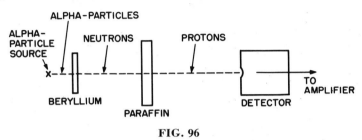

FIG. 96

Schematic diagram of apparatus used by Chadwick to measure the energy of protons knocked out of paraffin by neutrons.

was confirmed by Chadwick in 1932, and almost simultaneously Feather showed that the particles which emerged from the paraffin were protons. Chadwick then found that when alpha-particles from polonium were used to produce the unknown radiations by bombardment of beryllium, the protons knocked out of the paraffin by the unknown radiation had an energy of 5.65 mev. Similarly, when the radiations from beryllium were allowed to strike nitrogeneous material instead of paraffin, nitrogen nuclei of energy 1.61 mev were knocked in the direction of the original beam of radiation.

In order to pass through such large thicknesses of lead, the unknown radiations from beryllium must be either gamma-rays or neutral particles. Chadwick's data provided the means for deciding between these two possibilities. First consider a head-on collision between a photon and a motionless nucleus, as in the Compton effect discussed in Sec. 6.10. The nucleus will recoil in the *forward* direction (direction of the original photon), and the photon will rebound in the opposite direction. If m be the mass of the nucleus and W its kinetic energy, then from Eq. (318) the energy of the incident photon is

$$E = \frac{mc^2}{\left(1 + \dfrac{2mc^2}{W}\right)^{1/2} - 1} \tag{385}$$

Now if Chadwick's data for recoil protons and nitrogen nuclei are substituted into Eq. (385) on the assumption that the radiation from beryllium consists of photons, we find the values 54.1 mev and 103.5 mev for the initial energies of the photons. Since it seems unlikely that two different radiations are emitted by beryllium, with only one having effect in each case, the hypothesis of gamma radiation being emitted by beryllium seems unacceptable. Furthermore, since the energy of the alpha-particles from polonium which produce the unknown radiations from beryllium is only 5.30 mev, it seems unlikely that the radiations from beryllium could be so much larger. Thus we see that the gamma-ray hypothesis is rather unsuccessful.

Let us now consider the hypothesis that the radiations from beryllium consist of a stream of neutral particles of mass, m, and velocity, v. We will treat the case of head-on collision of such a particle with a nucleus, such that the nucleus recoils in the forward direction with velocity V, while the particle continues with velocity, v'. If the mass of the nucleus is M, the conservation equations take the form

$$\tfrac{1}{2}mv^2 = \tfrac{1}{2}mv'^2 + \tfrac{1}{2}MV^2 \tag{386}$$

$$mv = mv' + MV \tag{387}$$

Writing Eqs. (386) and (387) in terms of the energy of the bombarding particle, W and W', and the energy of the recoil nucleus, W_n, we find

$$W = W' + W_n \tag{388}$$

$$\sqrt{2mW} = \sqrt{2mW'} + \sqrt{2MW_n} \tag{389}$$

Eliminating the energy of the bombarding particle after collision, W', between Eqs. (388) and (389), for the energy of the recoil nucleus in the forward direction, we find the value

$$W_n = \frac{W(4mM)}{(m + M)^2} \tag{390}$$

If we substitute Chadwick's data for the energy of recoil protons and nitrogen nuclei into Eq. (390), we have the equations

$$1.61 = \frac{W(56m)}{(m + 14)^2} \quad \text{(nitrogen)} \tag{391}$$

$$5.65 = \frac{W(4m)}{(m + 1)^2} \quad \text{(hydrogen)} \tag{392}$$

Equations (391) and (392) provide two simultaneous equations in the unknown mass and energy of the incident particles. Solving these equations, we find

$$m = 1.16 \text{ amu}$$

$$W = 5.68 \text{ mev}$$

We see not only that the assumption of a neutral particle as the radiation from beryllium yields a single type of radiation, but also that the energy of the particle is of the same order of magnitude as the energy of the alpha-particles which produce the radiation. The neutral particle hypothesis is therefore much more satisfactory than the gamma-ray hypothesis because of both uniqueness and energy magnitude.

The neutral particle emitted by beryllium when bombarded with alpha-particles is called the *neutron*. The reaction by which neutrons are produced is as follows:

$$_4\text{Be}^9 + {}_2\text{He}^4 \rightarrow {}_6\text{C}^{12} + {}_0n^1$$

This reaction is still used as a source of neutrons, since the probability of an alpha-particle producing a neutron is high compared with most nuclear reactions. For example, one millicurie of radon mixed with enough beryllium to absorb all of the alpha-particles emitted by the radon will produce approximately 6700 neutrons per second. Today neutrons can be produced by the bombardment of a great number of different nuclei by various particles, but the original reaction is still one of the most prolific.

A more accurate determination of the mass of the neutron than that described above is provided by the photoelectric disintegration of the *deuteron* (heavy hydrogen nucleus) by gamma rays. If sufficiently energetic gamma rays strike deuterium, the following reaction takes place:

$$_1\text{H}^2 + hf \rightarrow {}_1\text{H}^1 + {}_0n^1$$

Experimentally the energy of the gamma-ray must be at least 2.21 mev before this reaction will take place. Remembering the equivalence of mass and energy, it is clear that the sum of the masses of the proton and neutron must be slightly greater than the mass of the deuteron. The energy brought in by the gamma ray is converted into the slight amount of additional mass needed to make the reaction take place.

As was described in connection with special relativity, only the sum of mass and energy is conserved. Since one atomic mass unit is equivalent to 931 mev of energy, the energy of the 2.21 mev gamma ray is equivalent to 0.00238 atomic mass units. Since the mass of the deuteron and the proton are known with great precision from mass spectrometry, the mass-energy balancing of the equation for the disintegration of the deuteron gives the equation

$$2.014718 + 0.00238 = 1.008128 + n$$

Solving this equation for the mass of the neutron, we obtain 1.00897 atomic mass units on the physical scale. The neutron is thus slightly heavier than the proton, and is distinguished from the proton chiefly by having no electrical charge.

9.3. BETA-DECAY AND THE NEUTRINO

When the energies of alpha-particles from various radioactive elements are measured by magnetic deflection, it is found that the alpha-particles of a given element all have the same energy or possibly several discrete energies. From this we conclude that there are discrete energy levels within nuclei which are analogous to the energy levels of the electronic structure of atoms. In addition, it is found that if an alpha-particle belongs to one of the less energetic groups, one or more gamma rays will be emitted which do carry off the remainder of the energy. Thus, application of the principle of conservation of energy to the emission energies of alpha-particles yields information regarding nuclear energy levels.

Now consider radioactive elements which emit beta-particles. By analogy with the case of alpha-particle emission, it might be expected that a beta-particle with less than the maximum amount of energy would be accompanied by one or more gamma rays carrying off the difference. Experimentally, however, the beta-particles from a given element have a wide and continuous distribution of energies. The energy distribution curve of a typical element is shown in Fig. 97. As shown in the diagram, the most probable energy is about half as great as the maximum energy, which is a definite value. Furthermore, beta-particles with less than the maximum value of energy are not followed by gamma-rays of appropriate energy, as occurs in the case

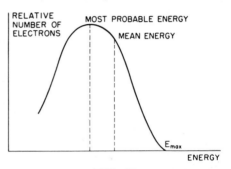

FIG. 97

Typical energy distribution of electrons from a beta-emitter.

of alpha-particle emission. As an example, the decay of $_1H^3$ to form $_2He^3$ plus an electron, represents a decrease in mass corresponding to 19.5 kev. This is in keeping with the energy of the most energetic electrons, which is 18.5 kev, but does not account for the lower energies of most of the electrons emitted.

The heat produced by electron emission can be measured calorimetrically by absorbing all the electrons emitted from a radioactive source and measuring the rise in temperature of the absorber. Calorimetric experiments of this sort show that the heat produced by electron emission corresponds to the average energy of the electron energy distribution curve, rather than to E_{max}. The problem is that while a definite energy, E_{max}, must be released during a disintegration, only a variable fraction of this energy is measurable, the remainder vanishing mysteriously.

The idea of nuclear energy levels is further strengthened by the study of elements which can decay in two different ways. For instance, ThC may emit an electron to form ThC′, which then emits an alpha-particle to form ThD, or ThC may emit an alpha-particle to form ThC″, which then emits an electron to form ThD. Clearly, the same total amount of energy must be released as ThC is converted into ThD in either way. As shown in Fig. 98, the total energy released in either branch can only be made the

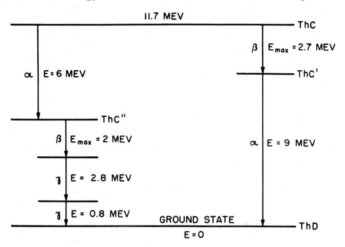

FIG. 98

Alternative paths by which ThC can decay to form ThD,
showing the energy involved in each transition.

same by taking for the energy of each electron emitted the maximum of the energy distribution curve, E_{max}. Apparently an energy E_{max} is released each time an electron is emitted, even though the electron itself does not always take all of this energy with it in the form of kinetic energy.

The momentum of the nucleus and the electron can be measured in various ways. It is found that the momenta of the electron and the recoil nucleus are not equal in magnitude and in opposite directions. If these were the only particles involved in electron emission, their momenta should be equal and opposite in order to conserve momentum, so we see that apparently conservation of momentum is also violated in electron emission.

A solution to this dilemma is to abandon the ideas of conservation of energy and momentum as applied to electron emission by nuclei. Most physicists are reluctant to do this, so in 1931 Pauli suggested an alternative: a previously unknown particle might carry away the undetected energy and momentum. This particle has been called the neutrino (little neutron). Since it would be electrically neutral and have little or no rest mass, it would pass through matter almost without any interaction. Such a particle would not violate the conservation principles, and yet it would be almost undetectable.

Belief in the existence of the neutrino was strengthened by the success of Fermi's theory of beta-decay, which was first proposed in 1934. By assuming an interaction between the electron, the neutrino, and the particles making up the nucleus, he was able to predict the energy distribution curves of positron and electron emitters. Until recently the success of this theory was the chief basis for belief in the existence of the neutrino. We will now describe the experiments through which the neutrino was finally detected.

Although neutrinos interact very weakly with matter, if they have sufficient energy they may occasionally produce certain reactions. If we let η stand for a neutrino and let $_{+1}\beta^0$ stand for a positron, one such reaction is the following:

$$\eta + {}_1H^1 \rightarrow {}_0n^1 + {}_{+1}\beta^0$$

In experiments begun in 1953 and culminating in 1956, Cowan and Reines verified the reaction above by detecting and identifying the positron and neutron produced.

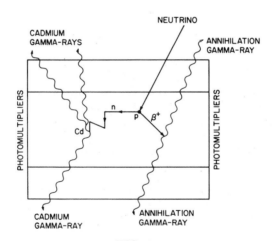

FIG. 99

Diagram of apparatus used by Cowan and Reines to detect the neutrino.

A nuclear reactor produced a flux of about 10^{13} neutrinos per square centimeter per second with high enough energies to make the reaction above take place. The chief difficulty lay in identifying the occasional reactions produced by neutrinos in the presence of a very large amount of background radiation. The apparatus used by Cowan and Reines is shown schematically in Fig. 99. The center tank contains cadmium chloride dissolved in water, the water providing the hydrogen targets. The positron quickly undergoes annihilation with the emission of two 0.51-mev gamma-rays in opposite directions. These annihilation gamma-rays produce scintillations in the liquid scintillator, and the scintillations are detected by groups of photomultipliers arranged at the ends of the tanks. Since the output of a photomultiplier is proportional to the energy of the gamma-ray striking the scintillation material, it is possible to distinguish between the annihilation gamma-rays and the gamma-rays of other energies. Thus, the positron produced by the neutrino is identified by the appearance in coincidence of two gamma-rays of energy 0.51 mev.

The neutron produced by the neutrino is slowed down by impacts with water molecules and in a few microseconds is captured by a cadmium nucleus. The excited cadmium nucleus decays with the emission of several gamma-rays with a characteristic total energy. These gamma-rays are detected by the photomultipliers and their energies determined from the outputs of the photomultipliers.

The pair of annihilation gamma-rays is used to start the sweep of an oscilloscope, the presentation being photographed. If characteristic gamma-rays from cadmium appear a few microseconds later, it becomes likely that both sets of gamma-rays come from a given neutrino. Neutrino events are observed about three times per hour, while the number drops almost to zero when the source of neutrinos (the nuclear reactor) is turned off. Thus, the observed events must be due to neutrinos being absorbed by protons. Later experiments with improved equipment have raised the counting rate due to neutrinos up to 44 counts per hour, and removed any lingering doubts as to the existence of the neutrino.

9.4. THE STRUCTURE OF THE NUCLEUS

As was mentioned in Sec. 8.6, the exact isotopic weights of all isotopes are very close to being integers on the $O^{16} = 16.00000$ scale. Since both the proton and the neutron have masses very close to unity, it would seem reasonable to consider one or both of them as constituents of nuclei. We will discard the alpha-particle and the deuteron as possibilities, since they are, almost certainly, composite particles. The gamma-ray, which is electromagnetic radiation, and the neutrino, which has neither rest-mass nor charge, can be excluded. The mesons and hyperons discussed in Chapter 11 are unstable particles with very short lifetimes, so we will not consider them as fundamental constituents of nuclei, although theories of nuclear binding force depend on mesons in the nucleus. The only remaining possibility is the electron, although according to the Fermi theory of beta-decay it is formed at the instant of emission. Reasons why the electron cannot be a permanent occupant of nuclei will be explained next.

The Heisenberg uncertainty principle discussed in Section 5.4 can be used to eliminate the electron as a possible permanent inhabitant of nuclei. Scattering experiments give estimates of nuclear dimensions of the order of 2×10^{-12} centimeters. Let us state Heisenberg's inequality in the form

$$(\Delta x) \cdot (\Delta p) \sim h$$

Then for a particle to be confined to the nucleus, so that the uncertainty in its position is no more than 2×10^{-12} centimeter, the uncertainty in its momentum must be at least as great as

$$\Delta p = \frac{h}{\Delta x} = \frac{6.6 \times 10^{-27}}{2 \times 10^{-12}} = 3.3 \times 10^{-15} \text{ gm-cm/sec}$$

Now the relativistic energy of a particle is related to its momentum according to the equation developed in Section 3.11 as follows:

$$W^2 = (pc)^2 + (m_0c^2)^2$$

If the momentum of a particle inside the nucleus is no more than the uncertainty in the momentum calculated above, this term in the energy equation will have the value

$$pc = 3.3 \times 10^{-15} \times 3 \times 10^{10} = 10^{-4} \text{ erg} = 60 \text{ mev}$$

After computing the total energy, W, the kinetic energy of a particle is computed by subtracting its rest-mass energy from its total energy.

Let us apply these ideas to the particles which are being considered as possible components of nuclei. For an electron, which has rest-mass energy of 0.5 mev, the total energy is almost exactly 60 mev. Thus, the kinetic energy of electrons confined to nuclei would be about 59.5 mev, even if there were only momentum due to the application of the Heisenberg principle to a confined particle. However, electrons emitted by naturally radioactive substances have energies of the order of a few mev, so that it appears unlikely that electrons could exist within nuclei for long. On the other hand, the rest-mass energy of a proton or a neutron is about 930 mev, so that the total energy of such a particle inside a nucleus is found to be 932 mev. Thus, the kinetic energy of a proton or neutron confined to a nucleus would be only about 2 mev, which is of the order of magnitude of the energy of particles emitted by nuclei. We thus conclude that while it is extremely unlikely that electrons can exist permanently inside of nuclei, protons and neutrons may do so.

We will construct nuclei from neutrons and protons, which are collectively known as *nucleons*, since they appear to be the most likely components.   Since the charge of a nucleus is equal to the atomic number of the element, we will build up nuclei by first taking a number of protons equal to the atomic number of the element, so that we will have the proper nuclear charge.   Enough neutrons are then added to bring the mass of the nucleus up to the mass number of the isotope in question.   In general, for an element of atomic number Z and mass number A, its nucleus consists of Z protons and $(A - Z)$ neutrons.   We see that the only difference between various isotopes of an element is in the number of neutrons in their nuclei. Similarly, isobars have the same number of nuclear particles, but the relative numbers of protons and neutrons are different.   Particles such as the deuteron and alpha-particle are of course composite particles, constructed in exactly the same way as other nuclei.   When various particles are emitted during a radioactive disintegration, the present idea is that these particles are formed at the instant of emission.   This explains why alpha-particles and electrons, for instance, may be emitted by unstable nuclei, even though these particles are not permanent residents of nuclei.   To sum up, the scheme of constructing nuclei from protons and neutrons is quite satisfactory, and it is quite unlikely that any changes will be made in this basic idea.

9.5. PARTICLE ACCELERATORS

After Rutherford had produced the first nuclear transmutations using alpha-particles from naturally radioactive elements, interest in nuclear bombardment grew rapidly.   Since the alpha-particles from naturally radioactive elements all have energies in the range of 4–8 mev, it would be highly desirable to be able to accelerate ions directly.   This would not only allow the energy of the ions to be adjustable, but would also allow the use of other ions aside from alpha-particles.   This section will be concerned with a brief description of the most successful of these ion accelerators.

Cockcroft and Walton completed the first of a long line of ion accelerators in 1930.   Their apparatus consisted essentially of a scheme for charging a number of condensers in parallel and discharging them in series, the switching being done by vacuum tubes.   The resulting high voltage is then applied between two electrodes in an evacuated accelerating tube.   Their first apparatus gave an energy of 0.3 mev to protons, while a later apparatus which was completed in 1932 gave a 10 microampere beam of protons at an energy of 0.7 mev.   Various other schemes for applying high direct voltages across an accelerating tube were tried at about the same time with varying degrees of success.   These methods include the use of transformers in cascade, Tesla coils, and even the use of atmospheric electricity, but none of these were successful enough to continue to be used for any length of time.

The electrostatic generator developed by Van de Graaff in 1931 reached the highest output of any machine of the direct applied voltage type.   Since this is the only machine of this type which is still being constructed and used, it will be described in some detail.   The principle of the *Van de Graaff generator* is that when any charge is transferred to a conductor, the charge will immediately distribute itself over the outside surface of the conductor.   Schematically, the design of such a machine is shown in Fig. 100.   Terminals E and G consist of many fine points, which give a corona discharge.   Thus, negative ions in the ionized air are repelled by E and are collected by the moving belt, which carries them up towards the conducting cap. Similarly, positive ions repelled by G are carried down the belt, so that the hemispherical cap gains electrons from E and loses positive charges at G, the result being that the cap is charged negatively. The charging rates of E and G are adjusted so as to be the same.

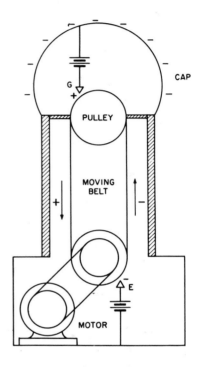

FIG. 100

Schematic diagram of a Van de Graaff electrostatic generator.

If the capacitance of the cap is C and it has a charge Q, then its potential is

$$V = \frac{Q}{C} \qquad (393)$$

For a sphere of radius r, the electrostatic field at its surface is

$$E = K' \frac{Q}{r^2} \qquad (394)$$

Since the capacitance of an isolated sphere is r/K', the relation between the potential of the cap and the electrostatic field at its surface is

$$V = rE \qquad (395)$$

The maximum potential of a given sphere will be attained just before the surrounding air breaks down and conducts a spark.   For example, if the radius of the cap is one meter and the electrostatic field for the breakdown of air is taken to be 3 million volts per meter, then the maximum voltage which such a machine could attain would be three million volts. In practice, however, the maximum voltage is limited by the leakage of charge from the cap rather than by the breakdown of the gas surrounding the machine. The highest voltages obtained with this machine have been less than 10 mev because of leakage losses. However, the loss of charge through leakage is also an advantage of this type of machine. By varying the charging rate in relation to the leakage losses, the voltage generated can be varied accordingly. This provides smooth and fine control of the output voltage, which is a great advantage in many types of experimental work.

Lawrence suggested a principle of particle acceleration which does not depend on the generation of extremely high direct voltages. Instead, ions receive many small increments of energy in succession while they are kept moving in a spiral path by a strong magnetic field. This principle of the *cyclotron* was proposed by Lawrence in 1929 and applied by Lawrence and Livingston in 1931. The machine is shown diagrammatically in Fig. 101.

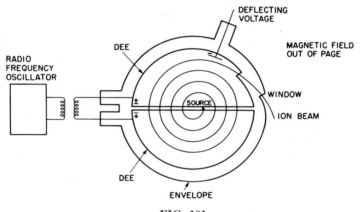

FIG. 101

Schematic diagram of a cyclotron.

Ions are provided by an ion source at the center of the machine. Two hollow electrodes called *dees* because of their shape are supported between the poles of a large electromagnet which produces a strong magnetic field perpendicular to the plane of the diagram. The whole interior of the dees is kept highly evacuated, so that ions can travel freely in circular orbits. Inside of the hollow dees, which are like a pill-box cut in two halves with the halves then separated slightly, there is no electric field, and charged particles move in circular orbits according to the equation

$$qvB = \frac{mv^2}{r} \qquad (396)$$

Thus the radius of a given orbit is

$$r = \frac{mv}{qB} \qquad (397)$$

Now suppose that an alternating voltage is applied across the gap separating the dees in such a phase that a particle is accelerated as it passes across this gap. The velocity of the particle is then increased and the next semi-circular orbit of the particle inside of a dee is larger in radius. The problem is to arrange things so that each time a particle arrives at the gap it will experience an accelerating electric field and gain some energy. Provided this can be done a sufficiently large number of times, ions of large energy can be obtained without the application of extremely large direct voltages.

The key to the successful operation of the cyclotron is seen when the time for a particle to traverse one semi-circle inside of a dee is computed. For an orbit of radius r, the time for a half revolution is

$$t = \frac{\pi r}{v} = \frac{\pi}{v}\left(\frac{mv}{qB}\right) = \frac{\pi m}{qB} \qquad (398)$$

Thus, the time for a half revolution depends only on the mass and charge of the ion and on the strength of the magnetic field, and not at all on the energy or velocity of the ion. If an alternating voltage is applied across the gap between the dees, the particle will be accelerated each time it passes the gap, provided that the frequency of the alternating voltage is

$$f = \frac{1}{2t} = \left(\frac{1}{2\pi}\right)\left(\frac{q}{m}B\right) \qquad (399)$$

If B is measured in gauss and numerical values of the charge and mass of common ions are substituted into Eq. (399), it is found that $f = 1525B$ for protons, and $f = 770B$ for deuterons or alpha-particles. Taking 10,000 gauss as a typical magnetic field, it is seen that the alternating voltage must have a frequency of the order of ten megacycles.

The energy acquired by an ion in its orbit inside the cyclotron is found by solving Eq. (397) for the velocity of the ion and substituting this value into the expression for the kinetic energy of a particle. The result is

$$E = \frac{1}{2}mv^2 = \frac{1}{2}mB^2r^2\left(\frac{q}{m}\right)^2 \qquad (400)$$

Using Eq. (399) to eliminate the values of B and q/m from Eq. (400), we find

$$E = 2\pi^2 mr^2 f^2 \qquad (401)$$

We see from Eq. (401) that the energy of a particle in an orbit of given radius is independent of the charge of the particle, while r and f are design constants of the machine [through Eq. (399)]. Thus, a cyclotron which produces 8 mev protons will produce 16 mev deuterons and 32 mev alpha-particles. We also see that ions which cross the gap when the accelerating voltage is not in the optimum phase for acceleration will still acquire the same energy; such particles will merely make more revolutions. Finally, the ions are brought outside the cyclotron where they can be used for bombardment of nuclei by deflecting the ion beam somewhat, as shown in Fig. 101.

Let us now consider the effects of the relativistic increase of the mass of particles with their velocity. Clearly this prevents the use of the cyclotron to accelerate electrons to any sizable energies, since Eq. (399) shows that the change of mass would throw the frequency of the alternating voltage out of synchronism with the time of revolution. Even for protons, a calculation shows that protons with an energy of 10 mev have a velocity of approximately 4.4×10^9 centimeters per second and a mass about 1.1% greater than the rest mass of a proton. Thus, even protons begin to fall out of step with the alternating voltage at these energies.

The relativistic increase of mass can be compensated for in several ways. Referring to Eq. (399), as long as the ratio B/m is kept constant, synchronism will be maintained. This could be achieved by designing the magnetic field so that it is greater at the outer orbits, where the particles have larger energies and thus greater masses, than at the center, where they are travelling slowly. A partial solution is to use higher voltages across the dees, so that the ions receive their energy in a smaller number of revolutions, thus minimizing disturbing effects. The best solution, however, is to vary the frequency applied to the dees in a way proportional to the increase in mass of the particles. This frequency modulation also compensates for the normal decrease of the magnetic field of a magnet from its center outward. *Frequency modulated cyclotrons* are now operating which accelerate ions to energies of 100–400 mev, so that disintegrations can be produced which are impossible with particles from radioactive nuclei which occur naturally.

The first accelerator which could give electrons large energies without the need for generating high direct voltages was developed by Kerst in 1940. In the *induction electron accelerator* or *betatron* a changing magnetic field serves two purposes. The changing magnetic field induces an accelerating electromotive force, while the magnetic field itself makes the electrons travel in circular orbits during the acceleration cycle. By maintaining the proper relationship between the magnitude of the magnetic field and its rate of change, the relativistic increases in mass of the electron can be compensated for and large energies can be acquired by electrons.

Consider an electron travelling in a circular orbit of radius, r, in a region where the magnetic field is increasing into the plane of the diagram, as shown in Fig. 102. If the total magnetic flux through this orbit changes from a value ϕ_1 to a value ϕ_2 in a time, t, then the average electromotive induced during this time interval is

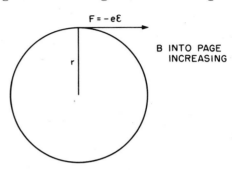

$$E = \frac{\phi_1 - \phi_2}{t} \qquad (402)$$

Now the electric field strength at the orbit is related to the electromotive force around the orbit by the equation

$$\mathcal{E} = \frac{E}{2\pi r} \qquad (403)$$

FIG. 102
Electron accelerated by a change of magnetic flux through a circular orbit.

Thus the force acting on an electron of charge $-e$ in this orbit is

$$F = -e\mathcal{E} = \frac{-eE}{2\pi r} = \frac{e(\phi_2 - \phi_1)}{2\pi rt} \qquad (404)$$

Now for a circular orbit of radius, r, for the momentum, Eq. (397) gives the value

$$mv = Ber \qquad (405)$$

Thus, for the electron to remain in an orbit of a given radius, any change in its momentum must accompany a change in the value of the magnetic field at the orbit, the relation being

$$(mv)_2 - (mv)_1 = (B_2 - B_1)er \qquad (406)$$

Returning to Eq. (404), the impulse produced by the electric force is related to the change in momentum according to the equation

$$(mv)_2 - (mv)_1 = Ft = \frac{e(\phi_2 - \phi_1)}{2\pi r} \qquad (407)$$

Comparing Eqs. (406) and (407), we see that for a circular orbit of a given radius, the following relation must hold between the change in the strength of the magnetic field at the orbit and the change in the magnetic flux through the plane of the orbit:

$$B_2 - B_1 = \frac{\phi_2 - \phi_1}{2\pi r^2} \qquad (408)$$

Now the flux through a circle can be expressed in terms of the average magnetic field throughout the circle, $\overline{B}$, by the equation

$$\phi = \overline{B}(\pi r^2) \tag{409}$$

Comparing Eqs. (408) and (409), we see that the relation between the value of the magnetic field at the orbit and the average value of the magnetic field throughout the area bounded by the orbit is

$$B_2 - B_1 = \tfrac{1}{2}(\overline{B}_2 - \overline{B}_1) \tag{410}$$

Thus, for the electron to be accelerated in a circular orbit of constant radius, the change in the magnetic field at the orbit must be just one half the change of the average magnetic field throughout the orbit. In the special case when the initial magnetic field is zero throughout the orbit, the average field throughout the orbit must change in such a way that it is always just twice the strength of the magnetic field at the orbit. If the condition of Eq. (410) is satisfied, electrons can be accelerated even though their masses change radically during the acceleration cycle.

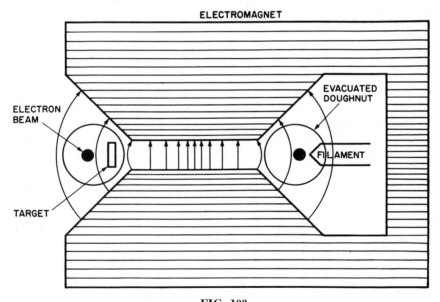

FIG. 103
Cross-section of a betatron or induction electron accelerator.

The varying magnetic field is usually produced by applying an alternating voltage of 60–600 cycles per second to an electromagnet. The inductance of the electromagnet is tuned to resonance at the frequency of the applied voltage by using large condensers, which are one of the most expensive items in the construction of a betatron.   The average magnetic field throughout the area bounded by the orbit is made larger than the value of the magnetic field at the orbit by tapering the pole tips of the electromagnet, as shown in Fig. 103.   Near the end of the accelerating cycle the iron at the center of the electromagnet saturates, so that Eq. (410) is no longer satisfied.   This causes the orbit to become smaller, so that the electrons spiral in towards the inner wall of the accelerating tube and strike the target.   One disadvantage of the betatron is that the target must be enclosed in the accelerating tube, since it is difficult to deflect the beam out of the betatron.

A betatron giving electrons energies of 250 mev is in operation at the University of Illinois and other betatrons developing energies of the order of 100 mev have been built.   However, electrons travelling in a circular orbit experience a very large centripetal acceleration, which results in the radiation of electromagnetic radiation.   The loss of energy due to radiation makes the construction of even larger betatrons uneconomical.   This difficulty is avoided in the *linear accelerator*, since the electrons quickly reach a velocity almost equal to the velocity of light at fairly low energies and experience very little further acceleration.   Increments of energy are given to the electrons either by having them pass through a series of cavities, which have voltages applied in the proper phases, or by electrodes properly spaced and phased with voltages which continually accelerate a pulse of electrons.   The energy acquired by an electron is approximately proportional to the length of the accelerator, so that it is possible to increase energy output by increasing the length of the accelerator.   Machines of this sort have reached energies of approximately one bev, and in principle very much higher energies could be obtained with a sufficiently long accelerator.   When heavy ions are accelerated in a linear accelerator, higher beam currents than in cyclotrons can be obtained for particles with energies of the order of 100 mev.

In order to reach very high energies using the cyclotron or betatron principles requires building huge magnets.   Since the price of such a machine increases approximately as the cube of the energy attained, new ideas must be used to reach energies measured in bev.   The *proton synchrotron* avoids using large magnets by using a combination of the cyclotron and betatron principles, and by using a magnet in the shape of a circular ring of C cross-section.   The magnetic field is maintained only in the gap of the C cross-section, rather than throughout the area of the ring.   The protons are accelerated once each revolution as they pass through the accelerating electrodes, to which a radio-frequency voltage is applied.

First consider the cyclotron-like orbits, where we are interested in the particles which arrive at the accelerating gaps just as the voltage is zero and decreasing, so that the particles acquire no energy at the gaps.   Particles which arrive at the gaps too early will encounter an opposing electric field at the gaps and will be slowed down.   After several such decelerations, these particles will eventually be slowed down until they circumnavigate an orbit in just the correct time.   Similarly, particles which arrive at the gaps too late will find an accelerating electric field and will be speeded up until they are travelling around the orbit in synchronism with the alternating voltage applied to the gaps.   We then have particles all travelling in a stable, self-maintaining orbit with an energy which depends on the magnetic field strength at the orbit and the frequency of the applied alternating voltage.

To increase the energy of particles in one of these *phase-stable orbits*, we change either the frequency or the magnetic field strength, or both.   If the change is slow enough, the particles will continue in the same orbits due to the phase stability described in the paragraph above.   The advantage of this scheme is that the radius of a phase-stable orbit increases only slightly with the energy of the particles, so that a large expanse of magnet is not needed.   In addition, the increase in the magnetic field accelerates the particles by an induced electromotive force, but the betatron flux condition does not have to be satisfied to keep the particles in stable orbits.

The first proton synchrotron in operation was the *cosmotron* at the Brookhaven National Laboratory at Upton, N.Y. in 1952, which produced an energy of 3 bev.   After this and several other similar machines were built, it was found that greatly improved focussing of the beam could be obtained by using a series of alternate diverging and converging magnetic lenses of great strength.   This allows using smaller magnets, more protons per pulse, and greater energy output.   In 1959 the European Organization for Nuclear Research, CERN, operated its *alternating gradient proton synchrotron* at 28.3 bev.   Protons are given an energy of 50 mev in a linear accelerator and then enter the ring-shaped structure, which is 200 meters in diameter.   Similar machines reaching even higher energies are under construction, and 30 bev was attained at Brookhaven during 1960.

9.6. INDUCED RADIOACTIVITY

The first transmutations produced by Rutherford and other workers yielded extremely minute quantities of stable isotopes already found in nature. The equation for the nuclear reaction had to be deduced using the Rutherford-Soddy rule, and direct identification of the product nucleus could not be made, since the number of atoms transformed was too small to be detected chemically.   In this section we shall discuss the discovery of nuclear reactions where the product nucleus was unstable, so that its existence could be detected through its radioactivity, even when minute amounts of material were transformed.

Joliot and Curie bombarded boron with alpha-particles from polonium in 1934. They found that positrons were emitted by the target, even after the source of alpha-particles had been removed. This positron activity was found to have a definite half-life of about ten minutes. Similarly, when aluminum was bombarded with alpha-particles a positron activity of about three minute half-life was observed.

The conclusion to be drawn from the experiment above is that new elements were being formed which emitted positrons in order to achieve stability. If this hypothesis were true, the new element might be chemically different from boron and thus separable from it by ordinary chemical procedures. The primary reaction suggested by Joliot and Curie was the formation of a previously unknown isotope of nitrogen according to the reaction

$$_5B^{10} + {}_2He^4 \rightarrow {}_0n^1 + {}_7N^{13}$$

It was then assumed that the new nitrogen isotope decayed by the emission of a positron, the reaction being

$$_7N^{13} \rightarrow {}_6C^{13} + \beta^+$$

To confirm this hypothesis, chemical procedures were used which would separate nitrogen from boron, and the positron activity was found to follow the chemistry of nitrogen.

This discovery of *induced radioactivity* was tremendously important, since the products of such a reaction could be identified from their chemistry. The minute traces of the products of transmutations can be followed in chemical reactions by observing the characteristic radioactive properties of each isotope: type of particle emitted, energy of particle, and half-life of emitter. Once the chemical nature of a radioactive isotope is discovered by comparing its chemistry with the chemistry of known elements, the atomic number of the *radio-isotope* is known immediately. With this information, the results of a nuclear transmutation could be deduced with certainty. In addition, this discovery of induced radioactivity is important because it makes possible a very wide range of radio-isotopes which can be produced by suitable transmutations.

Since the discovery of induced radioactivity occurred at about the same time as the discovery of the neutron and the construction of the first machines to accelerate ions, new induced radioactivities were discovered rapidly. Beginning in 1934 Fermi bombarded most of the elements in the periodic table with neutrons, since it seemed plausible that an unchanged particle might enter a nucleus more easily than an ion. A large number of induced radioactivities were found. Since the addition of a neutron makes the nucleus too heavy for its charge, electrons are usually emitted as the unstable isotope achieves stability. Radioactive isotopes of all of the elements are now known, and many of these can be produced in a variety of ways.

9.7. NUCLEAR REACTIONS

A quantity which is important in describing the probability that a given bombarding particle will produce a particular nuclear transmutation is the *capture cross-section*, σ. If we define the following quantities:

N = number of bombarding particles per square centimeter

Q = number of target nuclei per square centimeter

n = number of nuclei transmuted per square centimeter,

then the capture cross-section is defined as follows:

$$\sigma = \frac{n}{NQ} \tag{411}$$

The cross-section of a nuclear reaction is the probability that a single bombarding particle will react with a single target nucleus, and its dimensions are square centimeters. However, the capture cross-section is not an inherent geometric factor, but depends on the nature of the bombarding particle and the target nucleus, as well as the energy of the bombarding particle. In fact, the result of bombardment of a given nucleus with a given particle is not necessarily unique, so the type of transmutation must also be specified, if there are several competing reactions taking place.

Values of cross-sections for various reactions range from 10^{-32} to 10^{-20} square centimeters. A convenient unit for expressing cross-sections is the *barn*, which is defined as 10^{-24} square centimeters. A cross-section of one barn is fairly large, representing a fairly likely reaction, and therefore a nucleus which is easy to hit. This may indeed be the origin of the term.

In all nuclear reactions, energy and momentum are conserved, provided it is understood that mass and energy are equivalent. In addition, the Rutherford-Soddy rule applies to all reactions, so that nuclear charge and mass numbers are also conserved. In a typical nuclear reaction, the bombarding particle and the target nucleus are known, and the nature of the light product particle (proton, neutron, etc.) is determined from its characteristics. Using the Rutherford-Soddy rule, the nature of the product nucleus is determined. After this rough balancing has been done, the detailed balancing of momentum and energy is carried out. If the total mass of the products is less than the total mass of the initial particles, the loss in mass in the reaction will appear as kinetic energy shared by the product particles, or may be emitted in the form of gamma-radiation. If the masses of the various particles are known, the energies of the product particles can be computed by the usual rules of dynamics.

The *Q-value* of a nuclear reaction is defined as the difference between the sum of the masses of the initial particles (bombarding particle and target nucleus) and the sum of the masses of the product particles (product nucleus and product particle). If the *Q*-value is positive, the reaction is *exoergic* and energy is released by the nuclear reaction. If the *Q*-value is negative, the reaction is *endoergic*; clearly, an endoergic reaction cannot take place at all unless enough kinetic energy is supplied by the initial particles to create the required increase in mass. However, an energy equal to *Q* is not sufficient to make an endoergic reaction take place, since the bombarding particle would have momentum before the impact, while the product particles would have no momentum. Thus, the *threshold energy*, which is the minimum energy which will make an endoergic reaction take place, is greater than the *Q*-value. This situation is analyzed at the end of this chapter.

In computing values of *Q*, in principle the masses of bare nuclei should be used. However, since many isotopic masses have been determined with mass spectrometers, customarily the masses of neutral atoms are tabulated. We will show now that this is no handicap, except in reactions where electrons or positrons are involved. Consider the typical reaction given by the equation

$$_5B^{10} + {}_1H^2 \rightarrow {}_5B^{11} + {}_1H^1$$

If six electrons are added to each side of the equation, the nuclei become neutral atoms, while the mass difference between the two sides of the equation is unchanged. Thus, we can use the masses of neutral atoms in computing the *Q*-value for this reaction. (The masses of neutral hydrogen and deuterium should be used for the masses of the proton and deuteron, of course.) The masses of the neutral atoms are found to be as follows:

$$\begin{array}{ll} {}_5B^{10} = 10.016119 & {}_5B^{11} = 11.012790 \\ {}_1H^2 = \underline{2.014740} & {}_1H^1 = \underline{1.008145} \\ \phantom{{}_1H^2 = }12.030589 & \phantom{{}_1H^1 = }12.020940 \end{array}$$

Since the mass of the initial particles exceeds the mass of the product particles by 0.009919 atomic mass units, this is an exoergic reaction. Since one amu is equivalent to 931 mev, the *Q*-value of this reaction is 9.23 mev, which is shared by the product particles in the form of kinetic energy.

Now consider a reaction in which an electron is involved, such as

$$_6C^{14} \rightarrow {}_7N^{14} + \beta^-$$

In this reaction, if six electrons are added to each side, the carbon nucleus will be neutralized. The additional electron necessary to neutralize the nitrogen nucleus may be considered to be the electron emitted in the reaction, as far as computing Q-values is concerned. Thus, the mass of the electron emitted is effectively included by using the mass of neutral nitrogen in computations. Since the masses of these atoms are

$$_6C^{14} = 14.007687 \qquad _7N^{14} = 14.007520$$

this reaction is an exoergic reaction, with a mass difference of 0.000167 amu or 0.155 mev. The rule for computing Q-values in reactions including electrons is to ignore the electron, as its mass will be included in the mass of the neutral product atom.

The case is somewhat different when positrons are emitted, as in the following reaction:

$$_7N^{13} \rightarrow _6C^{13} + \beta^+$$

When seven electrons are added to neutralize the nitrogen nucleus, an excess of two electrons is left on the right-hand side of the equation. Thus, if neutral atomic masses are used, two electronic masses must be added to the total mass on the right-hand side of the equation. In this case we have

$$_7N^{13} = 13.009864 \qquad \begin{aligned} _6C^{13} &= 13.007478 \\ 2\beta^+ &= \underline{0.001098} \\ & 13.008576 \end{aligned}$$

Thus this is an exoergic reaction with a mass loss of 0.00129 amu, corresponding to a release of energy of 1.20 mev.

The rule for computing Q-values from masses of neutral atoms may be summed up by saying that neutral masses may always be used, unless electrons or positrons are involved. If electrons are involved, their masses are ignored, whereas two electron masses must be added to the mass of the product for each positron emitted. If electrons or positrons are accounted for in this way, the masses of neutral atoms may always be used.

Relativistic effects begin to become important when the kinetic energy of a particle is about one tenth of its rest-mass energy. Thus, relativistic expressions must always be used for any electrons appearing in nuclear reactions, since the rest-mass energy of an electron is only 0.511 mev. Since the rest-mass energy of a proton or neutron is about 934 mev, classical expressions can be used for these particles if their energies are less than about 100 mev. Similar considerations apply to other particles. The discussions of nuclear dynamics in this book will be confined to energies where relativistic expressions are not needed.

As a typical example of a nuclear reaction we shall consider the reaction $_5B^{10}(d,p)_5B^{11}$. This reaction was discussed in connection with the computation of Q-values from values of neutral atomic masses, and the Q-value of this reaction was found to be 9.23 mev.   Suppose the energy of the incident deuterons is 4.00 mev, and it is required that we find the energy of the protons emitted at an angle of 30° to the forward direction.   This bom-

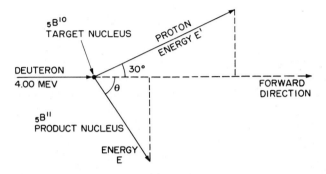

FIG. 104
Nuclear reaction analyzed in text.

bardment situation is shown in Fig. 104.   The equation expressing conservation of energy then takes the form

$$9.23 + 4.00 = E + E' \qquad (412)$$

Assuming that the product nucleus goes off at an angle θ with the forward direction, momentum components must be conserved.   Since energies are usually of prime interest, it is more convenient to write $p = mv = \sqrt{(2mE)}$ in the momentum equations, which then take the form:

$$\sqrt{2 \times 2 \times 4} = \left(\frac{1}{2}\sqrt{3}\right)\sqrt{2 \times 1 \times E'} + (\cos\theta)\sqrt{2 \times 11 \times E} \qquad (413)$$

$$0 = \frac{1}{2}\sqrt{2 \times 1 \times E'} - (\sin\theta)\sqrt{2 \times 11 \times E} \qquad (414)$$

In Eqs. (413) and (414), the mass numbers of the nuclei have been used in place of the exact isotopic weights; this is accurate enough for almost all purposes.   The angle, θ, may be eliminated between Eqs. (413) and (414) by solving them for the terms in θ, squaring each equation, and then adding. Using the identity $\sin^2\theta + \cos^2\theta = 1$, we find

$$22E = \frac{E'}{2} + 16 - (\sqrt{3})(\sqrt{16})\sqrt{2E'} + \frac{3}{2}E' \qquad (415)$$

Using Eq. (412) to eliminate E and collecting terms, we have

$$22(13.23 - E') = 2E' - \sqrt{(96E')} + 16 \qquad (416)$$

Cancelling some common factors and solving for the term in $\sqrt{E'}$, we find

$$\sqrt{6E'} = 6E' + 4 - 11 \times 6.62 \tag{417}$$

Squaring Eq. (417) to eliminate the radical and collecting terms, we have

$$(E')^2 - 23.1E' + (131.5)^2 = 0 \tag{418}$$

The solutions of Eq. (418) are found to be $E' = 12.95$ and $E' = 10.25$. The corresponding values of E are 0.28 mev and 2.98 mev. However, substitution of these solutions back into the original equations, Eqs. (413)–.(414), shows that the second of these solutions is spurious, having been introduced during the algebraic manipulations. The correct solution is that $E' = 12.95$ mev, $E = 0.28$ mev. Other problems in nuclear dynamics are solved by a similar procedure.

In many cases the problem is worked backward. That is, the energies of the product particle and nucleus are measured at a particular direction, and the equations are solved for Q. Knowing the exact masses of the initial particle, initial nucleus, and product particle, the mass of the product nucleus can be computed from the Q-value. In this way the mass of a radio-isotope which is produced only in minute quantities can be determined

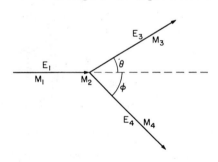

with great precision. A typical bombardment situation is shown in Fig. 105. A bombarding particle of mass M_1 and kinetic energy E_1 strikes a motionless target particle of mass M_2. The product nucleus, having a mass M_3, an energy E_3, goes off in a direction making an angle θ with the forward direction. The light product particle has a mass M_4, an energy E_4, and goes off in a direction making an angle ϕ with the forward direction. Usually the energy of the light particle, E_4, is measured in some particular direction ϕ and Q is computed. Since M_1, M_2, and M_4 are known with great accuracy, it can be seen below how M_3 can then be determined with similar accuracy.

FIG. 105
Typical nuclear bombardment reaction.

From the definition of Q given earlier in this section, we have

$$Q = (M_1 + M_2) - (M_3 + M_4) \tag{419}$$

It should be noted that Q is positive for an exoergic reaction and negative for an endoergic reaction. From conservation of energy,

$$E_1 + Q = E_3 + E_4 \tag{420}$$

As in the numerical example above, it is convenient to introduce kinetic energy into the momentum equations by using the identity $p = \sqrt{2ME}$. Conservation of momentum components in the forward direction and in a direction perpendicular to the forward direction yield the following two equations:

$$\sqrt{2M_1E_1} = \sqrt{2M_3E_3}\cos\theta + \sqrt{2M_4E_4}\cos\phi \qquad (421)$$

$$0 = \sqrt{2M_3E_3}\sin\theta - \sqrt{2M_4E_4}\sin\phi \qquad (422)$$

The angle θ can be eliminated between Eqs. (421) and (422) by using the identity $\sin^2\theta + \cos^2\theta = 1$, as was done before. The result is

$$M_1E_1 - 2\sqrt{M_1E_1M_4E_4}\cos\phi + M_4E_4 = M_3E_3 \qquad (423)$$

When the value of E_3 from Eq. (420) is substituted into Eq. (423) and the resulting equation is solved for Q, we find

$$Q = E_1\left(\frac{M_1}{M_3} - 1\right) + E_4\left(\frac{M_4}{M_3} + 1\right) - 2\frac{\sqrt{M_1E_1M_4E_4}}{M_3}\cos\phi \qquad (424)$$

Since it is found that Q is always a small fraction of an atomic mass unit, mass numbers may be used in place of exact isotopic masses in Eq. (424).

The result of bombarding a given type of nucleus with a given particle is not always unique. According to Bohr's theory of nuclear reactions, two steps take place in such a bombardment. First, the incident particle combines with the target nucleus to form a *compound nucleus*. In the bombardment of boron with deuterons, this first stage is represented by $_5B^{10} + {}_1H^2 \rightarrow {}_6C^{12}$. In a time of the order of 10^{-12} second the compound nucleus disintegrates to form the reaction products. The complete equation for the bombardment of boron is

$$_5B^{10} + {}_1H^2 \rightarrow {}_6C^{12} \rightarrow {}_5B^{11} + {}_1H^1$$

In most nuclear equations, however, the compound nucleus is omitted. The mode of disintegration is not directly connected with the nature of the original particle and nucleus, but rather depends on what competing disintegrations of the compound nucleus are energetically possible. Practically every conceivable combination of bombarding particle and product particle has been observed in some nuclear reaction, and almost any reaction can be made to occur if the bombarding particle carries enough energy into the system.

As an example of a bombardment in which the result is not unique, consider the bombardment of aluminum by deuterons. The following reactions have been observed to occur:

$$_2\mathrm{He}^4 + {}_{12}\mathrm{Mg}^{25} \text{ (stable)}$$

$$_{13}\mathrm{Al}^{27} + {}_1\mathrm{H}^2 \rightarrow {}_{14}\mathrm{Si}^{29} \nearrow\searrow {}_1\mathrm{H}^1 + {}_{13}\mathrm{Al}^{28} \rightarrow \beta^- + {}_{14}\mathrm{Si}^{28} \text{ (stable)}$$

$$_0 n^1 + {}_{14}\mathrm{Si}^{28} \text{ (stable)}$$

After the formation of $_{13}\mathrm{Al}^{28}$ by bombardment, it decays by the emission of an electron to form $_{14}\mathrm{Si}^{28}$.   In the reaction above it is interesting to note that the compound nucleus, $_{14}\mathrm{Si}^{29}$, is a stable isotope which is found in nature.   However, because of the large, exoergic Q-value of this reaction, the silicon nucleus is formed in a very high state of energy excitation.   The relative probabilities of the three modes of disintegration of the compound nucleus depend on the energy of the bombarding deuteron.

When the product nucleus is unstable, as in the case of the isotope $_{13}\mathrm{Al}^{28}$ in the example above, it will usually achieve stability by adjusting its nuclear charge by means of the emission of a positron or an electron.   Thus, an artificial isotope which is lighter than a stable isotope of the same element will usually emit a positron, in order to decrease its atomic number.   Similarly, an isotope which is too heavy will usually emit an electron, in order to increase its nuclear charge.   Examples of these disintegrations are provided by the sodium isotopes, the only stable one being $_{11}\mathrm{Na}^{23}$.   The decay schemes of the artificial isotopes of sodium are as follows:

$$_{11}\mathrm{Na}^{22} \rightarrow \beta^+ + {}_{10}\mathrm{Ne}^{22} \text{ (stable)}$$

$$_{11}\mathrm{Na}^{23} \text{ (stable)}$$

$$_{11}\mathrm{Na}^{24} \rightarrow \beta^- + {}_{12}\mathrm{Mg}^{24} \text{ (stable)}$$

For the same reason, nuclear reactions which maintain the ratio of nuclear charge to nuclear mass approximately constant, often produce stable products.   Examples of reactions of this kind are (α,p), (d,α), and (p,α). Finally, the absorption of a neutron by a nucleus often makes the nucleus too heavy for stability, so that such processes usually produce electron emitters.

If the bombarding particle has sufficient energy, more than one product particle may be produced.   For instance, bombardment of bismuth with 32 mev alpha-particles yields the reaction

$$_{83}\mathrm{Bi}^{209} + 2\mathrm{He}^4 \rightarrow {}_{85}\mathrm{At}^{211} + 2_0 n^1$$

At very high energies *spallation* may occur, where the nucleus is smashed into fragments.   When oxygen is bombarded with 90 mev neutrons, the result may be either two protons, two neutrons, and three alpha-particles, or a neutron and four alpha-particles.   Alternatively, heavy nuclei may undergo *fission*, where the nucleus breaks up into two moderate-sized fragments plus a few elementary particles.   This process will be discussed in the next chapter.

Finally, it should be noted that nuclear bombardment can produce previously unknown elements, of which no isotopes are known on earth. At present, man-made elements have filled in some gaps in the periodic table and extended the table up through element 102, the new elements having been named neptunium (93), plutonium (94), americium (95), curium (96), berkelium (97), californium (98), einsteinium (99), fermium (100), mendelevium (101), and nobelium (102).

ADDITIONAL READING

Cork, James M., *Radioactivity and Nuclear Physics*.   Princeton: D. Van Nostrand Co., 1957 (3rd Ed.).   An excellent text with many references to the literature.

Pollard, Ernest and Davidson, William L., Jr., *Applied Nuclear Physics*.   New York: John Wiley and Sons, 1951 (2nd Ed.).   Non-mathematical exposition of the uses of radioactivity.

Beyer, Robert T. (editor), *Foundations of Nuclear Physics*.   New York: Dover Publications, Inc., 1949.   Facsimiles of thirteen fundamental papers and an extensive bibliography.

PROBLEMS

1. Write down five reactions by which $_{27}Co^{58}$ could be produced.   (At least six have been observed.)

2. When tritium $(_1H^3)$ is bombarded with 4 mev deuterons, neutrons are produced.   Write the equation for this reaction and compute its Q-value in mev.

3. Compute the energy of the neutrons emitted in the forward direction in the reaction of Problem 2.   (*Ans.* 20.9 mev)

4. Compute the energy of the neutrons emitted perpendicular to the forward direction in the reaction of Problem 2.

5. When $_{38}Sr^{88}$ is bombarded with deuterons, $_{38}Sr^{89}$ is formed.   Consider the bombardment of a strontium target one millimeter thick by deuterons at a beam current of 200 microamperes.   Assuming that the cross-section for this reaction is 0.1 barn and the deuterons can pass completely through this thickness of strontium, compute the number of strontium atoms transmuted in one hour.   (*Ans.* 7.70×10^{14})

6. Refer to Problem 5.   If the cyclotron costs $20 an hour to operate and the half-life of $_{38}Sr^{89}$ is 55 days, compute the price per millicurie of radio-strontium produced.

7. When $_3\text{Li}^7$ is bombarded with 0.5 mev protons, two prolific reactions take place. A high-energy gamma ray may be emitted by $_4\text{Be}^8$, which subsequently disintegrates into two low-energy alpha-particles, or two high-energy alpha-particles may be produced. Compute the energy of the high-energy component of each of these reactions.

(*Ans.* 17.8 mev, 8.9 mev each)

8. When $_3\text{Li}^6$ is bombarded with very slow neutrons, alpha-particles and tritium atoms are produced. (This is one way to produce tritium.) If the energy of the alpha-particles is measured to be 1.93 mev, compute the mass of tritium.

9. Estimate the threshold energy for the occurrence of $(n,2n)$ reactions.

(*Ans.* 5 − 10 mev)

10. Put numerical values in Eq. (399) and show that if B is measured in gauss, the required frequency for cyclotron acceleration of protons is $f = 1525B$ and for alpha-particles or deuterons the required frequency is $770B$.

11. Show that if the frequency of a cyclotron is measured in megacycles and the radius of its dees in inches, then, if particles of mass number M are accelerated, their energy will be given by

$$E \text{ (ev)} = 132Mf^2r^2$$

12. As was mentioned in Sec. 9.7, endoergic reactions do not take place until the energy of the bombarding particle, E_1, is sufficiently greater than Q for momentum to be conserved. Treat Eq. (424) as a quadratic equation in the variable $\sqrt{E_1}$ ánd derive the following expression for the threshold value of E_1 by requiring that E_1 be real:

$$E_1 = \frac{(M_3 + M_4)Q}{M_1 - M_3 - M_4 + (M_1M_4/M_3) \sin^2\phi}$$

13. Consider the production of $_4\text{Be}^7$, using protons as bombarding particles. Write down the four possible bombardment reactions not involving spallation reactions or the use of radioactive isotopes as a target, by which $_4\text{Be}^7$ could be produced.

14. Refer to Problem 13. If you use protons of energy 1.8 mev, determine quantitatively whether or not each of the possible reactions will actually take place. Decide which element you would actually choose to bombard.

15. An accelerator beam produces k radioactive atoms per second in a target. If the radioisotope produced has a disintegration constant λ, show that the number of radioactive atoms, N, after bombardment for a time, t, is given by

$$N = \frac{k}{\lambda}(1 - e^{-\lambda t})$$

16. Refer to Problem 15. If $k = 10^8$ per second, compute the time to induce an activity of one millicurie in a radioisotope of half-life 3 hours.

chapter ten

nuclear fission and
applications of nuclear physics

The discovery of nuclear fission was probably the most important single development in the study of physics, from the point of view of the common man. From this discovery to the nuclear pile reactor and the atomic bomb was a step that revolutionised socio-political and economic conditions in the world for all time. In this chapter we shall trace the development of this aspect of nuclear physics, and will also discuss other applications of nuclear physics.

10.1. THE DISCOVERY OF NUCLEAR FISSION

After the discovery of induced radioactivity by Joliot and Curie in 1934, Fermi and others conducted a systematic search for neutron-induced radioactivities. When heavy elements, such as uranium and thorium, were bombarded by neutrons, many activities were induced, most of them being electron emitters. At first it was believed that *transuranic elements*, lying beyond uranium in the periodic table, were being produced. A typical process by which element 93 might be produced by the neutron bombardment of uranium is as follows:

$$_{92}U^{238} + {}_0n^1 \rightarrow {}_{92}U^{239} \rightarrow \beta^- + {}_{93}X^{239}$$

Unfortunately, the number of new activities induced by the bombardment of heavy elements soon increased to the point where even the postulation of transuranic elements through element 97 did not account for the facts.

No plausible decay scheme similar to the decay schemes of the families of naturally radioactive elements could account for all the known activities.

During 1938 Curie and Savitch found an activity which was precipitated with lanthanum $(Z = 57)$, but they still believed the radioactivity was due to a heavy element. At the same time, Hahn and Strassman found an activity which followed the chemistry of barium $(Z = 56)$ and which was accompanied by an activity which was the same as that of a known radio-isotope of krypton $(Z = 36)$. At first they thought they were dealing with radium, which is similar chemically to barium, but finally, exhaustive chemical tests convinced them that the activity was due to an isotope of barium. The question was how an isotope of barium could appear when uranium was bombarded with neutrons.

To solve this dilemma Hahn and Strassman hesitantly suggested that perhaps bombardment of uranium with neutrons did not produce a slightly heavier nucleus, but rather that the uranium nucleus broke up into two moderate sized fragments. The reaction might be as follows:

$$_{92}U^{238} + _0n^1 \rightarrow _{92}U^{239} \rightarrow _{56}Ba + _{56}Kr + \text{neutrons}$$

This fragmentation of the uranium nucleus was named by Meitner and Frisch *nuclear fission*. Immediately the whole world began the study of the fission of the heavy elements. Very quickly it was found that thorium $(Z = 90)$ and proto-actinium $(Z = 91)$ also underwent fission, and a large number of fission products were soon identified chemically. It is now known that any heavy element may undergo fission if it is bombarded with sufficiently energetic particles.

The mass-numbers of the isotopes involved in fission were unknown at the time. For the purpose of calculation we shall use the masses of the heaviest naturally occurring isotopes of barium and krypton, and show that a very large amount of energy is liberated in a fission process. Now the heaviest natural isotopes of barium and krypton are $_{56}Ba^{138}$ and $_{36}Kr^{86}$. Since the sum of these mass-numbers is only 224, the above equation for the fission of uranium shows that 15 neutrons must be emitted in the fission process. Assuming that the reaction above is correct, we then have

$$_{92}U^{238} + _0n^1 \rightarrow _{56}Ba^{138} \qquad + _{36}Kr^{86} + 15 \text{ neutrons}$$
$$238.14 + 1.00897 \quad 137.916 + 85.939 + 15(1.00897)$$
$$\text{Total} = 239.15 \qquad\qquad \text{Total} = 238.99$$

If this were the correct reaction, 0.16 amu would be converted into energy in the fission process, which would involve an energy release of about 150 mev per fission. This is several orders of magnitude greater than the energies released in ordinary nuclear reactions.

The isotopes used above in the calculation of the energy released in fission are not the correct ones. It is likely that these elements are not the direct products of fission, but instead are daughters of the primary products. For instance, radioactive barium may be produced in the following observed chain:

$$_{54}Xe^{139} \rightarrow \beta^- + {}_{55}Cs^{139} \rightarrow \beta^- + {}_{56}Ba^{139}$$
$$\text{(40 sec)} \qquad \text{(9.5 min)} \qquad \text{(85 min)}$$

In addition, the number of neutrons emitted during fission is not of the order of 15, but rather approximately 2.5 on the average in the case of $_{92}U^{235}$. However, the important facts are still true, regardless of the exact isotopes involved in a given fission; a large amount of energy is liberated in fission and a number of neutrons are produced.

The energy released in a single fission is enormous compared to the energy involved in other natural processes. For instance, the kinetic energy of a gas molecule at room temperature is about 0.04 electron-volts. The energy of an iron atom in a bullet travelling at 3000 feet per second is about 0.23 ev. Even though hydrogen and oxygen combine quite violently, the amount of energy released per atom of hydrogen is only about 1.3 ev, and the limit for chemical processes is an energy release of about 2–5 ev per molecule formed. This should be compared with the average energy per fission of 185 mev which Henderson found by a calorimetric method in 1940. A new and exceedingly powerful energy source had been discovered, if a way could be found to produce nuclear fissions on a large scale and to utilize the energy produced.

10.2. SUSTAINED NUCLEAR REACTIONS

The possibility of a sustained release of nuclear energy was suggested by the fact that more than one neutron was released in each fission of a nucleus. If x is the average number of neutrons emitted per fission and if k is the probability that a neutron will produce a fission, then a sustained reaction is only possible if $kx \geq 1$. This is the same as saying that, on the average, at least one neutron from each fission must itself produce a fission. Neutrons which escape the fissionable material or are absorbed without producing fission reduce the value of k. Since approximately 2.5 neutrons are emitted in each fission of an atom of $_{92}U^{235}$ on the average, this isotope might take part in a sustained nuclear reaction if k could be made large enough.

There are many difficulties in using $_{92}U^{235}$ in a nuclear chain reaction. The absorption of neutrons with the production of fission is most probable in the case of *thermal neutrons* (neutrons with the energy of random motion predicted by the kinetic theory of gases) with energies of the order of 0.03 electron-volts. However, the neutrons emitted in fission are *fast neutrons*, with energies of several mev. Some means must be found to slow the fission neutrons down to thermal energies, where the extremely high cross-section of 400–500 barns of $_{92}U^{235}$ for fission is observed. In doing this, not so many neutrons can be lost through absorption or diffusion that k becomes too small, or no sustained reaction can take place.

Many of the neutrons produced in fission will diffuse out of the mass of uranium and be forever lost to the fission process. This loss, however, is proportional to the surface area of uranium and thus to r^2, while the rate of production of neutrons by fission will be proportional to the volume of uranium and thus to r^3. By making the volume of uranium large enough we can make the relative loss of neutrons by diffusion as small as necessary. The minimum size at which a sustained fission reaction will take place is called the *critical size*. The critical size for uranium is a sphere of approximate radius 1–4 inches. Provided that enough fissionable material is available, the loss of neutrons by diffusion out of the mass will not, in itself, prevent a chain reaction.

A much more important difficulty is obtaining enough pure $_{92}U^{235}$. Natural uranium consists of approximately only one part in 140 of $_{92}U^{235}$, the remainder being almost entirely the heavy isotope, $_{92}U^{238}$. The heavier isotope may also capture neutrons, and since it is so much more plentiful, this will be a serious loss. If the heavy isotope captures fast neutrons, it will itself undergo fission and thus produce more neutrons, which will help the fission process. However, this is not very probable and the neutrons produced by fission are soon slowed down to lower energies by multiple collisions. Unfortunately, the heavy isotope has a large cross-section for the absorption of neutrons of energy about 25 electron-volts, and this absorption does not produce fission. Thus, before the neutrons can be slowed down to thermal energies where they will be highly effective in producing fission in the light isotope, most of them will be absorbed by the heavy isotope, without producing fission. These neutrons are lost to the process. For this reason a lump of natural uranium cannot explode spontaneously or undergo a nuclear chain reaction, since the abundant heavy isotope will absorb nearly all the fission neutrons produced without producing enough fissions to keep the process going.

One obvious solution to this problem is to remove the heavy isotope, so that all fission neutrons will eventually be slowed down and produce fission in nuclei of the light isotope. Since isotopes are chemically the same, any method of separation must use the small difference between masses of 235 and 238. In fact, most separation methods involve the square root of the ratio of these masses, which is very close to unity. The first small samples of uranium highly enriched in the light isotope were produced by *electromagnetic separation*. If uranium ions are passed through a mass spectrometer, the ions of the light isotope will be deflected somewhat more than the ions of the heavy isotope, so that collection of the light isotope is possible. Using the 184-inch cyclotron magnet from Berkeley, during the winter of 1944–1945, large scale production of uranium enriched in the light isotope began.

The most successful separation process is provided by the method of *thermal diffusion* through porous barriers. At a given temperature, a gas molecule containing the light isotope will have a slightly higher speed, so that when the gas is forced through a semi-permeable membrane or barrier a slightly larger proportion of the light molecules will get through. Unfortunately, the only suitable gas for the separation of the uranium isotopes is UF_6, which is a highly corrosive and poisonous gas. The engineering difficulties were overcome and the plant at Oak Ridge, Tennessee, uses 4000 successive thermal diffusion cycles to produce satisfactory enrichment of the light isotope. Production of the light isotope by this method began early in 1945. The thermal diffusion process is still used, and in fact another large thermal diffusion plant was opened after World War II.

Two other methods of separating the isotopes of uranium were tried in 1944, but they have since been abandoned. The small difference in the masses of the isotopes allows them to be separated in a centrifuge, but this was never developed beyond the pilot-plant stage. A more successful method is the *thermal diffusion tower*, which consists of a cylindrical column with a heated wire down its axis. If the gas UF_6 is in such a column, the molecules containing the light isotope will rise up the hot central wire while the heavier molecules will drop down the cool outer cylinder, thus providing some separation. This can be continued through a cascade of towers and was used with some success, but the most important applications of this process are to the separation of the isotopes of the light gases, such as neon and argon, where the mass ratio differs more from unity than is the case for uranium.

10.3. THE NUCLEAR PILE REACTOR

Another solution to the problem of the absorption of fission neutrons by the abundant, heavy isotope was suggested by Fermi. A means must be provided for slowing the fission neutrons down to thermal energies without allowing them to come in contact with nuclei of $_{92}U^{238}$, which would absorb the neutrons. Fermi's idea was to use a *moderator*, which would slow down neutrons by collision without absorbing any neutrons. The basic idea is shown in Fig. 106. The fast neutrons emitted in fission would immediately enter the moderator, where after a number of collisions they would be slowed down to thermal energies. Eventually these thermal neutrons would re-enter the uranium, where they could only be absorbed by $_{92}U^{235}$, with the production of another fission. Any fast neutrons which were absorbed by the heavy isotope before reaching the moderator would produce fission of the heavy isotope, which would be no disadvantage, but no neutrons of moderate energy would be available to be absorbed by the heavy isotope without producing fission.

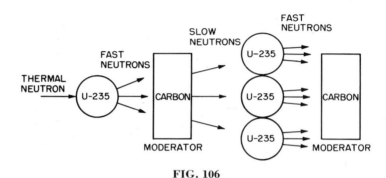

FIG. 106

Action of a moderator in slowing down fast neutrons emitted in fission reactions to thermal energies, at which neutrons are most effective in creating more fissions.

The problem was to design a mixture of uranium and a moderator which would satisfy these requirements. A good moderator must be light, in order to be able to absorb a large fraction of the energy of a neutron in each collision. Needless to say, a good moderator must not itself absorb neutrons. The possibilities for moderators reduce to $_1H^2$, $_2He^4$, $_4Be^9$, and $_6C^{12}$ when these requirements are made. The choice suggested by Fermi and Szilard was carbon. The design was to be one with lumps of uranium of a size smaller than the mean free path of fast neutrons in uranium. These lumps of uranium were then to be embedded in the body of the carbon moderator. Homogeneous piles, however, using *heavy water* (deuterium oxide) as a moderator, have been used in place of the heterogeneous carbon piles.

The first *nuclear pile reactor* was built in Chicago, Illinois during 1942. Lumps of uranium and carbon were added to form an oblate spheroid. As the number of layers was increased, the neutron intensity increased quite rapidly. On December 12, 1942, this first nuclear pile reactor was operated at a power level of 200 watts, which could have been increased except for the dangerous flux of neutrons. Since cadmium is an extremely good absorber of thermal neutrons, cadmium rods were introduced into the pile to control the reaction. By monitoring the neutron intensity, cadmium rods can be inserted or removed automatically in order to maintain a desired power level. Since about 1% of the neutrons emitted in fission are delayed by as much as 0.01 second relative to the absorption of a neutron by a nucleus, the pile reactor builds up and dies down rather slowly. This is fortunate, since the relatively slow time constant allows the cadmium controls to become effective before the pile explodes.

The first use of nuclear pile reactors was to provide a strong flux of neutrons which was used to produce element number 94, plutonium, by the bombardment of the heavy isotope of uranium. This was done because calculations by Bohr and Wheeler had shown that this hitherto unknown element would undergo fission by slow neutrons. Plutonium has the great advantage over $_{92}U^{235}$ of being chemically different from uranium, and it can be separated from the heavy uranium isotope by more or less ordinary chemical procedures. Thus, fissionable material can be separated from the interfering heavy isotope of uranium more easily than by any methods involving the weights of isotopes.

In order to produce plutonium, the size of the moderating lumps is adjusted so that some neutrons leave the moderator with energies of the order of 25 electron-volts. When these moderately fast neutrons re-enter the pile, they are absorbed by the heavy isotope of uranium without producing fission. The resulting nucleus is unstable and decays in the first of a series of radioactive disintegrations. The complete chain by which uranium is converted gradually into plutonium is

$$_{0}n^{1} + {}_{92}U^{238} \rightarrow {}_{92}U^{239} \xrightarrow[\text{23 min.}]{} \beta^{-} + {}_{93}Np^{239} \xrightarrow[\text{2.33 days}]{} \beta^{-} + {}_{94}Pu^{239}$$

Since the half-life of plutonium is 25,000 years, once it is separated from the uranium pile it can be stored indefinitely.

Plutonium produces approximately the same fission products as $_{92}U^{235}$ when it undergoes fission, although its fission is somewhat more energetic and the average fission process produces 3.0 neutrons, compared with 2.5 neutrons from $_{92}U^{235}$. Since plutonium produces only about half as many delayed neutrons from fission as the light isotope of uranium does, it is an excellent material to use when a rapid nuclear chain reaction is desired, as in the case of an explosion. However, to produce one gram of plutonium a day by the method explained above requires a pile operating at a power level of about 1000 kilowatts. Such a pile would have a radioactivity equivalent to 18 million curies and would be lethal at a distance of 10 meters. Despite these difficulties, plutonium was produced virtually by the ton at the production pile at Hanford, Washington. This pile operated at a power level of 1.5×10^{6} kilowatts and used the Columbia River for cooling.

As the pile is operated, the amount of light fission products increases continuously, while the amount of $_{92}U^{235}$ decreases. Since the fission products may absorb neutrons, they are said to *poison* the pile. In producing plutonium, a slug of natural or enriched uranium is irradiated in the pile until the optimum amount of plutonium has been produced; then the slug is removed from the pile. After allowing the slug to *cool* for a while until the short-lived radioactivities of the fission products disappear, the plutonium is removed chemically. Because of the tremendous intensity of radiation present in such a slug, all these processes must be performed either automatically or by remote control. It is a great tribute to the scientific and industrial people of this country that such a process could be carried through to yield the man-made element plutonium by the ton.

Many piles have been built throughout the world. Piles may be classified according to the type of moderator and its mode of introduction, speed of the neutrons used, coolant, use, and location. Piles have been built using deuterium oxide as a homogeneous moderator, but the majority use carbon as a heterogeneous moderator. A plutonium pile has been built which uses fast neutrons and no moderator at all, since neutron-absorbing impurities can be removed from plutonium. However, most piles use thermal neutrons or neutrons with energies of about 25 electron-volts. As a coolant it is possible to use water, helium, a liquid metal, or even no coolant at all, but air has been most commonly used. Piles have been built for the production of plutonium, for research purposes (mainly irradiation of materials with strong neutron fluxes), and for power production. In general, it may be said that there is no standardized pile, each one being designed to conform to the various factors of importance to the user of the pile.

10.4. THE ATOMIC BOMB

The inspiration for producing fissionable materials was the hope of producing a super-explosive which might shorten the war against Germany and Japan. In addition, the production by Germany of deuterium, which was known to be a good moderator in nuclear pile reactors, indicated that it too was working on the problem of releasing nuclear energy on a tremendous scale. About two billion dollars was risked on the production of a nuclear bomb by the United States, with results which are well known.

The problem in releasing nuclear energy on a large scale is the existence of a critical size of fissionable material. If the volume of material is too small, no sustained chain reaction can take place because of loss of neutrons by diffusion through the surface. On the other hand, a volume of fissionable material greater than the critical size will be triggered by the stray neutrons always present in cosmic radiation and will immediately explode. The situation is thus analogous to spontaneous combustion. As soon as two subcritical masses are brought together to form a mass greater than the critical mass, a stray neutron will initiate a chain reaction and the combined mass will explode.

One of the features of a nuclear bomb is the manner in which two or more sub-critical masses are shielded from each other during transport and how they are combined when the bomb is exploded. One method of bringing the two sub-critical masses together rapidly would be to fire one into the other. One difficulty in producing a true explosion is that the mass would blow itself apart as heat is developed by the chain reaction, so that fission would be stopped rather quickly. In the possible bomb

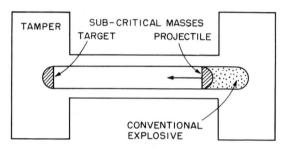

FIG. 107

Hypothetical method by which two sub-critical masses of fissionable material could be brought together quickly so as to produce an explosive chain reaction.

mechanism shown in Fig. 107, one function of the tamper is to confine the explosion, so that the chain reaction can proceed through a larger number of neutron generations. In addition, some neutrons will diffuse out of the fissionable material into the tamper, and after a while some neutrons may diffuse back from the tamper into the fissionable material, so that another function of the tamper is to act as a reflector of neutrons.

Another possible method is to embed a number of sub-critical pieces of fissionable material in a light plastic. Surrounding this are a number of sheets of conventional explosive, the whole assembly being spherical. If the sheets of conventional explosive are shaped properly, an implosion occurs when they are detonated. The sub-critical pieces of fissionable material are then fused into a super-critical piece and a nuclear chain reaction occurs. The implosion not only produces a super-critical mass of fissionable material, but also holds the nuclear reaction together for a number of neutron generations, thus playing the part of the tamper in the method described in the preceding paragraph. Undoubtedly the use of an implosion permits the size and weight of the resulting bomb to be much smaller than the bomb envisioned in Fig. 107.

Disregarding the details of the bomb mechanism, the first two "atomic" bombs were dropped on Hiroshima and Nagasaki in Japan in August, 1945. These bombs released an energy equivalent to 20,000 tons of TNT and are known as *nominal atomic bombs*.

10.5. NUCLEAR FUSION AND SOLAR ENERGY

In the preceding sections it was shown how energy could be released by fission of heavy nuclei into moderate-sized fragments, since mass disappeared in the process. Similarly, when light nuclei are combined together to form heavier nuclei, mass is lost. In this section we shall describe how the *fusion* of light nuclei provides the energy which the sun continually radiates.

The energy radiated by the sun keeps our planet alive, since 1.92 calories are received per square centimeter each minute. In more familiar units this amounts to 1.3 kilowatts per square meter or about 1.5 horse-power per square yard. From this we see that the total radiation from the sun amounts to about 1.2×10^{34} joules per year. Despite this tremendous amount of radiation, no change in the sun's temperature has been noticed nor has a change in the radiation received by the earth been observed. Clearly the sun is not a cooling body radiating energy as it cools, but rather some process must take place on the sun to produce this energy as it is radiated.

In 1938 Bethe suggested an explanation of the source of the sun's energy. According to Bethe's theory, the following nuclear reactions take place on the sun, where the temperature and pressure are exceedingly high:

$$_1H^1 + {}_1H^1 \rightarrow {}_1H^2 + \beta^+$$

$$_1H^1 + {}_1H^2 \rightarrow {}_2He^3 + \gamma$$

$$_2He^3 + {}_2He^3 \rightarrow {}_2He^4 + {}_1H^1 + {}_1H^1$$

The result of this series of reactions is the conversion of four protons into one alpha-particle, with the liberation of 26 mev of energy. The reactions above are believed to be the main source of the sun's energy, but the following series of reactions, proposed independently by Bethe and Weizsacker in 1938, also plays a part:

$$_1H^1 + {}_6C^{12} \rightarrow {}_7N^{13} \rightarrow \beta^+ + {}_6C^{13}$$

$$_1H^1 + {}_6C^{13} \rightarrow {}_7N^{14}$$

$$_1H^1 + {}_7N^{14} \rightarrow {}_8O^{15} \rightarrow \beta^+ + {}_7N^{15}$$

$$_1H^1 + {}_7N^{15} \rightarrow {}_8O^{16} \rightarrow {}_6C^{12} + {}_2He^4$$

The net result of this process is the conversion of four protons into an alpha-particle plus two positrons, with the nucleus of $_6C^{12}$ merely acting as a catalyst. The difference in mass between the two protons and two neutrons which make up the helium nucleus and the mass of a helium nucleus amounts to 0.03032 amu. When this mass disappears in the fusion process outlined above, 28.2 mev of energy appears for each nucleus of helium produced.

The first series of reactions given above is probably most important in the case of the sun, which is only moderately hot as stars go. In the case of very hot stars the carbon-nitrogen cycle becomes more important, while in the centers of red-giant stars, successive captures of alpha-particles lead to the synthesis of heavier elements. Thus, both the energy output of stars and the formation of a wide variety of elements is explained by these fusion reactions. It is interesting to note that the mass of our sun decreases at the rate of 4.4×10^6 tons per second. However, this amounts to only 6.3×10^{-14} of the sun's mass per year, so that there is no danger of the sun burning out soon. If the sun were to keep radiating at its present rate, it would lose half of its mass in a time of 8×10^{12} years.

Other light nuclei might be fused to form heavier nuclei if sufficiently high temperatures and pressures were available. There is in each case a disappearance of mass in such fusion processes, and a calculation quickly shows that the energy released per pound of material in these *thermonuclear processes* is of the same order of magnitude as the energy released by the fission of the heavy elements. Since the light elements are much more abundant than the heavy elements, this appears to be an extremely attractive source of energy. However, thermonuclear fusion processes require very high temperatures and pressures such as are found in the interior of a star.

The only source of extremely high temperatures and pressures on the earth appears to be the interior of an atomic bomb during its explosion. Because of the high energy density inside such an explosion, the particles there have temperatures measured in millions of degrees and pressures measured in hundreds of thousands of atmospheres. (Temperature, of course, is only defined in equilibrium processes, so this must be considered as an equivalent temperature, based on the energy of the particles.) At the end of about 10^{-4} second after the instant that the chain reaction starts, the ball of fire produced by the explosion has expanded to a radius of about 50 feet and its temperature has dropped to about 300,000°K. Any thermonuclear reaction involving an atomic bomb must therefore be completed in a very short time interval.

Let us now consider the thermonuclear reactions which take place at the temperature and pressure produced in the interior of an atomic bomb. Fusion of protons with protons, as in the Bethe cycle above, does not take place with great enough probability to be used in connection with a very short-lived atomic bomb. However, reactions involving deuterium, $_1H^2$, and tritium, $_1H^3$, occur with much greater probability, with tritium reactions being the easiest to produce. Various fusion reactions involving the isotopes of hydrogen are listed below.

$$_1H^2 + {_1}H^2 \rightarrow {_0}n^1 + {_2}He^3 + 3.2 \text{ mev}$$
$$_1H^2 + {_1}H^3 \rightarrow {_0}n^1 + {_2}He^4 + 17.6 \text{ mev}$$
$$_1H^3 + {_1}H^3 \rightarrow {_0}n^1 + {_0}n^1 + {_2}He^4 + 11 \text{ mev}$$

It should be noted that each of these reactions produces an energetic neutron, which can contribute to the fission process in uranium or plutonium.

Unfortunately, both of the heavy isotopes of hydrogen are scarce and expensive compared to ordinary hydrogen. Deuterium is stable, but only occurs with an abundance of 0.02% in nature. Tritium is radioactive, with a half-life of 12 years. One way of producing tritium is by the bombardment of lithium with neutrons (see Problem 8, Chapter 9), but this involves using up fissionable material in producing an intense source of neutrons. Thus, a so-called *hydrogen bomb* would probably consist of a mixture of deuterium and tritium, with all three reactions listed above occurring. Since the speed of a reaction is proportional to the concentration of the reactants, the deuterium and tritium would be used in liquid or solid form, enormously complicating the mechanism of the bomb. On the other hand, the amount of material used in a fusion bomb is not limited by any critical size, since the material is entirely inert until exposed to extremely high temperatures and pressures. Thus, in principle it is possible to build as large a fusion bomb as might be desired.

The first hydrogen fusion device was exploded at Einewetok Atoll in 1955. Undoubtedly, however, the complications introduced by liquefying or solidifying hydrogen made this device not transportable as a bomb. However, lithium hydride is a solid up to fairly high temperatures, so that fusion reactions involving lithium become attractive. Consider the following reactions:

$$_1H^2 + {_3}Li^6 \nearrow {_0}n^1 + {_4}Be^7 + 3.2 \text{ mev}$$
$$\searrow {_2}He^4 + {_2}He^4 + 22.4 \text{ mev}$$

$$_1H^2 + {_3}Li^7 \rightarrow {_0}n^1 + {_4}Be^8 + 14.9 \text{ mev}$$

It is very likely that transportable bombs using one or more of the above reactions have been constructed, with the fusionable nuclei being in close proximity in a molecule of lithium deuteride.

As was mentioned above, temperature is only defined for equilibrium. However, we can take Eq. (342) as the definition of temperature, so that the average kinetic energy per particle is given by $3/2kT$. It is easy to show that a temperature of $10^7°K$ corresponds to an energy of about 1300 ev, which is a very low energy as compared to that produced by cyclotrons and other particle accelerators. It is therefore easy to give particles very high equivalent temperatures by accelerating them through rather low voltages. It is not difficult to produce fusion reactions in this way, but it is very difficult to produce a sufficient number of fusion reactions to make the energy output exceed the energy input. Research now under way, using highly ionized gases or *plasmas*, shows promise of eventual success. The deuterium in sea-water alone would then supply man's energy needs for thousands of years to come, while it is estimated that energy from fissionable materials will only last a few centuries.

10.6. SOME APPLICATIONS OF NUCLEAR PHYSICS

Although radium was used in the treatment of cancer from the earliest days of radioactivity, the applications of nuclear physics were rather limited until the discovery of induced radioactivity in 1934. By suitable bombardment, a radioactive isotope of any element could be prepared, so that light elements could be studied. Today radioactive isotopes of every element are known. Many useful radio-isotopes can be obtained from the Atomic Energy Commission, either as fission products or as the result of irradiations of materials in the intense neutron flux of a nuclear pile reactor. Sources of this sort can be obtained with intensities of many millicuries. Certain other radio-isotopes cannot be prepared in this way, so they must be produced by bombardment of targets with high energy ions. Sources produced by ion-bombardment are usually of lower intensity, typical intensities being of the order of millicuries or microcuries. A number of useful radio-isotopes usually obtainable from the Atomic Energy Commission are listed in Appendix 3.

Since detectors of nuclear radiations can count individual nuclear events, extremely minute quantities of radioactive chemicals can be followed through various processes. Each radio-isotope can be followed by observing its characteristic radiation or half-life. In order to demonstrate the possible sensitivity of the use of *radioactive tracers*, consider $_{15}P^{32}$, which is an electron emitter of half-life 14.3 days. It can easily be shown that one gram of this radio-isotope would emit 6.3×10^{17} electrons per minute initially. Let us assume that in a particular experiment only 5% of the electrons are actually detected and that 30 counts per minute must be recorded in order to overcome the background count which is always present due to cosmic rays and other sources. Under these conditions, it would be possible to detect $600/6.3 \times 10^{17} = 9.6 \times 10^{-16}$ gram of $_{15}P^{32}$. Such a sensitivity is well beyond the reach of the analytical chemist, so the use of tracers opens wide fields of research.

Using tracers is not quite as simple as it might appear in the previous paragraph. Organic molecules are of great interest in many fields of research, but the only really satisfactory tracer among the four elements carbon, oxygen, hydrogen, and nitrogen is $_6C^{14}$, which has a half-life of 5720 years. A marginally useful tracer is $_1H^3$, which has a half-life of 12 years, but this radio-isotope emits an electron of energy only 14 kev, so that special counting techniques are required. In addition, when organic molecules are prepared with *tagged atoms* (radioactive isotopes), chemical exchange may take place. When chemical exchange takes place in the case of hydrogen, for instance, the atom of tritium does not remain with the tagged molecule, but will soon be widely distributed among all the organic molecules of the organism which contain hydrogen. Finally, the organism may be affected adversely either by the tracer itself or by accompanying stable isotopes (radio-isotopes are often not pure, but are used with chemical carriers to provide bulk), so that the amount of tracer which can be used may be limited.

Despite the handicaps and difficulties mentioned above, radioactive tracers are finding many applications in various fields of research. The absorption of the various components of fertilizer by plants has been studied with tracers, and progress has been made in understanding the basic process of photosynthesis by using radioactive carbon. Another interesting use of tracers is in testing piston rings. If radio-isotopes are used in making the piston rings, the wear of the piston rings can be computed from the amount of radioactivity appearing in the crank-case oil. The use of radio-isotopes in diverse branches of science and engineering rose roughly exponentially during the past 15 years and new applications are continually being made.

Neutrons produced by cosmic rays continually transmute nitrogen in the atmosphere into radioactive carbon, the reaction being $_7N^{14}(n,p)_6C^{14}$. While they are alive, plants and animals absorb amounts of stable and radioactive carbon in the proportions of about 10^{12} to 1. However, once the organism dies, the radioactive carbon decays into stable nitrogen and is not replenished. Since the half-life of $_6C^{14}$ is 5720 years, the activity due to this radio-isotope will drop to half-value in 5720 years. Thus, by comparing the ratio of stable to radioactive carbon in a specimen to the present ratio, we can determine the life of the specimen. In this calculation it is necessary to assume that the same rate of production of radioactive carbon has continued for thousands of years. This seems a very reasonable assumption and is almost certainly true. Another assumption we would have to make, which seems an uncertain one, is that no diffusion of radioactive carbon to or from the specimen has occurred. The dates obtained for radiocarbon, using a technique developed by Libby, are in keeping with the dates calculated by archaeological methods.

In the case of the nuclear pile reactor described above, the aim was to convert $_{92}U^{238}$ into plutonium, and to consider the heat produced by the conversion as a wasted by-product. Approximately 22,000 kilowatt-hours of energy are produced for each gram of plutonium made. To generate one million kilowatts continuously for a year would require the consumption of only about two tons of fissionable material. The large amount of energy produced from a small amount of fuel is at present the chief advantage of a reactor as a source of energy. Nuclear-powered submarines, for example, can stay at sea almost indefinitely, and nuclear-powered aircraft, too, are being developed. Nuclear power would also have obvious advantages in locations where other fuels are scarce or difficult to transport.

A number of reactors have been built to generate electrical power in competition with conventional power plants. In 1956 the first large reactor delivered about 80 megawatts at Calder Hall, England, and larger reactors are in operation or under construction. However, at present the cost of electrical power generated by reactors is approximately twice that of conventional power sources. Nevertheless as our supply of fossil fuels gradually decreases, it can be expected that more and more reactors will be built.

Nuclear reactors have one advantage over conventional power sources in that under proper conditions they may produce more fuel than they use. In *breeder reactors* some neutrons are used to convert $_{92}U^{238}$ into $_{94}Pu^{239}$, as was described earlier in this chapter. Since the heavy isotope of uranium is relatively useless, any fissionable material which is produced is a net gain. An even more promising possibility is the conversion of thorium into fissionable material in the following series of reactions:

$$_{0}n^{1} + _{92}Th^{232} \rightarrow _{92}Th^{233} \xrightarrow[\text{23.5 min.}]{} \beta^{-} + _{91}Pa^{233} \xrightarrow[\text{27.4 days}]{} \beta^{-} + _{92}U^{233}$$

The product of these reactions, $_{92}U^{233}$, is fissionable with slow neutrons and is therefore a suitable nuclear fuel. It can be chemically separated from thorium and, since it has a half-life of 16,300 years, it can be stored indefinitely. Thorium is much more common than uranium; thus the amount of nuclear energy available to mankind is greatly increased by using thorium as a breeder material.

This section on the applications of nuclear physics should be concluded with a few remarks on the health and safety aspects of radioactive materials. Charged particles, such as alpha-particles and electrons, penetrate tissue very little, so that their effects are mainly confined to the skin, where severe burns may be produced.   Gamma rays are much more penetrating and do damage through the electrons produced in tissue by the photo-electric effect, the Compton effect, and by pair formation.   Neutrons are also very penetrating and do damage by means of protons knocked out of organic material or protons produced by (n,p) transmutations.   For all these radiations, the Roentgen unit is defined as the amount of radiation which will produce one electrostatic unit of ions of a given sign per cubic centimeter of standard air.   The Roentgen unit thus measures the energy absorbed from the radiation and not the total intensity of the radiation.

The ill-effects of over-exposure to nuclear radiations are the same as in the case of X-rays.   (The reader should re-read Section 6.13.)   From experience a dose of 0.1 Roentgen unit per day or 0.3 Roentgen unit per week seems to be a safe maximum for workers who are exposed day after day.   However, all work involving radioactive materials should be performed only under the supervision of someone familiar with both the physical and physiological effects of radiations.   Despite the tremendous amount of radioactive material which was processed in the various plants producing the atomic bomb, no severe accidents occurred which were not the result of the individual's violation of safety procedures.   If suitable precautions are taken, every experiment in nuclear physics can be performed in such a way as to be safe to the experimenter.

ADDITIONAL READING

Smyth, H. D., *Atomic Energy for Military Purposes*.   Princeton: Princeton University Press, 1945.   The first authoritative account of the development of the atomic bomb.   This is the famous "Smyth Report."

Glasstone, Samuel (editor), *The Effects of Nuclear Weapons*.   Washington: U. S. Atomic Energy Commission, 1957.   This is the most complete and authoritative account available of the effects of nuclear explosions.

Evans, Robley D., *The Atomic Nucleus*.   New York: McGraw-Hill Book Company, Inc., 1955.   A standard reference in the field of nuclear physics.

PROBLEMS

1. Compute the power developed continuously by fission of one lb of plutonium per day.   (Assume 200 mev per fission.)   At the rate of 0.5 cent per/kwhr, what would be the value of this power?

   (*Ans.* 4.3×10^5 kw; \$51,000 per day)

2. Assume that in separating $_{92}U^{235}$ from natural uranium electromagnetically a beam current of 10 milliamperes is used. If the ions are doubly charged, how long would such a device have to operate in order to produce one gram of pure $_{92}U^{235}$?

3. Derive an expression for the maximum energy lost by a neutron in an elastic collision with a nucleus. Use this expression to explain why only light elements are satisfactory as moderators in nuclear pile reactors.

4. Compute the fractional loss of energy by a neutron in a collision with an atom of $_6C^{12}$.

5. Use the result of Problem 4 to calculate the number of collisions which a neutron would have to undergo with atoms of $_6C^{12}$ to reduce the energy of the neutron from 1 mev to 0.1 ev. Assume maximum energy loss in each collision.   (*Ans.* 49)

6. The heat of combustion of TNT, $C_6H_2(CH_3)(NO_2)_3$, is 820,700 calories per mole. What mass of uranium would ideally give off an energy in fission equivalent to 20,000 tons of TNT (the nominal atomic bomb)?

7. Compute the rate at which helium is being produced by the sun.
$$(Ans.\ 2 \times 10^{16}\ \text{tons/year})$$

8. Compute the energy released when one kilogram of helium is formed by the fusion of deuterium and tritium. Compare this with the energy released by the nominal atomic bomb of Problem 6.

9. 500 millicuries of $_{15}P^{32}$ are mixed with ten tons of phosphate fertilizer, which is then applied to a field of lettuce. 43 days later the ashes of a head of lettuce are found to emit 650 electrons per minute. How many grams of fertilizer has the head of lettuce absorbed?   (*Ans.* 0.0432 gm)

10. 9.4 millicuries of $_{27}Co^{58}$ are mixed with 50 grams of steel to make a piston ring. This isotope is a positron emitter with a half-life of 72 days. After using the piston ring for 60 days, it is found that 30 positrons are emitted per minute by a cubic centimeter of the crank-case oil. If the total volume of crank-case oil is two liters, compute the weight of material worn off the piston ring.

11. The radiation rate from the radioactive fall-out of an atomic bomb falls off with time as $t^{-1.2}$. Assume an initial rate of 200 Roentgens per hour one hour after the explosion. Compute the dose accumulated in 8 hours and in an infinite time, both times beginning one hour after the explosion.
$$(Ans.\ 355\ \text{Roentgens};\ 1000\ \text{Roentgens})$$

chapter eleven

cosmic rays and mesons

In the three preceding chapters we have described nuclear reactions which, in most cases, involve energies of the order of a few mev. In addition, bombardment by ions of known and adjustable energy allowed control of nuclear reactions. In this chapter we shall consider nuclear reactions which are produced by cosmic rays. These reactions often involve energies of billions of electron-volts; therefore, very interesting processes can occur which are impossible at lower energies. However, man has very little control over either the number or energy of the bombarding particles, so that clear-cut experiments under laboratory conditions are not easy to perform. Despite this handicap, much information about nuclei and nuclear reactions has been obtained from these super-energy reactions.

11.1. THE DISCOVERY OF COSMIC RAYS

As early as 1785 Coulomb found that a charge leaked off an insulated electroscope in an unexplained manner. A century later Boise showed that leakage across the insulation was not responsible for this loss of charge. In 1903 Rutherford and Cooke found that about ten ions were formed per cubic centimeter of air each second in an electroscope. Furthermore, if the electroscope were shielded with lead, the rate of ion production dropped about 40%. If this ionization were produced by radiation entering the electroscope, part of it must necessarily be very penetrating in order to pass through lead. Rutherford and Cooke decided that this ionization was caused by radioactive contaminants in and near the electroscope.

This theory was revised in 1910 when Gockel found that an electroscope would discharge more rapidly at an altitude of three miles than at the earth's surface. However, less radioactive contamination should occur at high altitudes, since the radioactive elements are all very heavy.

During 1911 and later years, Hess used balloons to carry instruments up to heights of several miles. He found that at a height of three miles the ionization was already about three times as great as at sea level. The variation of ionization with altitude near the surface of the earth is shown in Fig. 108. However, in 1958 Van Allen discovered two toroidal-shaped

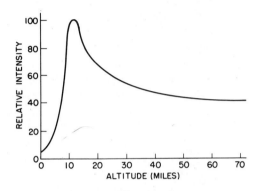

FIG. 108
Variation of cosmic-ray intensity with altitude.

belts of extremely intense radiation known as *Van Allen radiation*. One belt extends from an altitude of about 500 miles up to about 3000 miles, while the other belt extends from an altitude of about 9000 miles to 13000 miles. In both of these radiation belts the intensity is about 1000 times greater than expected for cosmic radiation. As will be discussed in Section 11.3, it is believed that these belts consist of low-energy electrons and protons trapped by the earth's magnetic field.

In addition to his discovery of the increase in ionization near the surface of the earth, Hess found that ionization intensity remained constant at all times and at all seasons of the year. Therefore, he concluded that the sun did not cause this ionization, although it is now known that a small part of the cosmic-ray intensity is due to the sun. On this evidence Hess suggested that the ionization must be caused by some very penetrating radiation coming from the upper atmosphere or from outer space (the cosmos). These radiations are now called *cosmic rays*, but in the past the name *Hess-rays* was sometimes used. It is now known, however, that this ubiquitous radiation is not entirely due to cosmic radiation. At sea level various other sources of ionization are present.

Typical values of the number of ions produced per cubic centimeter are as follows: wall contamination, 4.0; air contamination, 0.2; earth contamination, 3.0; cosmic radiation, 1.5; total: 8.7. At a given point on the earth the cosmic radiation itself is nearly constant, suggesting that the source of these radiations is far removed from our own solar system. The problem is, first, to determine the nature and source of these radiations and, second, to investigate their interactions with matter on the earth.

11.2. CHARACTERISTICS OF COSMIC RAYS

The introduction of Wilson's cloud chamber in 1911 gave physicists an instrument with which to study individual cosmic-ray particles. If a strong magnetic field is applied to the chamber, the paths of charged particles are curved. From the direction of the curvature of the tracks, the sign of the particle's electrical charge can be deduced. From the track's appearance and magnitude of curvature, the type of particle and its momentum are deduced. From its momentum, the particle's energy can be computed. If enough cloud-chamber photographs are taken, it is found that a number of different particles with charges of both signs are present in the radiation. There is also a wide variation in the energies of various particles. Also, the types of particles observed, and their energy distributions, depend on the altitude at which photographs are taken. The reason for this will be explained later.

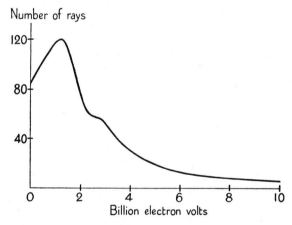

FIG. 109

Distribution of energies of cosmic-ray particles at sea level. (From *Cosmic Rays*, by Leprince-Ringuet: Prentice-Hall, 1950.)

The distribution of energies of cosmic-ray particles at sea level is shown in Fig. 109. An outstanding feature of the curve is the very high energies possessed by most of the particles. In fact, the most probable energy, which corresponds to the peak of the curve, is about 2×10^9 electron-volts.   This value should be compared with the energies of the particles emitted by radioactive nuclei, which are only a few mev.   Cosmic-ray energies as high as 10^{19} ev have been observed and there is no reason for believing that even this enormous energy is the upper limit.

In 1938 Auger discovered extensive showers of particles which would almost simultaneously actuate Geiger counters hundreds of meters apart. Some showers in air consist of as many as a hundred million particles. Since the total energy of all the particles in some very large showers has been found to be as high as 10^{19} ev, the primary cosmic ray which initiated the shower must have had an energy at least as large as this.

The intensity of cosmic rays can be attenuated by shielding the detecting instrument with layers of an absorbing material, such as water or lead. When the absorption curves of cosmic rays in lead are measured at sea level, and then at an altitude of 3500 meters, the curves shown in Fig. 110

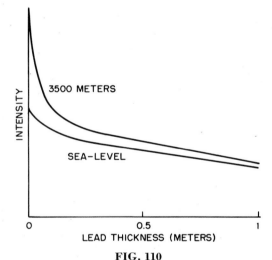

FIG. 110

Absorption of cosmic rays in lead at sea level and at an altitude of 3500 meters.

are found.   From the shapes of the curves, it is clear that two different absorption coefficients must be assigned if the absorption is assumed to follow an exponential law, as is the case for X-rays.   From the curve at the higher altitude, it is seen that the *soft component* is stopped by a few centimeters of lead, while even a meter of lead does not completely absorb the *hard component*.   Since atmospheric absorption is equivalent to the absorption of ten meters of water, or one meter of lead, the soft component cannot be a primary cosmic-ray constituent.   It must be created at all levels of the atmosphere by the hard component — otherwise no trace of the soft component would be observed at sea level. We shall discuss the processes involved in the creation of the soft component in the atmosphere later in the chapter.

The properties of the two components of cosmic rays are found to be quite different. As may be seen in Fig. 110, the relative intensity of the soft component increases quite rapidly with altitude, but the intensity of the hard component increases only slightly. In addition, for the soft component the absorption of materials is proportional to the square of the atomic number of the absorber, whereas the absorption coefficient for the hard component is proportional to the first power of the atomic number of the absorber. Clearly, interpretation of observations on cosmic rays at various altitudes is quite complex. To unravel this problem we must first study the hard component, since this is undoubtedly the primary cosmic radiation. A knowledge of the nature of the hard component may then lead us to an understanding of the processes by which the soft component is created at various levels in the atmosphere. In the following section we shall see that the effect of the earth's magnetic field on the primary cosmic-ray particles provides considerable information about these particles.

11.3. THE EFFECT OF THE EARTH'S MAGNETIC FIELD ON COSMIC RADIATION

The magnetic field of the earth provides us with a huge spectrometer to use in connection with the primary cosmic-ray particles. Since electromagnetic waves are not affected by a magnetic field, and since charged particles have deflections dependent on the sign of their electrical charges, we can discriminate between the three possibilities, somewhat as was done in connection with the alpha, beta, and gamma rays emitted by radioactive nuclei.

Although the earth's magnetic field is only about 0.5 gauss at the surface of the earth, it acts on charged particles for a very large distance. Since the earth's magnetic field can be quite well simulated by a magnetic dipole at the center of the earth, the field of the earth falls off as the inverse cube of the distance from the center of the earth. For instance, at a distance of 8000 miles from the center of the earth, the strength of the magnetic field is still about one-tenth of a gauss. Thus, because of the large distance over which deflection can take place, even particles of energies in billions of electron-volts can suffer large deflections.

If we look down at the North pole, as in Fig. 111, the magnetic field of the earth is out of the page. As shown in the diagram, the deflection of positively charged particles which approach the earth is such that any positively charged particles which reach the earth will arrive predominantly from the west. Similarly, negatively charged particles should arrive predominantly from the east. Thus, if the primary cosmic radiations consist of charged particles predominantly of one sign, then there should be a difference in cosmic-ray intensities measured in westward directions, as compared to intensities measured in eastward directions. Such a difference has been observed and is known as the *east-west effect*.

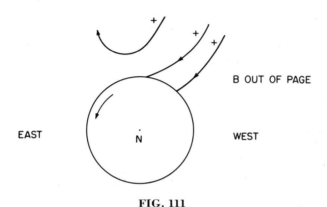

FIG. 111

View of equatorial plane of the earth, looking southward. The deflections of various positively charges particles are shown.

The east-west effect for cosmic-ray particles can be studied by constructing a *cosmic-ray telescope*. In this instrument several Geiger counters are mounted in a straight line, and are the axis of the telescope. The pulse outputs of the counters are connected to the input of a circuit, such as the one shown schematically in Fig. 112, for the case of three counters. Normally all three vacuum tubes conduct, and there is a large voltage drop across the load resistor. The negative voltage pulse from a Geiger counter will cut off its amplifying tube, but as long as at least one tube still conducts, there will still be a large voltage drop across the common load resistor. However, if a particle passes through all three counters simultaneously, all three vacuum tubes will be cut off. In this case there is no voltage drop across the common load resistor and the output voltage rises to the full B-plus supply voltage, giving a large positive pulse. This positive pulse, which occurs only when a particle passes through all three counters simultaneously, is used to drive a recording circuit. Since a count will not be recorded unless all three counters are excited simultaneously, this is called a *coincidence circuit*.

By pointing the axis of the cosmic-ray telescope in various directions, and observing the number of coincidences at each direction, the variation

of intensity with azimuth can be studied.   Observations show a definite
east-west asymmetry and indicate a preponderance of positively charged
particles in the primary radiation.

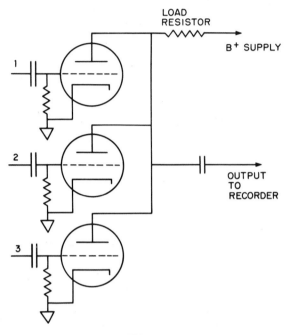

FIG. 112
Circuit for recording coincidences in three counters.

The detailed problem of trajectories of charged particles approaching
the earth from various directions, was worked out by Stormer, and later
by Lemaitre and Vallarta.   Since the North magnetic pole is not coincident
with the North geographic pole, the *magnetic latitude* must be used instead
of the geographic latitude in these calculations.   The *magnetic equator*,
for instance, may be defined as the locus of points where the magnetic
field vector of the earth is horizontal.   The aspect of the problem which is
of interest in connection with cosmic rays is the determination of the
energies of particles which can reach the earth as a function of direction
and magnetic latitude.

Lemaitre and Vallarta showed that the earth could be divided into
three regions with respect to the arrival at the earth of particles of a given
energy.   In the region near the North pole, particles can arrive from any
direction, since the earth's· magnetic field is mainly directed toward the
center of the earth.   In the intermediate region, particles can reach the
earth only from directions which lie within a complicated cone, which is

tipped westward for positively charged particles.   In the forbidden zone near the equator, no particles of the given energy can reach the earth, regardless of their initial directions.   These various zones are shown in Fig. 113.   A proton must have an energy of about ten billion electron-volts in order to arrive at the magnetic equator, while protons of smaller energies can arrive only at higher latitudes.

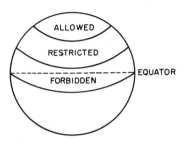

The belts of Van Allen radiation referred in Section 11.1 are believed to be due to low-energy charged particles, probably electrons and protons.   A charged particle approaching the earth will move in a helical path centered on a magnetic line of force.   As the particle approaches either magnetic pole, the spiral becomes tighter and tighter until finally the path reverses.

FIG. 113
Zones of the earth which can be reached by primary particles of a fixed energy.

Thus, a given particle moves back and forth between the northern and southern hemispheres while drifting slowly around the earth, with electrons drifting from west to east, while protons drift in the opposite direction.   At the end of each trajectory the particle dips into the upper atmosphere and loses energy by collisions.   Eventually the particle loses so much energy that it is stopped in the atmosphere.   It is believed that the sun supplies new particles continually to make up for losses to the atmosphere, although the energies of particles of solar origin do not appear to be high enough.   Another possible source of charged particles is the decay of free neutrons produced by cosmic rays, which would produce both protons and electrons.   Additional observations and refinements to the theory will undoubtedly explain the origin of the charged particles, their energy distribution, and why they occur in two belts rather than one.

From the preceding discussion, we see that the theory of cosmic-ray trajectories predicts an east-west asymmetry in the cosmic-ray intensity at a given point on the earth if particles of a given sign predominate among the primary particles.   This east-west asymmetry is observed and indicates that the primary cosmic-rays are positively charged.   In addition, if any substantial fraction of the primaries are charged particles, there should be a variation of intensity with latitude.   This variation at sea level is shown in Fig. 114.   However, measurements at high altitudes show an increase in intensity all the way to the magnetic poles.   The flattening of the curve at sea level as shown in Fig. 114, is due to the absorption of low energy particles in the atmosphere, even though these particles have enough energy to penetrate the earth's magnetic field.

Although most of the primaries appear to be positively charged, it should not be concluded that they are all protons. In 1948 Bradt and Peters reported the discovery of nuclei among the cosmic-ray primaries observed at high altitudes. More recent measurements show that the

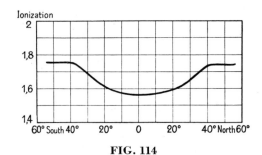

FIG. 114

Variation of ionization per cubic centimeter at sea level with magnetic latitude. (From *Cosmic Rays*, by Leprince-Ringuet: Prentice-Hall, 1950.)

primaries consist approximately of 77% protons, 20% helium ions, and the remaining 3% of ions of heavier atoms. It is interesting to note that the relative abundances of ions in the primary cosmic rays is quite similar to the abundances determined from the spectra of stars.

11.4. MESONS AND HYPERONS

Although cosmic rays are an important subject of research in themselves, particularly to the astro-physicist, the extremely high energies of the primaries makes them even more interesting as bombarding particles. Until 1952 no accelerators were in operation which could give energies in billions of electron-volts, although such energies are common for cosmic-ray particles. Many remarkable nuclear reactions were first observed as a result of cosmic-ray bombardment and the first information regarding the positron and various mesons came from observations on cosmic rays. Recently, however, it has been possible to produce very high-energy particles in the laboratory, as described above in Section 9.5, so that these high-energy reactions can be studied under controlled conditions.

As described briefly in Section 6.11, in connection with the absorption of X-rays by pair formation, positrons were first observed by C. D. Anderson in 1932 in cloud-chamber photographs of cosmic rays. A track was found which had the appearance of an electron track, but curved in the opposite direction in the magnetic field in which the cloud chamber was immersed.   This was only the first of a series of remarkable discoveries in such photographs.

In 1936 Anderson and Neddermyer found another exceptional track in chamber photographs.   A particle traversed part of the chamber which was in a magnetic field, and then passed through a lead plate.   Since the track was more curved on one side of the lead plate than on the other, the direction of the trajectory was known.   The particle finally stopped in the vapor of the chamber.   The energy, as deduced from the particle's range in the vapor, could only be made consistent with the energy deduced from the curvature of its track by hypothesizing a particle of mass inter-mediate between the masses of the electron and proton.   Various measure-ments during 1937 and 1938 estimated the mass of this new particle at about 220 electron masses.   The particle has been variously named the *meson*, the *mesotron*, and the *yukon* (after Yukawa; see below), but the term meson is now universally accepted.   Thus, cosmic-ray observations led to the discovery of a second new particle.

Before continuing with a discussion of experimental observations on the meson, we shall first consider Yukawa's theory of nuclear forces, which was announced in 1935.   In order to account for the binding forces between protons and neutrons making up nuclei, Yukawa postulated the existence of a particle of about the mass of the meson, which would serve as an adhesive to hold nuclei together.   Briefly, his theory is as follows. First, consider the interaction force between two electrons, e_1 and e_2. According to *classical ideas*, we say that the electrons exert forces on one another to agree with Coulomb's law.   According to *quantum mechanics*, however, they may just as well be considered to interact through the emission and absorption of photons.   The electron emitting a photon loses momentum, while the electron absorbing a photon gains momentum.   The result of this exchange of photons is a change in the momentum of each particle, which is exactly the effect of a force acting between the particles. Since this change in momentum is a result of an exchange of photons, this type of force is called an *exchange force*.   In the form of an equation where primes indicate that the momentum of the particle has changed from its initial value, we have

$$e_1 + e_2 \rightarrow e_1' + hf + e_2 \rightarrow e_1' + e_2'$$

The photon involved in this interchange of momentum is a *virtual* (unob-servable) *photon*, since it violates conservation of energy, and it may be considered a mathematical construct without direct physical reality.

In order to explain the forces which bind the particles in a nucleus together, Yukawa postulated an exchange force of the sort described above between nucleons.   Thus, neutrons and protons could exchange momentum through the medium of a "heavy quantum," and in that way exert forces on one another. In addition, the heavy quantum, which from now on will be called a *meson*, would also allow nucleons to exchange charge. For instance, when a proton dissociates and emits a positive meson, μ^+, we have the following reaction, where capital letters refer to one particle and small letters to the other:

$$p + N \rightarrow \text{n} + \mu^+ + N \rightarrow n + P$$

The net result of this reaction is that the particles have exchanged charge as well as momentum. Similarly, a neutron can emit a negative meson, converting itself into a proton according to the reaction

$$n + P \rightarrow p + \mu^- + P \rightarrow p + N$$

The forces between like particles require the emission of a neutral meson, according to the following reactions:

$$n + N \rightarrow n + \mu^0 + N \rightarrow N + n$$
$$p + P \rightarrow p + \mu^0 + P \rightarrow P + p$$

The mesons postulated by Yukawa to account for the short-range forces between nucleons are virtual and cannot be observed, since they violate conservation of energy. However, if the nucleons acquire sufficient kinetic energy, they may create an observable meson. For instance, in a collision between a neutron and a proton, the neutron may emit a negative meson. In this case, the observed products of the collision will be two protons and a negative meson.

The Heisenberg uncertainty principle permits us to estimate the mass of the meson. In Section 5.4 it was stated that the product of the uncertainties in the simultaneous measurement of any two quantities which are classically called *canonically conjugate*, is $h/4\pi$. Equation (229) was stated in terms of the pair of variables, momentum and position, but holds equally well for the pair of variables energy and time. For the uncertainties in the simultaneous measurement of the energy and time of a particle, we then have the equation

$$\Delta E \, \Delta t \geq \frac{h}{4\pi} \tag{425}$$

A virtual meson may violate conservation of energy for a time short enough to satisfy Eq. (425). Thus, if the meson travels between the nucleons with the speed of light, c, the greatest distance the meson could travel without observably violating conservation of energy is given by

$$R = c \, \Delta t = c \, \frac{h}{4\pi \, \Delta E} \tag{426}$$

If the mass of the meson, μ, is related to the uncertainty in its energy by the relation from relativity, $\Delta E = \mu c^2$, we can write Eq. (426) in the form

$$R = \frac{h}{4\pi c \mu} \tag{427}$$

Solving for the mass of the meson from Eq. (427), we have

$$\mu = \frac{h}{4\pi c R} \tag{428}$$

Now the range of nuclear forces can be measured by nuclear scattering experiments, and typical values are of the order of 10^{-13} centimeters. Using this value for R, the greatest distance the virtual meson can travel, we find for the mass of the meson:

$$\mu = \frac{6.62 \times 10^{-27}}{4\pi \times 3 \times 10^{10} \times 10^{-13}} = 1.76 \times 10^{-25} = 1760 \times 10^{-28} \text{ gram}$$

Compared with the mass of the electron, 9.1×10^{-28} gram, we see that the mass of a virtual meson would be approximately 200 electron masses. This is in remarkably good agreement with the present value for the mass of the meson of 206 electron-masses considering the approximations involved in the quantum mechanical estimate.

The Yukawa theory also required that the meson be unstable, decaying into an electron and a neutrino in a time of the order of a microsecond. The emission of electrons by radioactive nuclei, even though no electrons exist permanently inside nuclei, is explained as a process in which a neutron emits a negative meson.   This negative meson then decays into an electron and a neutrino according to the following reaction:

$$n \rightarrow p + \mu^- \rightarrow p + \beta^- + \eta$$

The net result is that an electron is observed to be emitted by the nucleus, while a neutron inside the nucleus is converted into a proton.   The conversion of a neutron into a proton raises the atomic number of the element by one unit, which is in agreement with the Rutherford-Soddy rule. Thus, the Yukawa hypothesis accounts at least qualitatively for beta-decay.   Experimentally, however, electrons are observed with energies of the order of a few mev, while the rest-mass energy of the meson is about 100 mev.   In order to conserve momentum and still allow the electron to carry away only a fraction of the energy available when the meson decays, two neutrinos must be emitted.   Experimentally, there is no direct evidence for the emission of two neutrinos.

The average lifetime of the meson has been measured by various experimenters.   A typical arrangement is shown in Fig. 115.   The two

Geiger counters are connected in coincidence, as explained earlier in this chapter in connection with cosmic-ray telescopes. The voltage pulse from counter 1 is delayed a known and adjustable time before entering the coincidence circuit. Suppose a meson passes through counter 1 and then

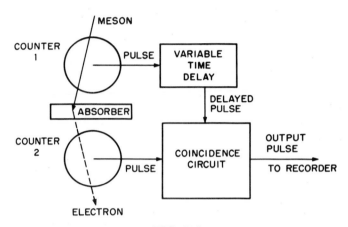

FIG. 115
Arrangement for measuring the average lifetime of mesons.

decays in the absorbing plate. The electron produced by the meson's decay will traverse counter 2 after a time which is the lifetime of that particular meson. If the voltage pulse from counter 1 is delayed by just this amount, a coincidence will be registered by the coincidence circuit. The time delay of the voltage pulse from the first counter is varied and the relative numbers of mesons with various corresponding lifetimes are measured.

If the decay of the meson is assumed to be a statistical process, similar to the radioactive decay of nuclei, then the number of mesons which have a lifetime, t, is related to the average lifetime of the meson, T, by the equation

$$N = N_0 \exp\left(\frac{-t}{T}\right) \tag{429}$$

Thus, the average lifetime of the meson can be deduced from measurements of the relative number of coincidences, N/N_0, as a function of the delay time introduced, t. For positive mesons, values of the average lifetime are found to be about 2.2 micro-seconds, which is in good qualitative agreement with the lifetime deduced by Yukawa. However, the lifetime of negative mesons is found to be considerably less than this value, particularly in absorbers of high atomic number. Apparently, negative mesons are easily captured by nuclei, which have a positive charge, so that the loss of negative mesons, both through capture by nuclei and through radioactive decay, is measured in this case. When a negative meson is captured by a nucleus, a violent nuclear explosion may occur, giving a *star* of nuclear fragments. This will be discussed further in the following section on cosmic-ray processes.

For a number of years it seemed that the Yukawa theory of the meson might eventually be modified so as to give exact agreement with experiment. Certainly the semiquantitative agreement between the theory and observations on cosmic ray mesons was too impressive to ignore. The success of Yukawa's theory and later refinements of it in accounting for nuclear forces, beta-decay, and other difficult aspects of nuclear theory gave added confirmation of the whole scheme. From 1947 on, however, a succession of new particles were discovered and the apparent agreement between theory and experiment was destroyed.

In 1947 Powell, Occhialini, Lattes, and Muirhead reported the discovery of a meson somewhat heavier than the cosmic-ray meson first observed by Anderson. This meson was named the *pi-meson;* it has a mass of 273 electron-masses. Furthermore, the pi-meson is the primary meson corresponding to Yukawa's theory, and the earlier-known cosmic-ray meson, now called the *mu-meson,* is a secondary meson produced by the decay of a pi-meson according to the following schemes:

$$\pi^{\pm} \rightarrow \mu^{\pm} + \eta$$

In addition, there is a neutral pi-meson which decays in the following way:

$$\pi^0 \rightarrow \gamma + \gamma$$

The lifetime of the charged pi-mesons is about 2.5×10^{-8} seconds while that of the neutral pi-meson is less than 10^{-15} seconds. With the development of large accelerators, it became possible to study these reactions very extensively, so that masses and lifetimes of various mesons could be accurately measured.

The picture was further beclouded in 1957 by the discovery by Franzinetti and Morpurgo of an even heavier meson known as the *K-meson.* The charged K-mesons have a mass of about 966 electron-masses and a lifetime of about 10^{-8} second. However, they decay in a variety of ways, some examples of which are shown below:

$$
K^{\pm} \nearrow \pi^{\pm} + \pi^{+} + \pi^{-} \\
\rightarrow \pi^{\pm} + \pi^{0} \\
\searrow \mu^{\pm} + \eta
$$

In addition, there is a neutral K-meson with a mass of about 973 electron-masses and a lifetime of about 10^{-10} seconds. The principal mode of decay of this meson is as follows:

$$K^0 \rightarrow \pi^+ + \pi^-$$

In addition to the complications introduced by the discoveries of the various mesons described above, a variety of unstable particles, intermediate in mass between the neutron and the deuteron, have been observed. These particles are known as *hyperons,* and were first detected in cosmic-rays by Rochester and Butler in 1947, but have since been produced by high-energy accelerators. The first hyperon was called the *neutral lambda particle,* Λ^0, because of the characteristic V-shaped tracks left by its decay products. This hyperon has a mass of 2182 electron-masses and a life-time of about 3×10^{-10} seconds. Its principal mode of decay is as follows:

$$\Lambda^0 \rightarrow p + \pi^-$$

The proton and negative pi-meson leave a V-shaped track in a cloud-chamber or bubble-chamber. In addition, sigma-particles and xi-particles, with masses in the range 2300–2600 electron-masses, have been observed. Again it must be said that the exact part played by these various hyperons is as yet unknown.

In Section 6.11 the formation of positron-electron pairs was discussed. Since the electron and positron differ only in the sign of their charge, the positron is said to be the *anti-particle* of the electron or more simply the *anti-electron.* If enough energy is available, anti-electrons can be produced, while if an electron combines with an anti-electron, their masses are converted into annihilation radiation. Similarly, the *anti-proton* should exist, which would be identical with the proton except for having a negative charge. Proton-anti-proton pairs were first produced by Chamberlain and his co-workers in 1955. Protons of energy 6.2 bev struck a copper target and the resulting anti-protons were identified by their charge-to-mass ratio and by their speed. Furthermore, very high-energy tracks were observed in a bubble-chamber when a proton and an anti-proton took part in pair annihilation.

In general, anti-particles and particles have the same mass but opposite charges, if they are charged particles. They also have magnetic moments of the same magnitude but of opposite sign. In 1956 Segre and his co-workers reported the identification of the *anti-neutron* and the observation of annihilation between a neutron and anti-neutron. It is believed that, in general, all particles, including mesons and hyperons, have anti-particles, although some anti-particles seem to be indistinguishable from the corresponding particle.

11.5. COSMIC RAY PROCESSES AND THE ORIGIN OF COSMIC RAYS

The extensive showers of particles mentioned in Section 11.2 can now be understood. If the primary cosmic ray particles are sufficiently energetic the mesons and hyperons discussed in the preceding section can be produced and they produce additional particles by decaying. Furthermore, when a highly energetic charged particle is suddenly decelerated in a collision with a nucleus, electromagnetic radiation known as *bremsstrahlung* or *braking radiation* is produced. This electromagnetic radiation may then form an electron-positron pair as was described in Section 6.11. These particles may themselves produce bremsstrahlung, and the continuation of this process through many generations can produce an extensive shower.

Multiple tracks, called *stars*, all starting from a single point, are often observed in photographic emulsions and cloud-chamber photographs. The branches of a star may be the tracks of protons, mesons, hyperons, fragments of nuclei, and, possibly, other particles. Stars may originate through the decay or mutual annihilation of various particles and also through the complete disruption or spallation of a nucleus.

While the details of the interactions of cosmic rays with various substances on the earth are becoming increasingly better understood, the origin of these cosmic radiations remains a matter of hypothesis and speculation. Since this problem is not susceptible to direct investigation as yet, enormous extrapolations must be made from the rather scanty data on the primary cosmic radiations. Although several hypotheses regarding the origin of these radiations seem plausible, none has yet been generally accepted.

Variations of the cosmic ray intensity at a point on the earth should be observed corresponding to the variations of the positions of the stars if certain stars emit cosmic rays and accelerate them to the observed energies. Observed variations of this sort are of very small amplitude, so it seems certain that the stars in our own galaxy are not responsible for cosmic rays. A variation of less than 1% between midnight and noon is observed, so that our sun may contribute a small amount to the total cosmic ray intensity observed at the earth. However, this small solar variation may be due to variations of the electrical conductivity of the earth's atmosphere with temperature, or to deflection of the primary cosmic-ray particles by the magnetic field of the sun. In any event, it seems unlikely that the primary cosmic-ray particles are given very large energies within stars, so that we must consider how charged particles could be given energies up to perhaps 10^{12} electron-volts in interstellar space.

Weak electric fields extending for enormous distances through interstellar space could give charged particles sufficiently large energies. However, it is hard to see how such an electric field could be maintained despite the movement of a large number of charged particles. Some sort of mechanism would have to be imagined which could maintain a constant potential difference across portions of space, despite the large flux of charged particles which would tend to cancel this potential difference.

A possible source of high energy particles might be the stellar explosions known as *novae* or *super-novae*. Occasionally stars do explode with the release of tremendous amounts of energy, but it is uncertain whether the relatively small number of explosions of this sort would account for the large amount of energy involved in the cosmic radiation of the universe. This theory is bolstered by the evidence regarding the connection between solar flares and short duration increases in the cosmic-ray intensity at the earth. Swann has shown that the changing magnetic field of the sun during a solar flare could accelerate protons to the energies observed for cosmic ray particles. However, not all flares are accompanied by increases in the intensity of cosmic radiation, so that a solar flare may merely serve as a source of charged particles which are then accelerated by the changing magnetic field of the sun.

Interstellar space is not an absolute vacuum, but contains on the average approximately one particle per cubic centimeter. However, this distribution of matter in space is not uniform, variations of as much as a factor of a hundred being possible. Alfven suggested that convection currents of the particles in interstellar space would establish magnetic fields in space, if most of the particles were ionized. These magnetic fields would occupy tremendous volumes and be rather stable. Fermi showed that if the region of such a magnetic field were moving, protons could gradually gain energy by collisions with particles in the magnetic field. This would be an extremely slow process covering a large volume of space, since on the average a proton would undergo an accelerating collision about once a year and would have a mean free path of the order of 10^{13} kilometers. The distribution in energy of the protons reaching the earth can then be calculated, with results which are in approximate agreement with the observed distribution of energies of cosmic-ray particles. To conclude, as we learn more about the nature of the primary cosmic radiation and its energy distribution, we will be better able to explain the origin of this mysterious but most interesting radiation.

ADDITIONAL READING

Leprince-Ringuet, Louis, *Cosmic Rays*. Englewood Cliffs, N. J.: Prentice-Hall, Inc., 1950. An excellent account of cosmic-ray investigations, with many photographs and plates.

Parker, E. N., "Origin and Dynamics of Cosmic Rays," *Physical Review*, **109**, 1328 (February 15, 1958). Survey and critique of various theories of the origin of cosmic-rays.

Treiman, S. B., "The Weak Interactions," *Scientific American*, **200**, No. 3, 72 (March, 1959). Discussion of the elementary particles, including mesons and hyperons, and their properties.

PROBLEMS

1. Find the radius of curvature of an electron of energy 10 bev in a uniform magnetic field of 18,000 gauss.   (*Ans*. 1850 cm)

2. Repeat Problem 1 for a proton of the same energy, and compare your results.

3. Referring to the results of Problems 1 and 2, compute the maximum deflection from a straight line which would be observed for the curved tracks of the electron and the proton, if the cloud chamber is 30 centimeters in diameter.   (*Ans*. 0.61 mm, 0.56 mm)

4. Prove that the maximum velocity which an electron can receive from a head-on collision with a heavy particle is twice the initial velocity of the heavy particle. (Ignore relativistic effects.)

5. Compute the maximum energy which an electron can receive in a collision with a 5 mev proton.   (*Ans*. 10.9 kev)

6. Consider a 10 bev proton in a region of space where the magnetic field is 0.001 gauss and increasing at the rate of 0.001 gauss per year. Treating this situation as a hyperbetatron, compute the energy gained by the proton per revolution, the time per revolution, and the energy gained per day.

7. Estimate the intensity of cosmic radiations at Lancaster, Pa. (40° north latitude) in Roentgens per day.   (*Ans*. 7.2×10^{-5})

8. Assume that a pi-meson at rest decays to form a mu-meson and a neutrino. Compute the kinetic energy of the mu-meson by the application of the principles of conservation of energy and momentum.

9. Referring to Problem 8, compute the dynamical mass of the neutrino produced by the decay of a pi-meson.   (*Ans*. 58.8 m_0)

appendix

TABLE 1. SOME ISOTOPIC WEIGHTS

Element	Z	A	Abundance(%)	Mass	Half-life	Radiation
Neutron	0	1		1.008986		
Proton	1	1		1.007582		
Alpha	2	4		4.002764		
Hydrogen	1	1	99.985	1.008145		
	1	2	0.015	2.014740		
	1	3		3.017005	12.26 yr	β^-(18 kev)
Helium	2	3	0.00013	3.016986		
	2	4	100	4.003874		
	2	5		5.01389	10^{-21} sec	n(0.97 mev)
	2	6		6.02083	0.82 sec	β^-(3.50 mev)
Lithium	3	5		5.01395	?	p(1.8 mev)
	3	6	7.5	6.017034		
	3	7	92.5	7.018232		
	3	8		8.025033	0.86 sec	β^-(13 mev)
Beryllium	4	7		7.019159	53.6 days	γ(0.478 mev)
	4	8		8.007849	?	2α(0.096 mev)
	4	9	100	9.015060		
	4	10		10.016716	2.5×10^6 yr	β^-(0.557 mev)
	4	11		11.02514	13.7 sec	β^-(11.5, 9.3 mev)
Boron	5	8		8.0268	0.6 sec	β^+(13.7 mev)
	5	9		9.016195	?	$p + 2\alpha$(0.28 mev)
	5	10	18.7	10.016119		
	5	11	81.3	11.012795		
	5	12		12.018168	0.022 sec	β^-(13.43 mev)
Carbon	6	10		10.02024	19.1 sec	β^+(1.9 mev)
	6	11		11.014922	20.40 min	β^+(0.980 mev)
	6	12	98.89	12.003816		
	6	13	1.11	13.007478		
	6	14		14.007687	5600 yr	β^-(0.1561 mev)
	6	15		15.01416	2.3 sec	β^-(4.3 mev)
Nitrogen	7	12		12.02278	0.0215 sec	β^+(16.6 mev)
	7	13		13.009864	10.1 min	β^+(1.24 mev)
	7	14	99.635	14.007520		
	7	15	˙0.365	15.004862		
	7	16		16011171	7.36 sec	β^-(various)
	7	17		17.0140	4.14 sec	β^-(3.7 mev)

Element	Z	A	Abundance (%)	Mass	Half-life	Radiation
Oxygen	8	14		14.013069	74 sec	β^+(1.83 mev)
	8	15		15.007767	2.05 min	β^+(1.68 mev)
	8	16	99.759	16.000000		
	8	17	0.037	17.004537		
	8	18	0.204	18.004855		
	8	19		19.00959	29.4 sec	β^-(2.9, 4.5 mev)
	8	20		20.01038	13.6 sec	β^-(2.69 mev)
Fluorine	9	17		17.007506	66 sec	β^+(1.748 mev)
	9	18		18.006646	1.87 hr	β^+(0.649 mev)
	9	19	100	19.004448		
	9	20		20.006350	11.2 sec	β^-(5.414 mev)
	9	21		21.0066	5 sec	β^-(5.7 mev)

TABLE 2. NATURALLY RADIOACTIVE ELEMENTS

Thorium series	Half-life	Radiation (energy in mev)
$_{90}Th^{232}$	1.39×10^{10} yr	$\alpha(3.98)$
$_{88}Ra^{228}$ (MsTh$_1$)	6.7 yr	$\beta^-(0.01)$
$_{89}Ac^{228}$ (MsTh$_2$)	6.13 hr	$\beta^-(1.11, 0.45)$
$_{90}Th^{228}$ (RdTh)	1.91 yr	$\alpha(5.42, 5.34)$
$_{88}Ra^{224}$ (ThX)	3.64 days	$\alpha(5.68)$
$_{86}Rn^{220}$ (Tn)	52 sec	$\alpha(6.28)$
$_{84}Po^{216}$ (ThA)	0.158 sec	$\alpha(6.77)$
$_{82}Fb^{2\ 2}$ (ThB)	10.64 hr	$\beta^-(0.35, 0.59)$
$_{83}Ei^{212}$ (ThC)	60.5 min	β^- 66%(2.25), α 34%(6.09)
$_{84}Po^{212}$ (ThC')	3.04×10^{-7} sec	$\alpha(8.78)$
$_{81}Tl^{208}$ (ThC'')	3.1 min	$\beta^-(1.80)$
$_{82}Pb^{208}$ (ThD)	stable	

Neptunium series

$_{93}Np^{237}$	2.20×10^6 yr	$\alpha(4.78)$
$_{91}Pa^{233}$	27.4 days	$\beta^-(0.257, 0.145)$
$_{92}U^{233}$	1.62×10^5 yr	$\alpha(4.82)$
$_{90}Th^{229}$	7340 yr	$\alpha(4.85)$
$_{88}Ra^{225}$	14.8 days	$\beta^-(0.320)$
$_{89}Ac^{225}$	10.0 days	$\alpha(5.80)$
$_{87}Fr^{221}$	4.8 min	$\alpha(6.30)$
$_{85}At^{217}$	0.018 sec	$\alpha(7.02)$
$_{83}Bi^{213}$	47 min	$\alpha(5.86)(2\%)$; $\beta^-(1.39)98\%$
$_{84}Po^{213}$	4.2×10^{-6} sec	$\alpha(8.34)$
$_{81}Tl^{209}$	2.20 min	$\beta^-(1.8)$
$_{82}Pb^{209}$	3.32 hr	$\beta^-(0.635)$
$_{83}Bi^{209}$	stable	

Actinium series

$_{92}U^{235}$	7.13×10^8 yr	$\alpha(4.39)$
$_{90}Th^{231}$ (UY)	25.64 hr	$\beta^-(0.094, 0.302)$
$_{91}Pa^{231}$	3.43×10^4 yr	$\alpha(5.02)$
$_{89}Ac^{227}$	21.8 yr	$\beta^-(0.046)98.8\%$; $\alpha(4.94)1.2\%$
$_{90}Th^{227}$ (RdAc)	18.4 days	$\alpha(5.97, 6.03, 5.75)$
$_{88}Ra^{223}$ (AcX)	11.68 days	$\alpha(5.72)$
$_{86}Rn^{219}$ (An)	3.92 sec	$\alpha(6.82)$
$_{84}Po^{215}$ (AcA)	1.83×10^{-3} sec	$\alpha(7.37)$
$_{82}Pb^{211}$ (AcB)	36.1 min	$\beta^-(1.4)$
$_{83}Bi^{211}$ (AcC)	2.16 min	$\alpha(6.61)99.7\%$; $\beta^-(?)0.3\%$
$_{84}Po^{211}$ (AcC')	0.52 sec	$\alpha(7.43)$
$_{81}Tl^{207}$ (AcC'')	4.78 min	$\beta^-(1.47)$
$_{82}Pb^{207}$ (AcD)	stable	

TABLE 3. SOME USEFUL RADIO-ISOTOPES

Element	Mass Number	Half-life	Beta (mev)	Gamma (mev)
Antimony.......	122	2.8 days	1.36,1.94	0.57
	124	60 days	0.65,2.37	1.71
Argon...........	37	34 days	K	none
Barium.........	131	12 days	K	0.22,0.50
Beryllium.......	7	43 days	K	0.485
Bismuth.........	210	5 days	1.17	none
Cadmium.......	115	2.5 days	0.6,1.13	0.65
Calcium.........	45	180 days	0.25	none
Carbon.........	14	5720 yr	0.154	none
Cesium.........	134	2.3 yr	0.64	0.57,0.79
Chlorine........	36	10^6 yr	0.64	none
Cobalt..........	60	5.3 yr	0.31	1.16,1.30
Copper..........	64	12.8 hr	$0.57e^-,0.66e^+$	1.35(weak)
Gold............	198	2.7 days	0.97,0.61	0.41,0.16
Hydrogen.......	3	12.1 yr	0.011	none
Iodine..........	131	8 days	0.60,0.32	0.37,0.64
Iridium.........	192	75 days	0.59	0.14,0.21,0.47,0.30
Iron............	55	4 yr	K	
	59	46.3 days	0.26,0.46	1.10,1.30
Mercury........	203	43.5 days	0.21	0.29
Nickel..........	63	300 yr	0.05	
Phosphorus......	32	14.3 days	1.712	none
Selenium........	75	125 days	K,e^-	0.10,0.27,0.45
Silver...........	110	225 days	$0.59,K$	0.66,0.90,1.40
Sodium.........	22	3 yr	$0.58e^+$	1.3
	24	14.8 hr	1.39	1.38,2.76
Strontium.......	89	55 days	1.48	none
Sulfur..........	35	87.1 days	0.619	none
Thallium........	204	3.0 yr	0.77	none
Tin.............	113	105 days	K,e^-	0.085
Titanium........	51	72 days	0.36	1.0
Wolfram........	185	73.2 days	0.43	none
Zinc............	65	250 days	K,e^-	1.14
			$0.32e^+(1.3\%)$	

TABLE 4. USEFUL CONSTANTS AND CONVERSION FACTORS

Taken from "A Survey of Atomic Constants" by J. A. Bearden and John S. Thomsen, The Johns Hopkins University (1955).

Symbol	Name of Constant	Value
e	electron charge	1.60209×10^{-19} coulombs
		4.80294×10^{-10} esu
m_0	electron rest-mass	9.1086×10^{-31} kg
e/m_0	specific electron charge	1.75888×10^{11} coul/kg
		5.27299×10^{17} esu/gm
c	velocity of light	2.997928×10^8 m/sec
N_0	Avogadro's number	6.0247×10^{23} (physical scale)
$m_0 N_0$	electron atomic weight	5.48760×10^{-4} amu (physical scale)
$m_0 c^2$	electron rest-mass energy	0.510984 mev
1 ev	electron-volt	1.60209×10^{-19} joule
M	proton mass	1.007596 amu
		$1836.13\ m_0$
h	Planck's constant	6.6254×10^{-34} joule-sec
		4.134×10^{-15} ev-sec
k	Boltzmann's constant	1.38049×10^{-23} joule/°K
		8.6168×10^{-5} ev/°K
F	Faraday constant	96520 coul (physical scale)
J	calorie in joules	4.1854 joules/calorie
R	Rydberg constant	109737.31 per cm
$h/m_0 c$	Compton wavelength	0.0242627 angstroms
hc/e	Duane-Hunt constant	12397.8 volt-angstroms
1 amu	atomic mass unit	931.14 mev
K'	Coulomb's law constant	8.98752×10^9 nt-met²/coul²

index